Encyclopaedia of
MODERN AIRCRAFT ARMAMENT

Encyclopaedia of
MODERN AIRCRAFT ARMAMENT

Christopher Chant

Patrick Stephens

First published 1988

British Library Cataloguing in Publication Data

Chant, Christopher
    Encyclopaedia of modern aircraft
    armament.
    1. Aerial gunnery
    I. Title
    623.74'61   UG1340

    ISBN 0-85059-862-1

Patrick Stephens Limited is part of the Thorsons Publishing Group, Wellingborough, Northamptonshire, NN8 2RQ, England

Printed in Great Britain by Richard Clay Limited, Chichester, Sussex

10 9 8 7 6 5 4 3 2 1

Contents

Introduction	9
Aeritalia G91R	10
Aeritalia G91Y	12
Aeritalia/Aermacchi/EMBRAER AMX	14
Aermacchi M.B.326K	16
Aermacchi M.B.339A	18
Aérospatiale CM.170-1 Magister	20
Aérospatiale SA 319B Alouette III Astazou	22
Aérospatiale SA 321G Super Frelon	24
Aérospatiale AS 332B/F Super Puma	26
Aérospatiale SA 341F Gazelle	28
Aérospatiale SA 365F Dauphin 2	30
Aéro L-39ZA Albatros	32
Agusta A 129A Mangusta	34
Agusta (Bell) AB.204AS	36
Agusta (Bell) AB.212ASW	38
Agusta (Sikorsky) ASH-3D/H Sea King	40
Beech T-34C-1	42
Bell Modernized AH-1S HueyCobra	44
Bell AH-1T Improved SeaCobra	46
Boeing B-52G Stratofortress	48
British Aerospace (Blackburn/HS) Buccaneer S.Mk 2B	54
British Aerospace (English Electric/BAC) Canberra B(I).Mk 8	56
British Aerospace (HS) Harrier GR.Mk 3	58
British Aerospace (HS) Hawk T.Mk 1A	61
British Aerospace (Hawker) Hunter FGA.Mk 9	64
British Aerospace (English Electric/BAC) Lightning F.Mk 53	66
British Aerospace (HS) Nimrod MR.Mk 2	68
British Aerospace Sea Harrier FRS.Mk 1	70
British Aerospace (BAC) Strikemaster Mk 88	72
Britten-Norman Defender	74

CASA C-101DD Aviojet	77
Cessna A-37B Dragonfly	80
Dassault-Breguet Alizé	82
Dassault-Breguet Atlantique 2	84
Dassault-Breguet Mirage IIIE	86
Dassault-Breguet Mirage IVA	90
Dassault-Breguet Mirage 5	92
Dassault-Breguet Mirage 2000C	94
Dassault-Breguet Mirage F1E	97
Dassault-Breguet Super Etendard	102
Dassault-Breguet/Dornier Alpha Jet A	104
Fairchild-Republic A-10A Thunderbolt II	107
FMA IA-58A Pucará	110
General Dynamics F-16A Fighting Falcon	112
General Dynamics F-111F	118
Grumman A-6E/TRAM Intruder	122
Grumman F-14A Tomcat	125
HAL Ajeet	128
Hughes (McDonnell Douglas) AH-64A Apache	130
Hughes (McDonnell Douglas) Model 500MD/TOW Defender	134
Ilyushin Il-28 'Beagle'	138
IAI Kfir-C2	140
IAI/McDonnell Douglas Phantom 2000	144
Lockheed F-104G Starfighter	146
Lockheed P-3C Orion Update III	149
Lockheed S-3A Viking	152
McDonnell Douglas A-4M Skyhawk II	154
McDonnell Douglas F-4E Phantom II	157
McDonnell Douglas F-15C Eagle	161
McDonnell Douglas F/A-18A Hornet	165
McDonnell Douglas/British Aerospace AV-8B Harrier II	170
Messerschmitt-Bölkow-Blohm PAH-1	175
Mikoyan-Gurevich MiG-15bis 'Fagot'	178
Mikoyan-Gurevich MiG-17F 'Fresco-C'	180
Mikoyan-Gurevich MiG-195 'Farmer-C'	182

Mikoyan-Gurevich MiG-21bisF 'Fishbed-N'	185
Mikoyan-Gurevich MiG-23MF 'Flogger-G'	189
Mikoyan-Gurevich MiG-25 'Foxbat-A'	192
Mikoyan-Gurevich MiG-27 'Flogger-D'	195
Mikoyan-Gurevich MiG-29 'Fulcrum'	198
Mikoyan-Gurevich MiG-31 'Foxhound'	200
Mil Mi-8 'Hip-E'	202
Mil Mi-24 'Hind-D'	205
Mil Mi-28 'Havoc'	208
Mitsubishi F-1	210
Nanchang Q-5 'Fantan-A'	212
Northrop F-5E Tiger II	214
Panavia Tornado IDS	217
PZL Mielec TS-11 Iskra-bis DF	224
Rockwell B-1B	226
Rockwell OV-10A Bronco	228
Saab 105Ö	230
Saab J 35F Draken	232
Saab JA 37 Viggen	235
SEPECAT Jaguar S	239
Shin Meiwa PS-1	242
SIAI-Marchetti S.211	244
SIAI-Marchetti SF.260W Warrior	246
Sikorsky UH-60A Black Hawk	248
Soko J-1 Jastreb	250
Soko G-4 Super Galeb	252
Soko Orao-B/CNIAR IAR-93B	254
Sukhoi Su-7BMK 'Fitter-A'	256
Sukhoi Su-17M 'Fitter-C'	259
Sukhoi Su-21 'Flagon-F'	262
Sukhoi Su-24 'Fencer-C'	264
Sukhoi Su-25 'Frogfoot-B'	266
Sukhoi Su-27 'Flanker'	268
Tupolev Tu-16 'Badger-G'	270
Tupolev Tu-22 'Blinder-B'	272

Tupolev Tu-26 'Backfire-B'   274

Tupolev Tu-28P 'Fiddler-B'   276

Tupolev Tu-95 'Bear-A'   278

Tupolev Tu-? 'Blackjack'   280

Vought A-7E Corsair II   282

Vought F-8E(FN) Crusader   286

Westland Lynx AH.Mk 1   288

Westland Sea King HAS.Mk 5   291

Xian F-7M Airguard   294

Yakovlev Yak-28P 'Firebar'   296

Yakovlev Yak-38 'Forger-A'   298

Acknowledgements and further reading   300

Index   301

Introduction

At all levels of modern warfare the combat aircraft can, and often does, exert a decisive influence on the outcome of events, and this importance is amply confirmed by the huge quantity of material written about modern combat aircraft. Yet in all this literature there appear to be two glaring omissions: specific reference to which weapons any particular aircraft can carry and a detailed analysis of the nature of those aerial weapons.

This book addresses the first of these limitations, and a companion volume on *Modern Aircraft Weapons* is in preparation to remedy the second shortcoming. That there are failings in these two fields can readily be checked: all too many modern reference books about aircraft state baldly that the type in question 'can carry 8,000 lb of ordnance on six pylons, including two air-to-air missiles', or words to the same effect. But the nub of the matter to those genuinely interested in the capabilities rather than just the performance of modern combat aircraft should be the types, numbers and dispositions of the whole range of weapons that can be delivered by the aircraft in question: reference works often forget that combat aircraft are in themselves only the platforms for the delivery of weapons, and that it is the weapons and the aircraft as a system that really count.

The selection of aircraft in this book is designed to reflect the types currently available for combat operations, and within each aircraft entry emphasis has been placed textually on current variants of the aircraft, on the internally and externally-carried ordnance, and on the sensors, sights etc, that allow the aircraft to perform its primary function with maximum capability. The accompanying photographs have been judiciously selected and their captions carefully written to highlight the armament, and the companion diagram highlights the basic type's external stores carriage, with emphasis on the location and rating of the hardpoints used to carry weapons, as well as the nature of the primary weapons (and, where space permits, the other stores) that can be accommodated under the hardpoints. Line drawings of aircraft are diagrammatic and are not intended to indicate comparative sizes.

The author cannot claim that the treatment is exhaustive, for the pace of development is extraordinarily rapid, and space within the book limited. With older aircraft types this does not present too great a problem, for their load-carrying capabilities were generally as modest as the weapon types available. But with more modern aircraft greater load-carrying capability is matched by an enormous diversity of weapon types, with a mass of further development under way for weapons of the immediate future. In the hope of securing export orders manufacturers now qualify their aircraft for the carriage of as many weapon types as possible, and this has been almost impossible to reflect in the book. The author's primary intention has thus been to illustrate the weapon types generally carried by any particular aircraft in service with the air force of its country of origin and with other weapons of importance included where space permits.

The author would like to take this opportunity to thank the professional colleagues and manufacturers who have aided so willingly and extensively in the preparation of *Modern Aircraft Armament*. Any errors are, of course, entirely the responsibility of the author.

Christopher Chant

Grantham,
Lincolnshire.

December 1987

Aeritalia G91R

Type: single-seat light attack, close support and reconnaissance fighter.

Internal armament: (Italian aircraft) four 0.5-in (12.7-mm) Colt-Browning M3 machine-guns plus 300 rounds per gun, or (Portuguese aircraft) two 30-mm DEFA 552 cannon plus 125 rounds per gun, both gun arrangements located in the sides of the forward fuselage.

Disposable armament: up to 1500 kg (3,307 lb) of disposable stores carried on four hardpoints (two under each wing).

Electronics and operational equipment: normal communication and navigation equipment, plus Bendix DRA-12A Doppler navigation and a SFOM sight.

Current variants and operators

G91R/1: initial production variant of the light attack and close-support aircraft originating from a 1954 NATO requirement and first flown in August 1956. Only Italy operates this model, which has an internal armament of four heavy machine-guns and is powered by a 5,000-lb (2268-kg) Rolls-Royce Viper Mk 803 non-afterburning turbojet.

G91R/1A: tactical reconnaissance variant of the G91R/1 introduced in 1959 and used only by Italy with a shortened nose for three forward and oblique cameras.

G91R/1B: version of the G91R/1 with locally-strengthened airframe and a number of detail modifications.

G91R/3: West German-built version of the G91/R1 with detail modifications and two cannon rather than four machine-guns. This type is now used only by Portugal.

G91R/4: version of the G91R/3 with the armament of the G91R/1. This type is now used only by Portugal.

G91T/1: Italian-built two-seat advanced and conversion trainer derivative of the G91R/1 with an internal armament of two 0.5-in (12.7-mm) machine-guns and provisions for disposable stores on two underwing hardpoints.

G91T/3: West German-built version of the G91T/1.

The G91 series resulted from a NATO requirement, but failed to secure anything like NATO-wide procurement. This is a G91R/3 reconnaissance fighter with a camera nose, two 30-mm DEFA cannon and four underwing hardpoints, the inner pair carrying BL755 cluster bombs.

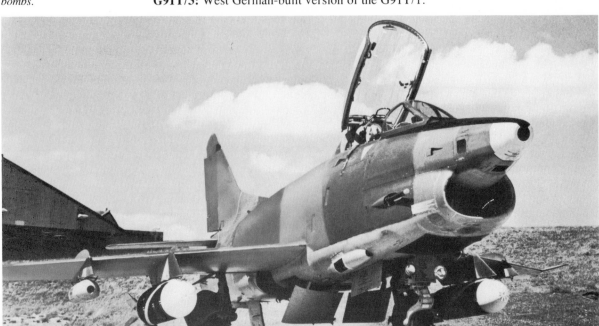

Aeritalia G91R/1

hardpoint rating

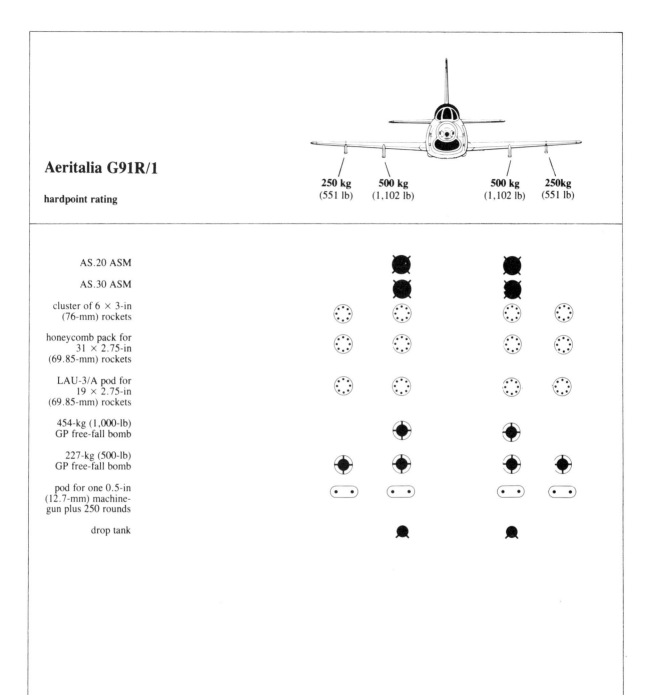

	250 kg (551 lb)	500 kg (1,102 lb)	500 kg (1,102 lb)	250kg (551 lb)
AS.20 ASM		●	●	
AS.30 ASM		●	●	
cluster of 6 × 3-in (76-mm) rockets	○	○	○	○
honeycomb pack for 31 × 2.75-in (69.85-mm) rockets	○	○	○	○
LAU-3/A pod for 19 × 2.75-in (69.85-mm) rockets	○	○	○	○
454-kg (1,000-lb) GP free-fall bomb		●	●	
227-kg (500-lb) GP free-fall bomb	●	●	●	●
pod for one 0.5-in (12.7-mm) machine-gun plus 250 rounds	◫	◫	◫	◫
drop tank		●	●	

Aeritalia G91Y

Type: single-seat light attack and close support fighter.

Internal armament: two 30-mm DEFA 552 cannon plus 125 rounds per gun in the sides of the forward fuselage.

Disposable armament: up to 1814 kg (4,000 lb) of disposable stores carried on four hardpoints (two under each wing).

Electronics and operational equipment: normal communication and navigation equipment, plus a CDC-5C-15 position and homing indicator; Sperry SYP twin-axis gyro platform; Bendix DRA-12A Doppler navigation; AiResearch air-data computer; Smiths Specto head-up display and Ferranti F195 ISIS-B sight.

The G91Y is essentially an updated and twin-engined version of the G91R, these two aircraft serving with the 8° Stormo 'Gino Primo' of the Italian air force, the type's sole operator.

Current variant and operator

G91Y: first flown in December 1966 for service from 1968, the G91Y is a simple yet useful development of the single-engined G91R series with a twin-engined powerplant (two 4,080-lb/1850-kg General Electric J85-GE-13A non-afterburning turbojets) for better performance with greater payload and the added reliability of two engines. The type is used only by Italy.

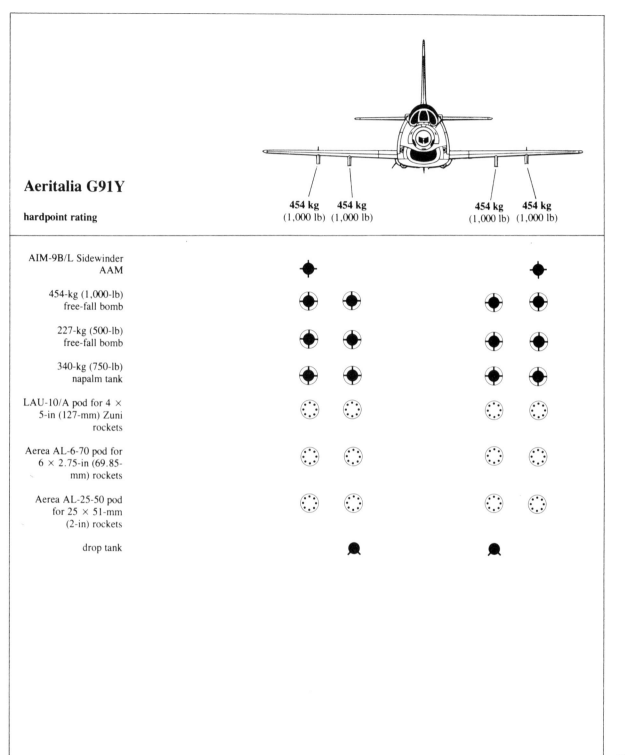

Aeritalia G91Y

hardpoint rating

	454 kg (1,000 lb)	454 kg (1,000 lb)	454 kg (1,000 lb)	454 kg (1,000 lb)
AIM-9B/L Sidewinder AAM	●			●
454-kg (1,000-lb) free-fall bomb	●	●	●	●
227-kg (500-lb) free-fall bomb	●	●	●	●
340-kg (750-lb) napalm tank	●	●	●	●
LAU-10/A pod for 4 × 5-in (127-mm) Zuni rockets	○	○	○	○
Aerea AL-6-70 pod for 6 × 2.75-in (69.85-mm) rockets	○	○	○	○
Aerea AL-25-50 pod for 25 × 51-mm (2-in) rockets	○	○	○	○
drop tank		●	●	

Aeritalia/Aermacchi/EMBRAER AMX

Type: single-seat attack aircraft.

Internal armament: (Italian aircraft) one 20-mm General Electric M61A1 Vulcan six-barrel rotary cannon plus 350 rounds in the lower port side of the nose, or (Brazilian aircraft) two 30-mm DEFA 554 cannon plus 125 rounds per gun in the underside of the nose.

Disposable armament: up to 3800 kg (8,376 lb) of disposable stores carried on seven hardpoints (one under the fuselage with side-by-side ejector racks, two under each wing, and two wingtip missile rails).

Electronics and operational equipment: normal communication and navigation equipment, plus as yet unspecified range-only radar; head-up display; head-down display; radar-warning receiver; laser ranger and marked-target seeker (in a lower fuselage bay where it can be replaced by any one of three pallet-mounted reconnaissance systems); stores management and delivery system; inertial navigation system; air-data computer; central computer and extensive electronic countermeasures such as the Elettronica ELT/555 pod system, plus provision for a reconnaissance pod.

Current variant and operators

AMX: originated as an Italian project for a G91 successor as lightweight counterpart to the Panavia Tornado, the AMX is now a joint Italo-Brazilian (70/30%) project against proposed procurement of 187 and 79 aircraft respectively. The first prototype flew in 1984 and service entry is due in 1989. The manufacturers are working on a considerable updating of the basic aircraft centred on its use as an anti-ship aircraft (with dedicated missile armament and considerably more sophisticated electronics such as the Thomson-CSF Agave radar in the shorter term, and the Ferranti Sea Vixen, Ericsson PS05, Fiat Grifo and Fiat/Westinghouse Altair in the longer term) or as a two-seat all-weather electronic warfare aircraft.

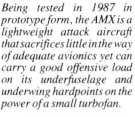

Being tested in 1987 in prototype form, the AMX is a lightweight attack aircraft that sacrifices little in the way of adequate avionics yet can carry a good offensive load on its underfuselage and underwing hardpoints on the power of a small turbofan.

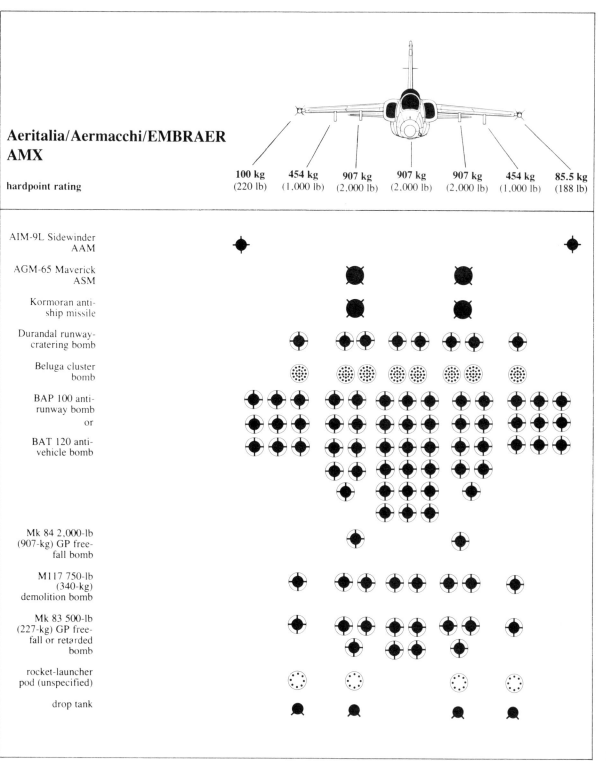

Aeritalia/Aermacchi/EMBRAER AMX

hardpoint rating

	100 kg (220 lb)	454 kg (1,000 lb)	907 kg (2,000 lb)	907 kg (2,000 lb)	907 kg (2,000 lb)	454 kg (1,000 lb)	85.5 kg (188 lb)

Weapons:

- AIM-9L Sidewinder AAM
- AGM-65 Maverick ASM
- Kormoran anti-ship missile
- Durandal runway-cratering bomb
- Beluga cluster bomb
- BAP 100 anti-runway bomb or BAT 120 anti-vehicle bomb
- Mk 84 2,000-lb (907-kg) GP free-fall bomb
- M117 750-lb (340-kg) demolition bomb
- Mk 83 500-lb (227-kg) GP free-fall or retarded bomb
- rocket-launcher pod (unspecified)
- drop tank

15

Aermacchi M.B.326K

Type: single-seat light attack aircraft.

Internal armament: two 30-mm DEFA 552 cannon plus 125 rounds per gun in the lower sides of the forward fuselage.

Disposable armament: up to 2500 kg (5,511 lb) of disposable stores carried on six hardpoints (three under each wing).

Electronics and operational equipment: normal communication and navigation equipment, plus Doppler navigation and provision for a sight ranging from a simple SFOM reflector type to a Ferranti LFS 5/102A gyro lead-computing type used (if desired) in conjunction with a laser rangefinder and a bombing computer. The type can also carry a reconnaissance pod.

Current variants and operators

M.B.326B: this is the oldest version of the M.B. 326 two-seat trainer series still in service, being the lightly-armed derivative for Tunisia of the 2,500-lb (1134-kg) Rolls-Royce Viper 11-engined unarmed M.B.326 that first flew in December 1957. The M.B.326B can carry an underwing load of 907 kg (2,000 lb).

M.B.326E: hybrid type used by Italy, combining the fuselage and powerplant of the M.B.326 with the wings and armament capability of the M.B.326GB.

M.B.326F: version of the M.B.326B for Ghana.

M.B.326G: uprated version with the 3,410-lb (1547-kg) Viper 20 Mk 540 turbojet and produced as the M.B.326GB for Argentina, Zaire and Zambia, and as the M.B.326GC (otherwise the EMBRAER EMB-326 Xavante) in Brazil for that country and Togo. The type was armed with two 0.5-in (12.7-mm) Colt-Browning M3 machine-guns plus 350 rounds per gun, and can carry 2500 kg (5,511 lb) of disposable stores on its six underwing hardpoints.

M.B.326H: Viper 11-engined armed trainer for Australia.

M.B.326K: single-seat operational trainer and light attack derivative of the M.B.326GB with the 4,000-lb (1814-kg) Viper Mk 632 turbojet, revised internal armament and the volume of the erstwhile rear cockpit used for additional fuel, avionics and the internal armament. The type was built in South Africa as the Atlas Impala Mk 2 with the Viper Mk 540 turbojet.

M.B.326L: two-seat version of the M.B.326K with the second cockpit restored to the detriment of inbuilt gun armament; the type is used by Dubai and Tunisia.

M.B.326M: two-seat trainer derivative of the M.B.326K for South Africa, where the type was built as the Atlas Impala Mk 1.

M.B.326 jet trainers of the Italian air force's Scuola Volo Basico Iniziale Aviogetti show off the type's trim lines with large and uncluttered wings well suited, in later models, to the addition of hardpoints for a substantial and varied offensive load.

Aermacchi M.B.326K

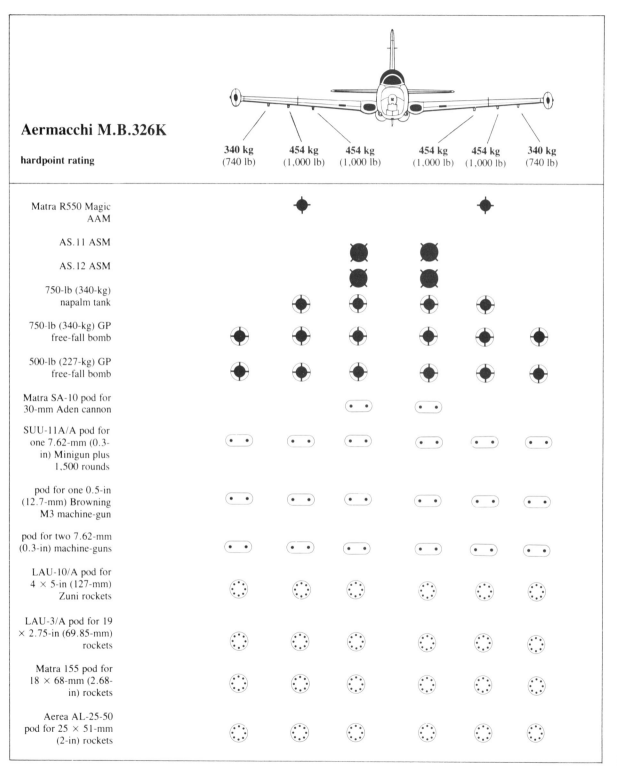

hardpoint rating	340 kg (740 lb)	454 kg (1,000 lb)	454 kg (1,000 lb)	454 kg (1,000 lb)	454 kg (1,000 lb)	340 kg (740 lb)
Matra R550 Magic AAM		●		●		
AS.11 ASM			●	●		
AS.12 ASM			●	●		
750-lb (340-kg) napalm tank		●	●	●	●	
750-lb (340-kg) GP free-fall bomb	●	●	●	●	●	●
500-lb (227-kg) GP free-fall bomb	●	●	●	●	●	●
Matra SA-10 pod for 30-mm Aden cannon			●	●		
SUU-11A/A pod for one 7.62-mm (0.3-in) Minigun plus 1,500 rounds	●	●	●	●	●	●
pod for one 0.5-in (12.7-mm) Browning M3 machine-gun	●	●	●	●	●	●
pod for two 7.62-mm (0.3-in) machine-guns	●	●	●	●	●	●
LAU-10/A pod for 4 × 5-in (127-mm) Zuni rockets	●	●	●	●	●	●
LAU-3/A pod for 19 × 2.75-in (69.85-mm) rockets	●	●	●	●	●	●
Matra 155 pod for 18 × 68-mm (2.68-in) rockets	●	●	●	●	●	●
Aerea AL-25-50 pod for 25 × 51-mm (2-in) rockets	●	●	●	●	●	●

Aermacchi M.B.339A

Type: two-seat trainer and light attack aircraft.

Internal armament: none.

Disposable armament: up to 1814 kg (4,000 lb) of disposable stores carried on six hardpoints (three under each wing).

Electronics and operational equipment: normal communication and navigation equipment, plus an Aeritalia 8.105.924 fixed reflector sight, or Saab RGS2 gyro sight, or Thomson-CSF RD21 gyro sight, and provision for a reconnaissance pod and Elettronica ELT/555 jammer pod.

Current variants and operators

M.B.339A: baseline variant of improved and updated version of the M.B.326 series with the same powerplant and basic design but with refined aerodynamics and a deeper forward fuselage to make possible a vertically staggered seating arrangement so that the instructor in the rear seat has a better field of vision. The type first flew in August 1976 and is used by Italy, Argentina, Dubai, Malaysia, Nigeria and Peru.

M.B.339B: version for Italy with optimized light attack capability.

M.B.339C: two-seat version of the M.B.339K Veltro 2 with much improved attack capability.

M.B.339K Veltro 2: this is the single-seat attack derivative of the basic two-seater, produced in a manner analogous to that which saw the evolution of the M.B.326K from the M.B.326G with an internal armament of two 30-mm DEFA 554 cannon plus 125 rounds per gun, and additional fuel plus avionics in the volume of the erstwhile rear cockpit. The type can be optionally provided with advanced items such as a head-up display and cathode-ray tube displays.

The M.B.339 two-seat trainer uses the same turbojet powerplant as the M.B.326 series, and has been developed into the single-seat M.B.339K Veltro 2 light attack aircraft, whose tip-tanks can leave all six hard-points free for weapons on most sorties.

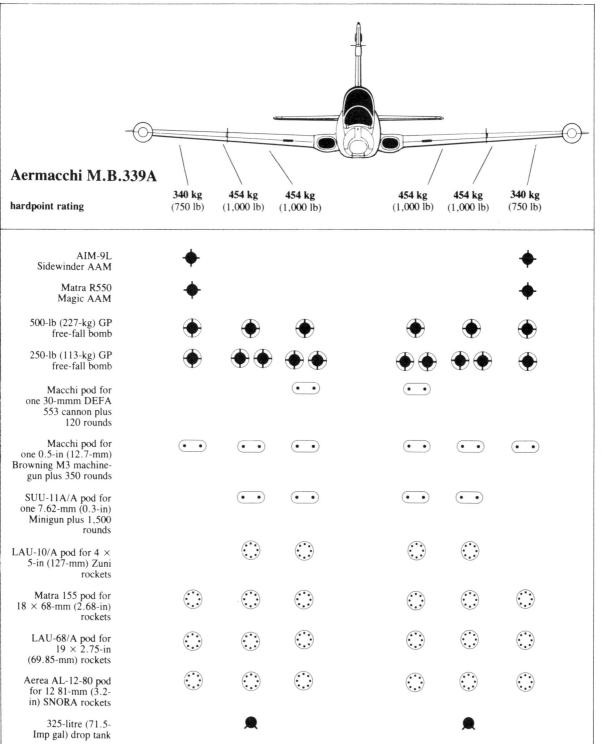

Aermacchi M.B.339A

hardpoint rating

	340 kg (750 lb)	454 kg (1,000 lb)	454 kg (1,000 lb)	454 kg (1,000 lb)	454 kg (1,000 lb)	340 kg (750 lb)
AIM-9L Sidewinder AAM	●					●
Matra R550 Magic AAM	●					●
500-lb (227-kg) GP free-fall bomb	●	●	●	●	●	●
250-lb (113-kg) GP free-fall bomb	●	●●	●●	●●	●●	●
Macchi pod for one 30-mmm DEFA 553 cannon plus 120 rounds			⬭	⬭		
Macchi pod for one 0.5-in (12.7-mm) Browning M3 machine-gun plus 350 rounds	⬭	⬭	⬭	⬭	⬭	⬭
SUU-11A/A pod for one 7.62-mm (0.3-in) Minigun plus 1,500 rounds		⬭	⬭	⬭	⬭	
LAU-10/A pod for 4 × 5-in (127-mm) Zuni rockets		⊙	⊙	⊙	⊙	
Matra 155 pod for 18 × 68-mm (2.68-in) rockets	⊙	⊙	⊙	⊙	⊙	⊙
LAU-68/A pod for 19 × 2.75-in (69.85-mm) rockets	⊙	⊙	⊙	⊙	⊙	⊙
Aerea AL-12-80 pod for 12 81-mm (3.2-in) SNORA rockets	⊙	⊙	⊙	⊙	⊙	⊙
325-litre (71.5-Imp gal) drop tank		⬤			⬤	

Aérospatiale CM.170-1 Magister

Type: two-seat trainer with secondary light attack capability.

Internal armament: two 7.5-mm (0.295-in) or 7.62-mm (0.3-in) machine-guns plus 200 rounds per gun in the upper side of the nose.

Disposable armament: up to 250 kg (551 lb) of disposable stores carried on two hardpoints (one under each wing).

Electronics and operational equipment: normal communication and navigation equipment, plus a gyro sight.

Current variants and operators

CM.170-1 Magister: baseline variant of the world's first custom-designed jet trainer, first flown in July 1952 and powered by two 400-kg (882-lb) Turboméca Marboré IIA turbojets, and able to carry a useful light armament. The type is used by France as well as the following: Algeria; Bangladesh; Belgium; Cameroun; Eire; El Salvador; Finland; Gabon; Guatemala; Israel; Lebanon; Libya; Morocco; Senegambia; Togo.

CM.170-2 Super Magister: uprated model with 480-kg (1,058-lb) Marboré VI turbojets for sprightlier performance.

CM.175 Zéphyr: arrestor hook version of the Magister for use by the French navy.

IAI Improved Fouga: this is the updated Israeli version with Marboré VI engines, modern avionics, a nose armament of two 7.62-mm (0.3-in) FN machine-guns plus 180 rounds per gun. There are four underwing hardpoints for the carriage of up to six rocket-launchers (one each on the two inner hardpoints and two each on the two outer hardpoints), or 250-lb (113-kg) Mk 81 bombs, or photo-reconnaissance pods. The type is also known as the AMIT (Advanced Multi-mission Improved Trainer).

In Israeli service the Magister has been beefed up and modernized as the AMIT trainer, but still retains the useful secondary light attack capability of which the Israelis made such good use in the 1967 'Six-Day War'.

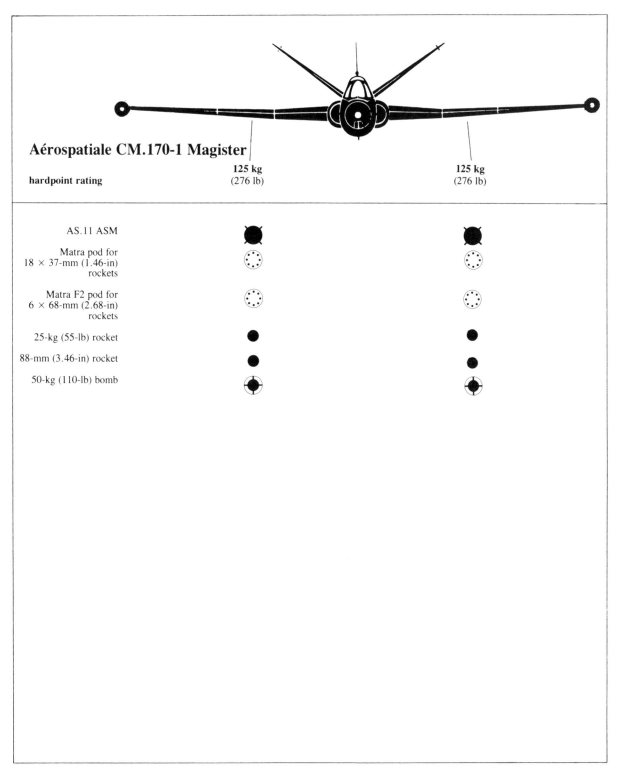

Aérospatiale CM.170-1 Magister

hardpoint rating

	125 kg (276 lb)	125 kg (276 lb)
AS.11 ASM		
Matra pod for 18 × 37-mm (1.46-in) rockets		
Matra F2 pod for 6 × 68-mm (2.68-in) rockets		
25-kg (55-lb) rocket		
88-mm (3.46-in) rocket		
50-kg (110-lb) bomb		

Aérospatiale SA 319B Alouette III Astazou

Type: multi-role helicopter.

Internal armament: one 7.62-mm (0.3-in) AA52 machine-gun plus 1,000 rounds, or one 20-mm MG151/20 cannon with 480 rounds, or one 20-mm M621 cannon with 350 rounds.

Disposable armament: up to 500 kg (1,102 lb) of disposable stores carried on four hardpoints (two on each of two outrigger pylons).

Electronics and operational equipment: normal communication and navigation equipment, plus (land version) an APX-Bézu 260 stabilized sight or (naval version) Omera-Segid ORB 31 radar and magnetic anomaly detection equipment with a towed 'bird'

Current variants and operators

SE 313B Alouette II: this was the world's first turboshaft-powered production helicopter and first flew in prototype form during March 1955. The type is powered by a 269-kW (360-shp) Turboméca Artouste IIC6 and can carry the same basic land-warfare weapons fit as the Alouette III. The Alouette series serves with air arms all over the world, notably those of Angola; Argentina; Austria; Belgium; Benin; Cameroun; Central African Republic; Chile; Congo; Denmark; Dominican Republic; Ecuador; Eire; Ethiopia; Finland; France; Gabon; Ghana; Greece; Hong Kong; India; Indonesia; Iraq; Ivory Coast; Jordan; Lebanon; Libya; Malaysia; Mexico; Morocco; Nepal; Netherlands; Nigeria; Pakistan; Peru; Portugal; Romania; Senegambia; Singapore; South Africa; Spain; Sweden; Switzerland; Tunisia; United Arab Emirates; UK; Venezuela; West Germany; Yugoslavia; Zaire; Zimbabwe.

SA 316B Alouette III: first flown as a prototype in February 1959, this is a much-improved Alouette II with greater payload and enclosed boom and a 425-kW (570-shp) Artouste IIIB turboshaft.

SA 318C Alouette II Astazou: upgraded Alouette II that first flew in February 1960 with the more economical 269-kW (360-shp) Turboméca Astazou IIA turboshaft and a strengthened transmission.

SA 319B Alouette III Astazou: upgraded Alouette III with the 448-kW (600-shp) Astazou XIV turboshaft for improved performance and payload.

Atlas Alpha XH-1: much improved derivative of the Alouette III under development in South Africa as a helicopter gunship with a revised forward fuselage for a gunner and pilot (the former forward of and below the latter), a belly-mounted GA1 20-mm cannon in a traversing/elevating mount, and stub wings for the carriage of a diversity of disposable weapons such as anti-tank missiles and rocket-launcher pods.

IAR-317 Airfox: gunship development of the Alouette III produced in Romania along the same basic lines as the XH-1 but with two fixed 20-mm cannon and provision for disposable loads of Soviet origins.

Aérospatiale SA 319B Alouette III Astazou

hardpoint rating	250 kg (551 lb)	250 kg (551 lb)	250 kg (551 lb)	250 kg (551 lb)
AS.11 ASM	●	●	●	●
AS.12 ASM		●	●	
Thomson-Brandt 68-12 pod for 12 × 68-mm (2.68-in) rockets	◉	◉	◉	◉
Thomson-Brandt 68-22 pod for 22 × 68-mm (2.68-in) rockets	◉	◉	◉	◉
Thomson-Brandt 68-36 pod for 36 × 68-mm (2.68-in) rockets	◉	◉	◉	◉
Mk 44/46 torpedo		●	●	

The Alouette III was one of the world's first truly successful armed helicopters, and though its primary installation of four AS.11 wire-guided missiles used in conjunction with the stabilized sight in the cabin roof is no longer an effective anti-tank system, the type retains a value against targets such as field fortifications and landing craft.

23

Aérospatiale SA 321G
Super Frelon

Type: five-crew anti-submarine helicopter.
Internal armament: none.
Disposable armament: up to 2000 kg (4,409 lb) of disposable stores carried on two hard points (one on each side of the fuselage).
Electronics and operational equipment: normal communication and navigation equipment, plus Thomson-CSF Sylphe panoramic search radar, Omera-Segid ORB 31D Heracles search and Exocet designation radar, Bendix ASQ-13 dunking sonar, and Doppler navigation.

Current variants and operators
SA 321G Super Frelon: first flown in November 1965, this is a massive yet capable ship- and shore-based anti-submarine helicopter intended primarily for the clearance of the approaches to France's nuclear submarine bases. The type may be updated with a SFIM autopilot plus automatic coupler, Crouzet Nadir navigation system, ORB 32WAS radar, Sintra-Alcatel HS-12 dunking sonar and Thomson-CSF Lamparo acoustic data-processing system. The similar SA 321GM and SA 321GV models are operated by the Libyan and Iraqi air forces respectively, the former having ORB 32WAS radar and sonar in the anti-submarine role, and the latter featuring provision for AM.39 Exocet anti-ship missiles.
SA 321J Super Frelon: export model with Turmo IIIC6 turboshafts. The type is operated by China (in the naval role with ORB 31D radar) and Zaire (VIP role without radar).
SA 321K Super Frelon: non-amphibious version for Israel, based on the commercial SA 321J and since refitted with 1,895-shp (1413-kW) General Electric T58-GE-16 turboshafts in place of the original Turmo turboshafts.
SA 321L Super Frelon: non-amphibious version for South Africa with Turmo IIIE6 turboshafts.
SA 321M Super Frelon: amphibious transport version for Libya with Turmo IIIE6 turboshafts and no radar.
Harbin Zhi-8: designation of the licensed version of the SA 321J produced in China but lacking the ORB 31D radar of the French-supplied helicopters: it is likely that considerable production will be undertaken in China after the first flight in June 1986.

The SA321G version of the Super Frelon was procured by the French navy mainly for the anti-submarine protection of the bases used by the country's nuclear submarines, but can also be used in the anti-ship role with an armament of two AM.39 Exocet air-launched missiles.

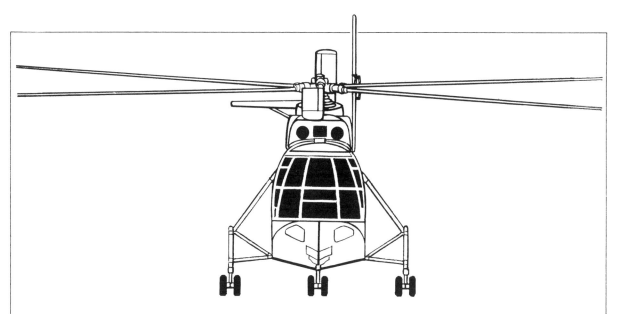

Aérospatiale SA 321G Super Frelon

hardpoint rating	**1000 kg** (2,205 lb)	**1000 kg** (2,205 lb)
AM.39 Exocet anti-ship missile	●	●
Mk 44/46 or L6 torpedo	● ●	● ●
250-kg (551-lb) mine	● ● ● ●	● ● ● ●
Mk 49/52/54 depth charge	● ● ● ●	● ● ● ●

Aérospatiale AS 332B/F Super Puma

Type: 24-seat multi-role helicopter.

Internal armament: two 7.62-mm (0.3-in) NF1 or FN-MAG macchine-guns plus 400 rounds, or one 20-mm M621 cannon plus 720 rounds.

Disposable armament: up to 1500 kg (3,307 lb) of disposable stores carried on two hardpoints (one on each side of the fuselage).

Electronics and operational equipment: normal communication and navigation equipment, plus a Decca or Nadir self-contained navigation system with roller map etc, and (naval helicopters) Bendix RDR 1400 or RCA Primus search radar in search-and-rescue machines, or Omera-Segid ORB 3214 panoramic search radar in anti-ship machines, or Alcatel HS-12 dunking sonar in anti-submarine machines.

Current variants and operators

SA 330B Puma: initial production version of this important tactical helicopter series first flown in April 1968 and powered by Turboméca Turmo IIIC6 turboshafts for a payload of 20 troops or 3200 kg (7,055 lb) of freight. The type has the same basic armament provision (cannon or machine-guns) as the AS 332 but generally carries only a cannon or machine-gun. Puma series helicopters have been sold to Abu Dhabi; Algeria; Argentina; Belgium; Brazil; Cameroun; Chad; Chile; Congo; Ecuador; Ethiopia; France; Gabon; Guinea; Indonesia; Iraq; Ivory Coast; Kenya; Kuwait; Lebanon; Malawi; Mexico; Morocco; Nepal; Nigeria; Oman; Pakistan; Portugal; Qatar; Romania; Senegambia; Singapore; South Africa; Spain; Sudan; Togo; UK; Zaire.

SA 330C Puma: export version of the SA 330B with Turmo IVC turboshafts.

SA 330E Puma: version of the SA 330B for the RAF.

SA 330H Puma: uprated version of the SA 330C.

SA 330L Puma: final production development of the basic Puma, with a number of detail modifications and improvements for delivery from 1976.

AS 332B Super Puma: much improved version first flown in September 1977 with greater performance and payload (21 troops or 4500 kg/9,921 lb of freight) but reduced maintenance requirements.

AS 332F Super Puma: naval version with revised sensors, and provision for two Mk 46 anti-submarine torpedoes, or two AM.39 Exocet anti-ship missiles, or six AS.15TT lightweight anti-ship missiles, or one AM.39 and three AS.15TT missiles.

AS 332M Super Puma: stretched version of the AS 332B with payload increased to 24 troops.

Armed with two Aerospatiale Exocet missiles for use against surface naval targets, an AS 332F Super Puma demonstrates its versatility as a weapons platform.

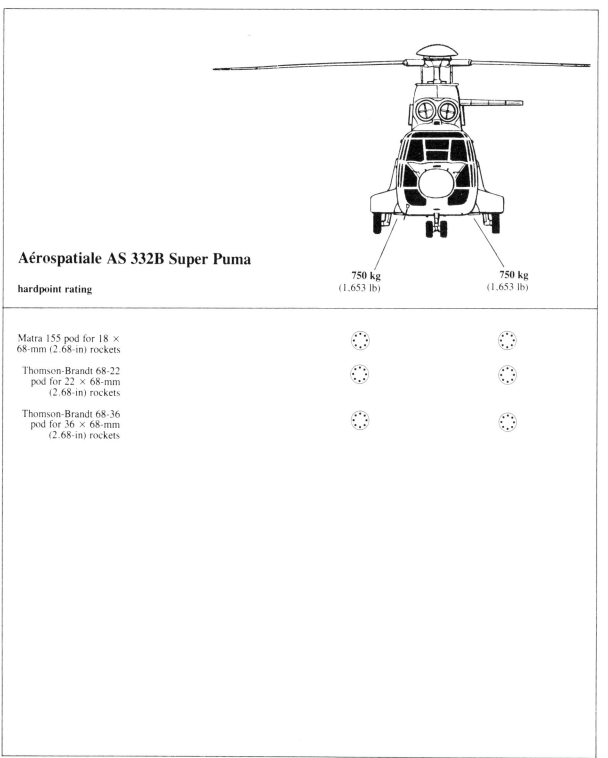

Aérospatiale AS 332B Super Puma

hardpoint rating

750 kg
(1,653 lb)

750 kg
(1,653 lb)

Matra 155 pod for 18 ×
68-mm (2.68-in) rockets

Thomson-Brandt 68-22
pod for 22 × 68-mm
(2.68-in) rockets

Thomson-Brandt 68-36
pod for 36 × 68-mm
(2.68-in) rockets

Aérospatiale SA 341F Gazelle

Type: five-seat multi-role helicopter.

Internal armament: provision for one Emerson Flexible Turret System (previously designated Mini-TAT) with one 7.62-mm (0.3-in) General Electric GAU-2B/A Minigun plus rounds on the side of the fuselage.

Disposable armament: up to 400 kg (882 lb) of disposable stores carried on two hardpoints (one on each side of the fuselage).

Electronics and operational equipment: normal communication and navigation equipment, plus an APX Bézu 334 stabilized sight (AS.11 or AS.12 installation) or an APX 397 stabilized sight (HOT installation).

Current variants and operators

SA 341B Gazelle: initial production version of the Gazelle for the British army; the type first flew in April 1967 and is powered by the 440-kW (590-shp) Turboméca Astazou IIIN turboshaft for a payload of three passengers or 700 kg (1,540 lb) of freight. The Gazelle has been sold to military operators in Abu Dhabi; Burundi; Cameroun; Ecuador; Egypt; Eire; France; Guinea; Iraq; Jordan; Kenya; Kuwait; Lebanon; Libya; Morocco; Qatar; Rwanda; Syria; UK; Yugoslavia.

SA 341C Gazelle: trainer and communications version of the SA 341B for the Royal Navy.

SA 341D Gazelle: communications version of the SA 341B for the RAF.

SA 341F Gazelle: basic version with the Astazou IIIC turboshaft for the French army. The SA 341F Canon subvariant has a 20-mm M621 cannon on the cabin side.

SA 341H Gazelle: export version of the SA 341 baseline series with the Astazou IIIB turboshaft.

SA 342K Gazelle: uprated version with the 650-kW (870-shp) Astazou XIVH turboshaft.

SA 342L Gazelle: improved export version based on the SA 342J civil helicopter.

SA 342M Gazelle: dedicated anti-tank version for the French army with the 640-kW (859-shp) Astazou XIVM turboshaft, Decca 80 Doppler navigation, an infra-red sight, exhaust deflectors and an armament of four or six HOT anti-tank missiles used in conjunction with an APX 397 sight.

France's primary anti-armour helicopter is the SA342M Gazelle, which carries four HOT tube-launched missiles and a SFIM APX 397 gyro-stabilized roof sight.

Aérospatiale SA 341F Gazelle

hardpoint rating	200 kg (441 lb)	200 kg (441 lb)
AS.11 ASM	●●	●●
AS.12 ASM	●	●
HOT anti-tank missile	●●	●●
pod for two 7.62-mm (0.3-in) AA52 or FN-MAG machine-guns	⊙	⊙
Thomson-Brandt 68-7 pod for 7 × 68-mm (2.68-in) rockets	⊙	⊙
Thomson-Brandt 68-12 pod for 12 × 68-mm (2.68-in) rockets	⊙	⊙
Matra HALMA pod for 10 × 68-mm (2.68-in) rockets	⊙	⊙

Aérospatiale SA 365F Dauphin 2

Type: two-seat anti-ship helicopter.
Internal armament: none.
Disposable armament: up to 500 kg (1,102 lb) of disposable stores carried on four hardpoints (two on each side of the fuselage).
Electronics and operational equipment: normal communication and navigation equipment, plus Thomson-CSF Agrion search and target-designation radar.

Current variants and operators

SA 361H/HCL Dauphin: first flown in June 1972 as replacement for the Alouette III series, the Dauphin has been developed in a number of civil and military forms. The SA 361H is powered by a single 1030-kW (1,380-shp) Turboméca Astazou XXB turboshaft, and can carry a crew of two plus eight passengers or 1363 kg (3,005 lb) of freight. Alternatively the type can be armed for the light battlefield role. The internal armament options include one 20-mm M621 cannon plus 500 rounds, or two 7.62-mm (0.3-in) AA52 or FN-MAG machine-guns plus 200 rounds per gun, and the disposable armament options are eight HOT anti-tank missiles (in two four-round packs used in conjunction with an APX 397 stabilized sight), or two pods each containing two 7.62-mm (0.3-in) machine-guns, or two pods each containing 22 68-mm (2.68-in) or 19 2.75-in (69.85-mm) rockets. Military operators of the Dauphin series are: Cameroun; China; Dominican Republic; Eire; France; Hong Kong; Ivory Coast; Malawi; Morocco; Saudi Arabia; Sri Lanka.
SA 365F Dauphin 2: this is the naval version of the SA 365 twin-engined series, powered by two 529-kW (710-shp) Turboméca Arriel 520M turboshafts; the type can carry eight passengers in the cabin, but is generally used in the anti-ship role. It can also be fitted with Omera-Segid ORB 32W or Bendix RDR search radar and equipment for the search-and-rescue role.
SA 365M Panther: powered by two 625-kW (838-shp) Turboméca TM333 turboshafts, this is the dedicated battlefield type able to transport a squad of infantry or, alternatively, operate in the close support role with two cabin-mounted 7.62-mm (0.3-in) FN-MAG machine-guns or 20-mm M621 cannon, and with a disposable armament of two Thomson-Brandt 68-22 pods each with 22 68-mm (2.68-in) rockets or eight HOT anti-tank missiles used in conjunction with a SFIM Viviane stabilized day/night sight with forward-looking infra-red sensor.
SA 366G: short-range search-and-rescue variant with two 680-shp (507-kW) Avco Lycoming LTS101-750A-1 turboshafts and used by the US Coast Guard under the designation HH-65A Dolphin.
Harbin Z-9 Zaitun: Chinese licence-built SA 365M.

Aérospatiale SA 365F Dauphin 2

hardpoint rating	125 kg (276 lb)	125 kg (276 lb)		125 kg (276 lb)	125 kg (276 lb)
AS.15TT anti-ship missile					

The SA 365F Dauphin 2 has a useful capability against small warships with its combination of Agrion radar (under the nose with its antenna folded back) and four AS.15TT missiles.

31

Aéro L-39ZA Albatros

Czechoslovakia

Type: single-seat light attack aircraft.
Internal armament: one 23-mm GSh-23L twin-barrel cannon plus 150/180 rounds in a semi-fixed pack under the fuselage.
Disposable armament: up to 1100 kg (2,425 lb) of disposable stores carried on four hardpoints (two under each wing).
Electronics and operational equipment: normal communication and navigation equipment, plus an ASP-3-NMU-39 sight and provision for an optical reconnaissance pod.

Current variants and operators

L-39C Albatros: first flown in November 1969, this is the replacement for the Aero L-29 'Maya' in all Warsaw Pact air forces (with the exception of that of Poland) for basic and advanced flying training. Other operators are Afghanistan, Cuba, Ethiopia, Guinea-Bissau; Iraq, Libya, Nicaragua, Syria and Vietnam. This model has two 500-kg (1,102-lb) hardpoints for the weapons training role.
L-39ZO Albatros: weapons trainer derivative of the L-39C with four underwing hardpoints for 1100 kg (2,425 lb) of disposable stores.
L-39ZA Albatros: dedicated attack aircraft with the rear cockpit replaced by additional fuel and avionics, and fitted with an under-fuselage gun pack.
L-39V Albatros: target-towing version of the basic trainer.
L-39MS Albatros: updated and uprated version of the L-39C entering service in 1987 with a 2400-kg (5,291-lb) turbofan, improved airframe and revised avionics. The greater power is designed to offer better performance rather than more payload.

The L-39 series has been developed in armed versions, but the relatively unstaggered seating of the two crew combines with the upswept flying surfaces to make the Albatros better suited for flying training than light attack.

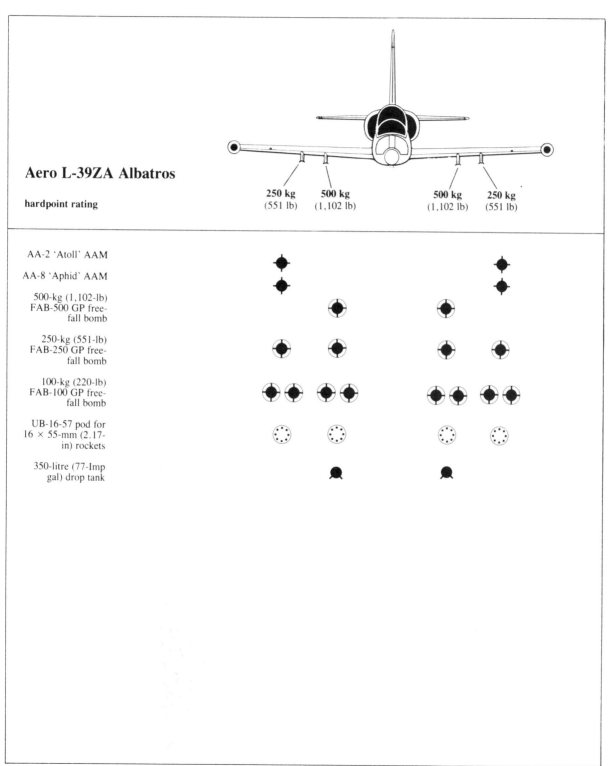

Aero L-39ZA Albatros

hardpoint rating

250 kg
(551 lb)

500 kg
(1,102 lb)

500 kg
(1,102 lb)

250 kg
(551 lb)

AA-2 'Atoll' AAM

AA-8 'Aphid' AAM

500-kg (1,102-lb)
FAB-500 GP free-
fall bomb

250-kg (551-lb)
FAB-250 GP free-
fall bomb

100-kg (220-lb)
FAB-100 GP free-
fall bomb

UB-16-57 pod for
16 × 55-mm (2.17-
in) rockets

350-litre (77-Imp
gal) drop tank

Agusta A 129 Mangusta

Type: two-seat anti-tank helicopter.

Internal armament: none.

Disposable armament: up to 1000 kg (2,205 lb) of disposable stores carried on four hardpoints (two under each stub wing).

Electronics and operational equipment: normal communication and navigation equipment, plus an M65 TOW sight with forward-looking infra-red sensor and laser rangefinder, an infra-red suppressor and a defensive suite including Elettronica/E-Systems radar-warning receiver, ITT radar jammer, Sanders infra-red jammer, and Perkin-Elmer radar and laser warning system.

Current variant and operator

A 129: first flown in September 1983, the A 129 is Europe's first custom-designed anti-tank helicopter and due to enter service in the later 1980s. Plans are currently under discussion for co-production of a Mk 2 version with more advanced weapons and a single-engined powerplant. Current orders are for Abu Dhabi and Italy.

The ordnance hardpoints of the Agusta A129 are clearly visible in this close-up shot of one of the world's most formidable attack helicopters.

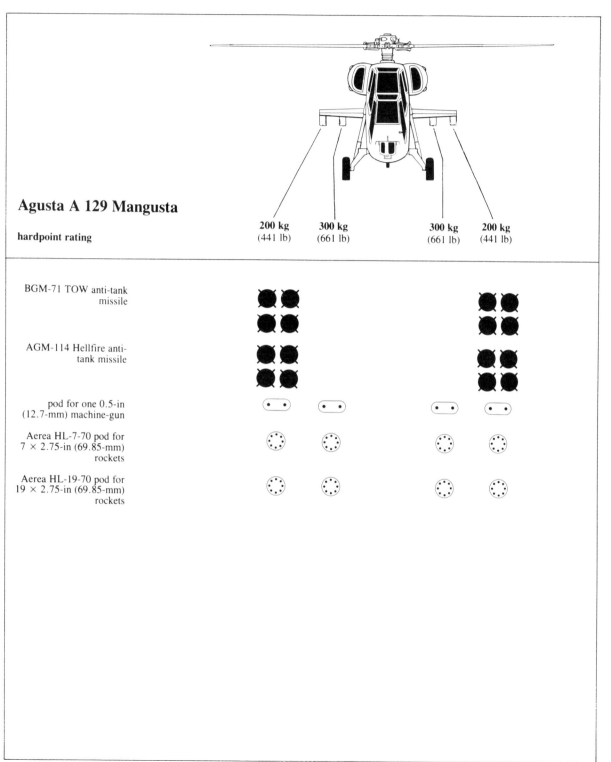

Agusta A 129 Mangusta

hardpoint rating

	200 kg (441 lb)	300 kg (661 lb)		300 kg (661 lb)	200 kg (441 lb)
BGM-71 TOW anti-tank missile	●● ●●			●● ●●	
AGM-114 Hellfire anti-tank missile	●● ●●			●● ●●	
pod for one 0.5-in (12.7-mm) machine-gun	⊙⊙	⊙⊙		⊙⊙	⊙⊙
Aerea HL-7-70 pod for 7 × 2.75-in (69.85-mm) rockets	⊛	⊛		⊛	⊛
Aerea HL-19-70 pod for 19 × 2.75-in (69.85-mm) rockets	⊛	⊛		⊛	⊛

Agusta (Bell) AB.204AS

Type: four-seat anti-submarine and anti-ship helicopter.

Internal armament: none.

Disposable armament: up to 500 kg (1,102 lb) of disposable stores carried on two hardpoints (one on each side of the fuselage).

Electronics and operational equipment: normal communication and navigation equipment, plus APS-195 search radar and Bendix ASQ-13B dunking sonar, and (with AS.12 installation) XM28 sight.

Current variants and operators

AB.204B: this is the Italian licence-built version of the Bell Model 204B multi-role helicopter, and can carry up to eight passengers in the cabin. This variant is operated by Austria, Greece, Italy, Somali Republic, Sweden and Turkey.

AB.204AS: Italian-developed version optimized for the detection and destruction of submarines and small surface units (fast attack craft, corvettes etc), and used by Italy and Spain.

The AB.204B generally operates without armament, but like many light and medium helicopters of the tactical variety can be fitted with a wide assortment of weapons should the situation require.

Agusta (Bell) AB.204AS

hardpoint rating

	250 kg (551 lb)	250 kg (551 lb)
Mk 46 or A 244S anti-submarine torpedo		
AS.12 ASM		

Agusta (Bell) AB.212ASW

Type: four-seat anti-submarine and anti-ship helicopter.
Internal armament: provision for an Emerson Dual Flexible Turret System for machine-guns or a cannon (usually not fitted).
Disposable armament: up to 500 kg (1,102 lb) of disposable stores carried on two hardpoints (one on each side of the fuselage).
Electronics and operational equipment: normal communication and navigation equipment, plus Canadian Marconi APN-208(V)2 Doppler navigation; Canadian Marconi CMA-708B/ASW tactical computing system; Bendix ASQ-13B dunking sonar; SMA/APS-705 search or (with Marte system) SMA/APQ-706 search and target designation radar and (with AS.12 installation) XM58 stabilized sight, or (for mid-course guidance of ship-launched Otomat missiles) TG-2 Teseo system, or (with Sea Killer installation) Marte target acquisition and missile guidance system.

Current variants and operators
AB.212: used by countries including Austria, Iran, Lebanon, Morocco, Saudi Arabia, United Arab Emirates and Zambia, this is the Italian licence-built version of the Bell Model 212, and is a utility type able to carry seven passengers or freight.
AB.212ASW: Italian development optimized for the anti-submarine and anti-ship roles with advanced sensors and weapons. The type is used by Iran, Italy, Peru, Spain, Syria, Turkey and Venezuela amongst others.

A considerable development of the Bell 212 series, the AB.212ASW features advanced sensors and weapon capability making it a highly effective platform against submarines (with weapons such as the torpedo seen here) and light surface vessels.

Agusta (Bell) AB.212ASW

hardpoint rating	250 kg (551 lb)	250 kg (551 lb)
Mk 46 or A 244S anti-submarine torpedo	●	●
Sea Killer Mk 2 anti-ship missile	●	●
AS.12 ASM	●	●
depth charge	◉	◉

Agusta (Sikorsky) ASH-3D/H Sea King

Type: four-seat anti-submarine and anti-ship helicopter.

Internal armament: none.

Disposable armament: up to 1400 kg (3,086 lb) of disposable stores carried on two hardpoints (one on each side of the fuselage).

Electronics and operational equipment: normal communication and navigation equipment, plus SMA/APS-705 search or (with Marte system) SMA/APQ-706 search and target designation radar; Bendix ASQ-13B dunking sonar; Doppler navigation; tactical computer system and (with Sea Killer installation) Marte target acquisition and missile guidance system.

Current variants and operators

ASH-3D/H Sea King: this is an upgraded Italian development of the basic Sikorsky SH-3D/H series with high capability against submarines and surface vessels. The variant is used by Italy, Iran and Syria amongst others, and can also double in two other roles, namely troop transport (31 troops) and search-and-rescue (25 survivors).

ASH-3D/TS: VIP transport version for Italy.

HH-3F: Italian-built version of the HH-3F Pelican search-and-rescue helicopter.

Demonstrating its potential as a missile platform is the Agusta ASH-3H variant of the basic Sea King design. The missile is an AM.39 Exocet.

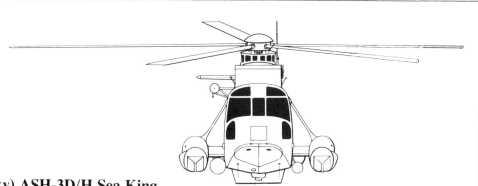

Agusta (Sikorsky) ASH-3D/H Sea King

hardpoint rating	700 kg (1,543 lb)	700 kg (1,543 lb)
Mk 46 or A 244S anti-submarine torpedo	⬤⬤	⬤⬤
AM.39 Exocet anti-ship missile	⬤	⬤
AGM-84 Harpoon anti-ship missile	⬤	⬤
Sea Killer Mk 2 anti-ship missile	⬤	⬤
AS.12 ASM	⬤⬤	⬤⬤
depth charge	⊕⊕	⊕⊕

Beech T-34C-1

Type: two-seat light attack and counter-insurgency aircraft.

Internal armament: none.

Disposable armament: up to 1,200 lb (544 kg) of disposable stores carried on four hardpoints (two under each wing).

Electronics and operational equipment: normal communication and navigation equipment, plus a Chicago Aerial CA-513 sight.

Current variants and operators

T-34A: initial production model for the US Air Force as a primary trainer powered by the 225-hp (168-kW) Continental O-470-13 piston engine. The type first flew in prototype form during December 1948.

T-34B Mentor: US Navy equivalent of the T-34A.

T-34C Turbine Mentor: straightforward turbine-engined version of the T-34B with a 400-shp (298-kW) Pratt & Whitney Canada PT6A-25 turboprop and other more modern features. The type first flew in September 1973.

T-34C-1: armed version of the T-34C designed for export (Algeria, Argentina, Ecuador, Gabon, Indonesia, Morocco and Peru) in the weapons training and counter-insurgency roles.

The armed version of the Mentor is the T-34C-1, which is used by countries such as Morocco mainly for flying and weapon training but remains available as a useful light attack and counter-insurgency type.

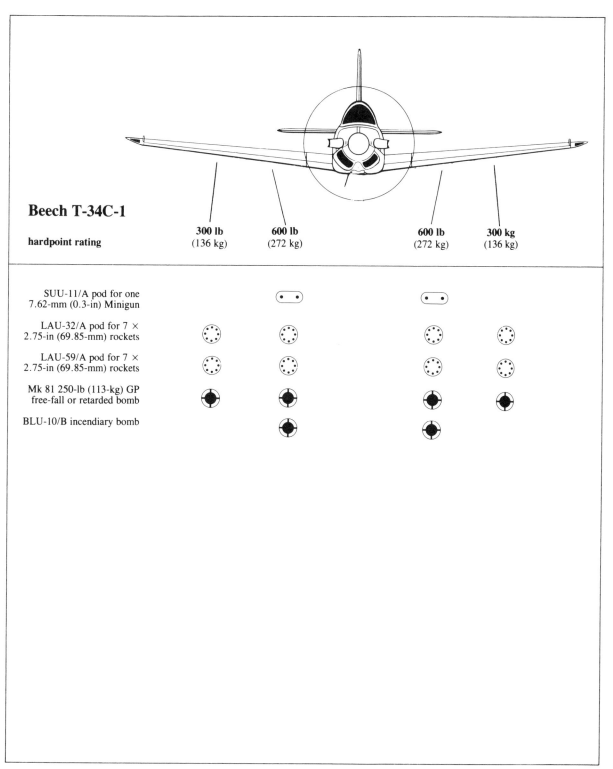

Beech T-34C-1

hardpoint rating

	300 lb (136 kg)	600 lb (272 kg)		600 lb (272 kg)	300 kg (136 kg)
SUU-11/A pod for one 7.62-mm (0.3-in) Minigun		⬭		⬭	
LAU-32/A pod for 7 × 2.75-in (69.85-mm) rockets	◉	◉		◉	◉
LAU-59/A pod for 7 × 2.75-in (69.85-mm) rockets	◉	◉		◉	◉
Mk 81 250-lb (113-kg) GP free-fall or retarded bomb	◉	◉		◉	◉
BLU-10/B incendiary bomb		◉		◉	

Bell Modernized AH-1S HueyCobra

Type: two-seat anti-tank and close support helicopter.

Internal armament: one General Electric Universal Turret (located under the nose) to accommodate most 20-mm or 30-mm cannon types, US aircraft being armed with a 20-mm General Electric M197 three-barrel rotary cannon plus 750 rounds.

Disposable armament: up to 2,000 lb (907 kg) of disposable stores carried on four hardpoints (two under each stub wing).

Electronics and operational equipment: normal communication and navigation equipment, plus an M65 stabilized TOW sight or Laser-Augmented Airborne TOW sight or Hughes FACTS (FLIR-Augmented Cobra TOW Sight); helmet-mounted sights; Kaiser head-up display; Hughes laser rangefinder; Rockwell laser marked-target seeker; Baldwin M138 stores management system; Teledyne digital fire-control system; Marconi air-data system; Sanders ALQ-144 infra-red countermeasures; E-Systems/ Loral APR-39 radar-warning receiver; ITT ALQ-136 electronic countermeasures; Tracor M130 chaff dispenser and Perkins-Elmer laser-warning receiver.

Current variants and operators

AH-1G HueyCobra: the HueyCobra was the world's first in-service helicopter gunship, evolved in the Vietnam War for a first flight during September 1965 as a derivative of the UH-1B/C utility helicopter. The type is powered by one 1,100-shp (820-kW) Avco Lycoming T53-L-13 turboshaft, and was tailored for helicopter escort and close support with a nose armament of one M28 turret (two 7.62-mm/ 0.3-in GAU-2B/A Miniguns plus 4,000 rounds per gun, or two M129 40-mm grenade-launchers plus 300 rounds per launcher, one GAU-2B/A and one M129) and four stub-wing hardpoints for four M159 pods (19 × 2.75-in/69.85-mm rockets), or four M157 pods (7 × 2.75-in/69.85-mm rockets), or two M18E1 pods (each with one 7.62-mm/0.3-in Minigun), or one M35 pod (one 20-mm M61A1 Vulcan six-barrel rotary cannon plus 1,000 rounds). Operators of the HueyCobra series include Egypt, Greece, Iran, Israel, Japan, Jordan, Pakistan, Spain, Turkey and the USA.

TH-1G HueyCobra: two-seat conversion trainer variant of the AH-1G.

Modified AH-1S HueyCobra: this is the US Army's primary anti-tank version, evolved via the AH-1Q interim anti-tank type (eight BGM-71 TOW missiles and M65 sight) and the uprated AH-1R (1,800-shp/1342-kW T53-L-703 turboshaft) with the best features of these two out-of-service variants. The designation Modified AH-1S covers 290 AH-1Gs adapted with the T53-L-703 and TOW armament plus improved offensive and defensive avionics.

Production AH-1S HueyCobra: improved version of the Modified AH-1S amounting to 100 new-build aircraft with flat-plate canopies, revised cockpits and instrumentation for genuine nap-of-the-earth flight.

Up-gun AH-1S HueyCobra: development of the Production AH-1S with the General Electric Universal Turret and the M138 stores-management system.

Modernized AH-1S HueyCobra: definitive AH-1S with all earlier improvements plus Doppler navigation; laser rangefinder; laser marked-target seeker; head-up display; ballistic computer; secure voice communications; jammers and other features.

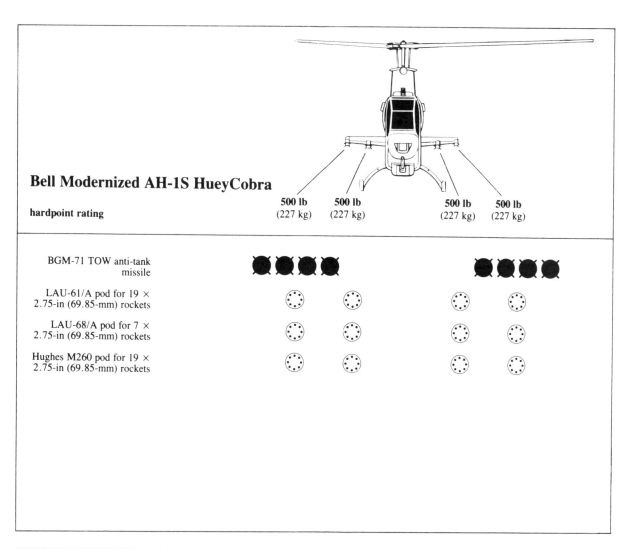

Bell Modernized AH-1S HueyCobra

hardpoint rating	500 lb (227 kg)	500 lb (227 kg)	500 lb (227 kg)	500 lb (227 kg)
BGM-71 TOW anti-tank missile	●	● ●	● ●	● ●
LAU-61/A pod for 19 × 2.75-in (69.85-mm) rockets	◉	◉	◉	◉
LAU-68/A pod for 7 × 2.75-in (69.85-mm) rockets	◉	◉	◉	◉
Hughes M260 pod for 19 × 2.75-in (69.85-mm) rockets	◉	◉	◉	◉

The single-engined AH-1S HueyCobra offers many tactical advantages over earlier models, including flat-plate canopies for minimum glint, and an advanced suite of sensors and weapons, here including eight TOWS and a turreted M197 20-mm cannon.

45

Bell AH-1T Improved SeaCobra

Type: two-seat close support and attack helicopter.

Internal armament: one General Electric Universal Turret (located under the nose) to accommodate most 20-mm or 30-mm cannon types, US aircraft being armed with a 20-mm General Electric M197 three-barrel rotary cannon plus 750 rounds.

Disposable armament: up to 2,200 lb (998 kg) of disposable stores carried on four hardpoints (two under each stub wing).

Electronics and operational equipment: normal communication and navigation equipment, plus an M65 stabilized TOW sight, M73 rocket sight, Sanders infra-red countermeasures, Tracor M130 chaff dispenser and a number of add-on items.

Current variants and operators

AH-1J SeaCobra: this was the version of the HueyCobra for the US Marine corps, differing from the US Army version primarily in having a 1,800-shp (1342-kW) Pratt & Whitney Canada T400-CP-400 coupled-turboshaft powerplant for greater survivability and additional power, offering more payload at the expense of reduced performance. The type first flew in October 1969 and is used by Iran, Israel, South Korea and the USA. The US aircraft have been upgraded in many instances to carry TOW or Hellfire anti-tank missiles, a night-flying capability having been added by the installation of night-vision cockpit equipment.

AH-1T Improved SeaCobra: much improved version of the AH-1J with dynamic features of the experimental Model 309 KingCobra and powered by the 2,050-shp (1528-kW) Pratt & Whitney Canada T400-WV-402 coupled turboshaft. The first AH-1T flew in May 1976.

AH-1W SuperCobra: first flown in 1986, this is essentially an up-engined version of the AH-1T with two 1,730-shp (1290-kW) General Electric T700 turboshafts for 65% greater installed power and much improved performance with heavier payload (the latter including TOW and Hellfire anti-tank missiles).

The most advanced version of the HueyCobra series currently in service is the AH-1W SuperCobra of the US Marine Corps. The type has excellent performance, advanced avionics and a primary armament of eight BGM-71 TOW anti-tank missiles and a three-barrel M197 20-mm cannon.

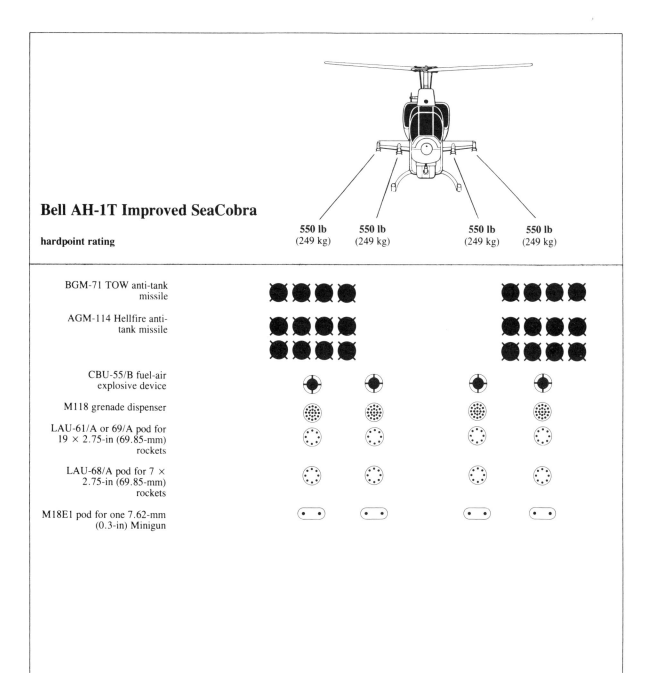

Bell AH-1T Improved SeaCobra

hardpoint rating

	550 lb (249 kg)	**550 lb** (249 kg)	**550 lb** (249 kg)	**550 lb** (249 kg)
BGM-71 TOW anti-tank missile				
AGM-114 Hellfire anti-tank missile				
CBU-55/B fuel-air explosive device				
M118 grenade dispenser				
LAU-61/A or 69/A pod for 19 × 2.75-in (69.85-mm) rockets				
LAU-68/A pod for 7 × 2.75-in (69.85-mm) rockets				
M18E1 pod for one 7.62-mm (0.3-in) Minigun				

Boeing B-52G Stratofortress

Type: six-seat strategic bomber and missile-carrier.

Internal armament: four 0.5-in (12.7-mm) Colt-Browning M3 machine-guns in a remotely-controlled tail installation.

Disposable armament: up to 50,000 lb (2,263 kg) of disposable stores carried in the 1,043-cu ft (29.53-cu m) weapons bay and on two hardpoints (one under each wing).

Electronics and operational equipment: normal communication and navigation equipment, plus a constantly updated (currently Phase VI) defensive electronics suite including Motorola ALQ-122 SNOE countermeasures system; Dalmo-Victor ALR-46 digital radar-warning receiver; Westinghouse ALQ-153 pulse-Doppler tail-warning receiver; ITT ALQ-172 deception noise jammers and Northrop ALQ-155(V) advanced electronic countermeasures system. Other electronic items are the ASQ-155 terrain-avoidance radar, the Electro-optical Viewing System comprising two steerable chin turrets (the port unit containing Westinghouse AVQ-22 low-light-level TV and the starboard unit containing Hughes AAQ-6 forward-looking infra-red); a satellite communications system; an ASG-15 tail turret fire-control system, and the Boeing-integrated Offensive Avionics System Phase I with Teledyne Ryan Doppler navigation; Honeywell ASN-131 inertial navigation system; IBM/Raytheon ASQ-38 analog bombing and navigation system; Lear Siegler attitude heading and reference system and McDonnell Douglas TERCOM (TERrain-COntour Matching) guidance.

Current variants and operator

B52-G Stratofortress: initially flown in April 1952 as the first genuinely inter-continental heavy bomber operated by the US Air Force's Strategic Air Command (still the only operator), the B-52 has gone through a number of variants before emerging as

A fully-updated B-52G of the Strategic Air Command lifts off in clean condition, though the normal load is six AGM-86B air-launched cruise missiles on each of two underwing hardpoints plus up to eight AGM-69A SRAMs on a rotary launcher in the weapons bay.

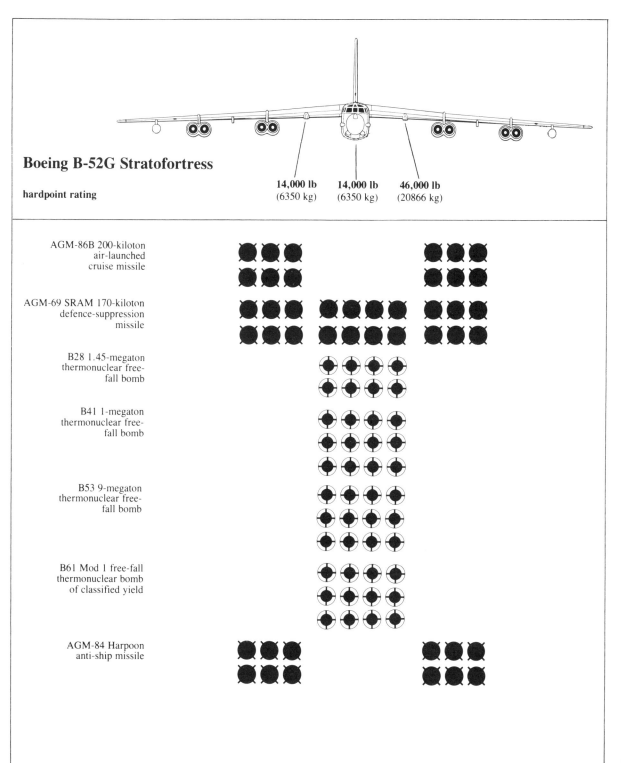

Boeing B-52G Stratofortress

hardpoint rating

14,000 lb
(6350 kg)

14,000 lb
(6350 kg)

46,000 lb
(20866 kg)

AGM-86B 200-kiloton
air-launched
cruise missile

AGM-69 SRAM 170-kiloton
defence-suppression
missile

B28 1.45-megaton
thermonuclear free-
fall bomb

B41 1-megaton
thermonuclear free-
fall bomb

B53 9-megaton
thermonuclear free-
fall bomb

B61 Mod 1 free-fall
thermonuclear bomb
of classified yield

AGM-84 Harpoon
anti-ship missile

Right *Over its impressively long service career the B-52 has been comprehensively updated, especially in its avionics systems. This is reflected on the flightdeck of this Stratofortress, in which the 1950s'-vintage central console for engine instruments is flanked by 1980s' vintage Electro-optical Viewing System computer-graphics CRTs for low-level navigation and terrain-avoidance within the context of the Strategic Radar Program update.*

Right *One of the many keys to the venerable B-52's continued viability is the advanced nature of the navigation and attack system, which has been steadily upgraded to ensure accurate low-level navigation. Seen here is the navigator's station on a B-52G.*

Below *A B-52G in flight with its two six-round clusters of white AGM-86B air-launched cruise missiles under the inner portions of the wings.*

the B-52G definitive turbojet-engined bomber in October 1958 with 13,750-lb (6237-kg) Pratt & Whitney J57-P-43WB engines, a remotely-controlled tail turret, a shorter vertical tail and a 'wet' wing to boost fuel capacity from 35,550 to 46,575 US gal (134571 to 176305 litres). The type was originally configured to carry free-fall nuclear weapons and two AGM-28A Hound Dog stand-off missiles under the wings, but by 1972 all surviving aircraft had been revised for the carriage of 20 AGM-69A SRAM missiles (eight in the weapons bay and six on each of two underwing launchers), the underwing launchers having since been altered for the carriage of 12 AGM-86B air-launched cruise missiles on six-round launchers. Aircraft not used for the ALCM programme are configured for long-range maritime patrol with an armament of AGM-84 Harpoon powered and GBU-15(V) unpowered anti-ship missiles.

B-52H Stratofortress: definitive model with 17,000-lb (7711-kg) Pratt & Whitney TF33-P-3 turbofans (boosting range by one-third compared with that of the B-52G), a 20-mm General Electric M61A1 Vulcan cannon in the tail turret with the ASG-21 fire-control system, revised electronic countermeasures and installation of terrain-avoidance radar. Electronics and improvements are similar to those of the B-52G and the weapons bay is to be configured for a rotary launcher for eight AGM-86B ALCMs, boosting the

Powered by TF33 tubofan engines rather than the more thirsty J57 turbojets of earlier models, the B-52H is the longest-ranged Strato-fortress model, and was also the last to enter service, though it too has been extensively updated since the middle 1960s. This aircraft sports the markings of Strategic Air Command's 379th Bomb Wing.

capacity of this model to 20 such missiles. When the Rockwell B-1B enters full service in the late 1980s, the surviving B-52Gs and B-52Hs are to be configured for the long-range tactical and operational bombing role with conventional weapons and stand-off submunition dispensers, including the GBU-15 glide bomb, AGM-130 rocket-assisted glide bomb and 'Popeye' 3,000-lb (1,361-kg) stand-off weapon.

Right *The primary key to Strategic Air Command's capability for global deployment and intercontinental strategic operations is the co-ordination of bombers and inflight-refuelling tankers, symbolized here as a B-52H takes on fuel from a KC-135 of SAC's huge tanker fleet.*

Below *View from the position of a KC-135 'boomer' as he flies the aerodynami-cally-controlled refuelling probe towards the receptacle of a waiting B-52H.*

52

Above *Ultimate production model of the mighty Strato-fortress, the B-52H posses-ses remarkable range and massive payload, and has been fully modernized with the Electro-optical Viewing System (identifiable by the chin bulges for its low-light-level TV and FLIR sensors), Offensive Avionics System, Phase VI ECM improve-ments and other electronics indicated by the mas of ex-ternal antennae and fair-ings.*

Above left *The B-52G was built with the inner portion of each wing stressed for a large pylon able to accom-modate one AGM-28 Hound Dog cruise missile, an obsolete weapon replaced by the AGM-69 SRAM and more recently the AGM-86B air-launched cruise missile, of wich twelve are carried (tandem triplets on each pylon). The bomb bay of the B-52G is too small to accom-modate the AGM-86's rotary launcher, and thus reserved for SRAM defense-suppres-sion missiles.*

Left *Tandem triplets of AGM-86B air-launched cruise missiles in folded configuration under the wings of a B-52G.* 53

British Aerospace (Blackburn/HS) Buccaneer S.Mk 2B

Type: two-seat low-level attack aircraft.

Internal armament: none.

Disposable armament: up to 16,000 lb (7258 kg) of disposable stores carried on the revolving door of the weapons bay and on four hardpoints (two under each wing).

Electronics and operational equipment: normal communication and navigation equipment, plus Ferranti Airpass III (Blue Parrot) radar (with long-range search, attack, ground mapping and terrain-avoidance capabilities); head-up display; Decca Doppler navigation; central air-data system; bombing computer; weapon-bay reconnaissance pack (one F97 night and six F95 day cameras); Marconi ARI.18228 radar-warning receiver system; and podded systems such as Westinghouse ALQ-101 electronic countermeasures.

The Buccaneer is of elderly design but still provides superb low-level flight characteristics and the ability to carry heavy loads over a considerable range. The bulged bomb-bay door accommodates extra fuel (with more receivable via the fixed inflight-refuelling probe). Under the port wing can be seen an AJ.168 Martel TV-guided air-to-surface missile (outboard) with its data-link pod (inboard).

Current variants and operators

Buccaneer S.Mk 2A: the Buccaneer first flew in April 1958 as a turbojet-engined naval strike aircraft and has since matured into an exceptional land-based low-level attack aircraft in its S.Mk 2 form with Rolls-Royce Spey turbofans. This mark lacks the capability for Martel air-to-surface missiles, and is used only by the RAF.

Buccaneer S.Mk 2B: improved version for the RAF with a bulged weapon-bay door for additional fuel capacity and provision for Martel missiles.

Buccaneer S.Mk 50: version for South Africa with a rectractable twin-rocket assisted take-off unit and provision for AS.30 air-to-surface missiles.

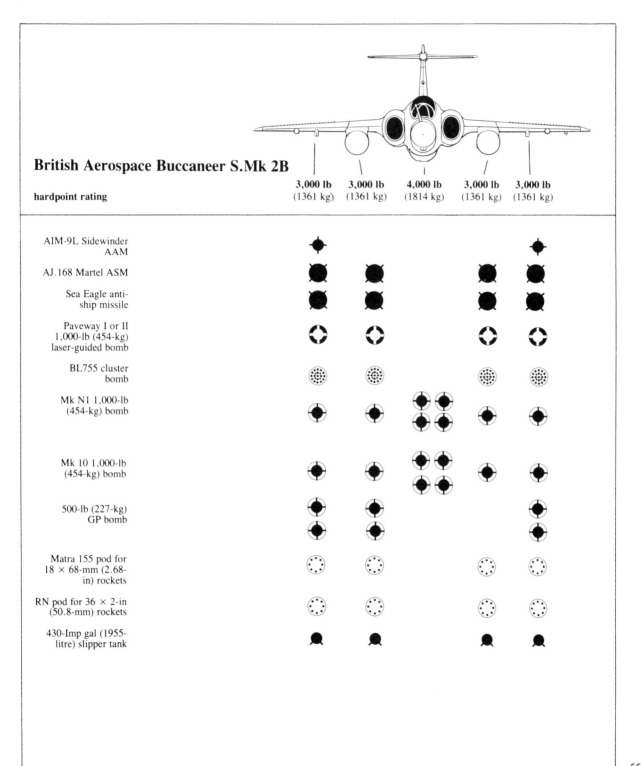

British Aerospace Buccaneer S.Mk 2B

hardpoint rating

	3,000 lb (1361 kg)	3,000 lb (1361 kg)	4,000 lb (1814 kg)	3,000 lb (1361 kg)	3,000 lb (1361 kg)
AIM-9L Sidewinder AAM					
AJ.168 Martel ASM					
Sea Eagle anti-ship missile					
Paveway I or II 1,000-lb (454-kg) laser-guided bomb					
BL755 cluster bomb					
Mk N1 1,000-lb (454-kg) bomb					
Mk 10 1,000-lb (454-kg) bomb					
500-lb (227-kg) GP bomb					
Matra 155 pod for 18 × 68-mm (2.68-in) rockets					
RN pod for 36 × 2-in (50.8-mm) rockets					
430-Imp gal (1955-litre) slipper tank					

British Aerospace (English Electric/BAC) Canberra B(I).Mk 8

Type: two-seat light bomber and intruder.

Internal armament: four 20-mm Aden cannon plus 500 rounds per gun in an optional ventral pack carried in the rear of the two-part weapons bay.

Disposable armament: up to 8,000-lb (3629-kg) of disposable stores carried in the weapons bay and on two hardpoints (one under each wing).

Electronics and operational equipment: normal communication and navigation equipment.

Current variants and operators

Canberra B.Mk 2: this was the initial production version of the Canberra, which had first flown in May 1949. The type is powered by two 6,500-lb (2948-kg) Rolls-Royce Avon Mk 101 turbojets and can carry two tandem triplets of 1,000-lb (454-kg) bombs internally. The variant is still operated by Argentina and Venezuela.

Canberra T.Mk 4: two-seat conversion trainer derivative of the B.Mk 2 used by Argentina and Venezuela.

Canberra B.Mk 6: definitive bomber model with 7,500-lb (3402-kg) Avon Mk 109 turbojets, updated avionics and two underwing hardpoints each rated at 1,000 lb (454 kg). The maximum disposable load is 8,000 lb (3629 kg), the underwing hardpoints being able to accommodate bombs, AS.20 or AS.30 air-to-surface missiles, and rocket-launcher pods. The type is used by Peru amongst others.

Canberra PR.Mk 7: photo-reconnaissance variant based on the B.Mk 6, and used by India and (in earlier form) by Venezuela.

Canberra B(I).Mk 8: night intruder version of the B.Mk 6 with a fighter-type cockpit for the pilot and the navigator/bomb-aimer positioned in the glazed nose. Aircraft of this basic type are used by India and Peru.

Canberra PR.Mk 9: definitive photo-reconnaissance version used by Chile and the UK.

Canberra B(I).Mk 12: version of the B(I).Mk 8 for South Africa and Venezuela.

Canberra E.Mk 15: navaid calibration model for the RAF.

Canberra T.Mk 17: definitive electronic countermeasures trainer for the RAF with V-bomber systems such as a radar-warning receiver and chaff dispenser.

Canberra T.Mk 19: electronically-silent trainer aircraft for the RAF.

Canberra T.Mk 22: radar trainer version for the Fleet Air Arm with Airpass III (Blue Parrot) radar.

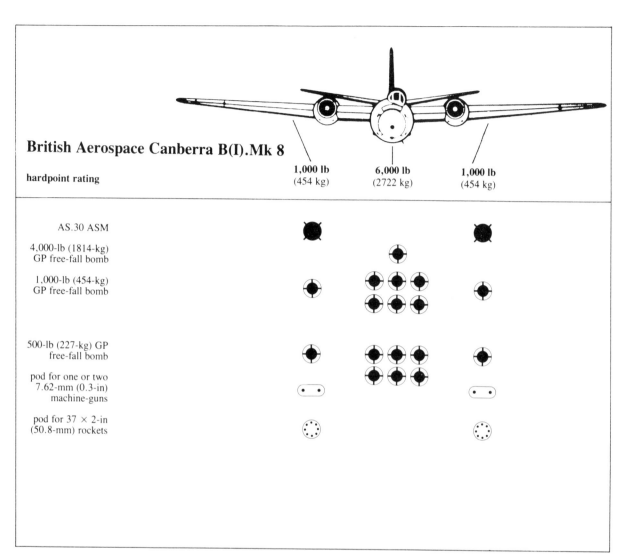

British Aerospace Canberra B(I).Mk 8

hardpoint rating	1,000 lb (454 kg)	6,000 lb (2722 kg)	1,000 lb (454 kg)
AS.30 ASM	●		●
4,000-lb (1814-kg) GP free-fall bomb		●	
1,000-lb (454-kg) GP free-fall bomb	●	● ● ● / ● ● ●	●
500-lb (227-kg) GP free-fall bomb	●	● ● ● / ● ● ●	●
pod for one or two 7.62-mm (0.3-in) machine-guns	●		●
pod for 37 × 2-in (50.8-mm) rockets	●		●

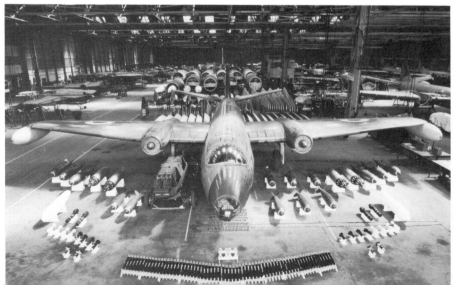

For its time the Canberra was a versatile aircraft, and this weapon display in front of a Canberra B(I). Mk 6 shows a number of practice weapons and their carriers as well operational weapons such as 'iron' bombs of various sizes, rocket-launchers and their weapons and, beside the fuselage, a detachable cannon pack for easy installation in the rear part of the weapons bay.

57

British Aerospace (HS) Harrier GR.Mk 3

A Harrier GR.Mk 1 (distinguishable from the GR.Mk 3 standard model by its lack of laser nose and fin-mounted radar-warning receiver) in a typical operational environment: this aircraft of No.1 Squadron based at RAF Wittering demonstrates off-airfield deployment with temporary snow camouflage and an external fit of two 30-mm cannon in the pods beneath the fuselage; two 100-Imp gal (455-litre) drop tanks on the inner underwing hardpoints; two Matra 155 rocket-launchers on the outer underwing hardpoints, and a practice bomb dispenser on the fuselage centreline.

Type: single-seat STOVL close support and reconnaissance aircraft.

Internal armament: (optional) two podded 30-mm Aden Mk 4 (modified) cannon plus 125 rounds per gun carried in place of the under-fuselage strakes.

Disposable armament: up to 8,000 lb (3269 kg) of disposable stores carried on five hardpoints (one under the fuselage and two under each wing) plus two wingtip stations for air-to-air missiles, though the Harrier is only cleared for vertical take-off with 5,300 lb (2404 kg) of stores.

Electronics and operational equipment: normal communication and navigation equipment, plus Smiths head-up display; Ferranti FE541 inertial navigation system; Smiths air-data computer; Marconi ARI.18223 radar-warning receiver; Ferranti Type 106 laser ranger and marked-target seeker; Tracor ALE-40 chaff dispenser; and one nose-mounted camera, plus provision for a reconnaissance pod.

Current variants and operators

Harrier GR.Mk 3: used only by the RAF, this is the current single-seat operational version of the series, which flew in P.1127 prototype form during October 1960 and developed via the Kestrel pre-production type and Harrier GR.Mk 1 initial service model. The GR.Mk 3 differs from the GR.Mk 1 in having a lengthened nose for the laser

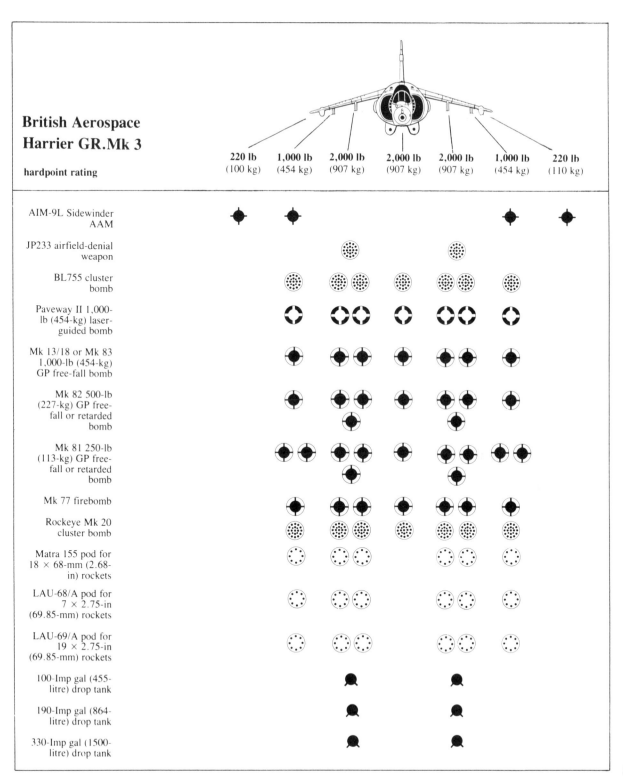

British Aerospace Harrier GR.Mk 3

hardpoint rating

Weapon	220 lb (100 kg)	1,000 lb (454 kg)	2,000 lb (907 kg)	2,000 lb (907 kg)	2,000 lb (907 kg)	1,000 lb (454 kg)	220 lb (110 kg)
AIM-9L Sidewinder AAM	●	●				●	●
JP233 airfield-denial weapon			●		●		
BL755 cluster bomb		●	●●	●	●●	●	
Paveway II 1,000-lb (454-kg) laser-guided bomb	●	●●	●	●●	●		
Mk 13/18 or Mk 83 1,000-lb (454-kg) GP free-fall bomb	●	●●	●	●●	●		
Mk 82 500-lb (227-kg) GP free-fall or retarded bomb	●	●●	●	●●	●		
Mk 81 250-lb (113-kg) GP free-fall or retarded bomb	●●	●●	●	●●	●●		
Mk 77 firebomb	●	●●	●	●●	●		
Rockeye Mk 20 cluster bomb	●	●●	●	●●	●		
Matra 155 pod for 18 × 68-mm (2.68-in) rockets	●	●●	●	●●	●		
LAU-68/A pod for 7 × 2.75-in (69.85-mm) rockets	●	●●	●	●●	●		
LAU-69/A pod for 19 × 2.75-in (69.85-mm) rockets	●	●●	●	●●	●		
100-Imp gal (455-litre) drop tank		●			●		
190-Imp gal (864-litre) drop tank		●			●		
330-Imp gal (1500-litre) drop tank		●			●		

ranger and marked-target seeker (increasing overall length by 15 in/38 cm) and greater thrust from its 21,500-lb (9752-kg) Pegasus Mk 103 vectored-thrust turbofan compared with the Harrier GR.Mk 1A's 20,500-lb (9299-kg) Pegasus Mk 102 and the Harrier GR.Mk 1's 19,000-lb (8618-kg) Pegasus Mk 101. The Harrier GR.Mk 3 can carry a reconnaissance pod fitted with optical cameras and infra-red linescan equipment.

Harrier T.Mk 4: two-seat combat-capable operational conversion and proficiency trainer variant of the GR.Mk 3, and thus fitted with that mark's radar-warning receiver and the laser ranger and marked-target seeker. This trainer version is also used by the Royal Navy as the Harrier T.Mk 4N and by the Indian navy as the Harrier T.Mk 60, though the latter is fitted with the avionics suite (less the Blue Fox radar) of the Sea Harrier.

AV-8A Harrier I: designation of the GR.Mk 3 equivalent for the US Marine Corps with the Pegasus Mk 103 turbofan but without the inertial navigation system and the laser ranger and marked target seeker. The US aircraft have Stencel rather than Martin-Baker ejector seats and are also fitted for USMC weapons, including Sidewinder air-to-air missiles.

TAV-8A Harrier I: equivalent of the Harrier T.Mk 4 for the US Marine Corps, but without the laser ranger and marked-target seeker and the radar-warning receiver.

AV-8C Harrier I: improved version of the AV-8A for the US Marine Corps with features of the McDonnell Douglas AV-8B Harrier II such as the under-fuselage lift-improvement devices, ALR-45 radar-warning receiver, ALE-39 chaff and flare dispenser, and secure voice communications.

AV-8S Matador: Spanish navy equivalent of the AV-8A.

TAV-8S Matador: Spanish navy equivalent of the TAV-8A.

British Aerospace (HS) Hawk T.Mk 1A

Type: two-seat advanced trainer with air-combat and light attack capability.

Internal armament: none.

Disposable armament: up to 6,800 lb (3084 kg) of disposable stores carried on five hardpoints (one under the fuselage and two under each wing).

Electronics and operational equipment: normal communication and navigation equipment, plus a Ferranti F195 sight (Saab RGS2 sight in Finnish aircraft) and options for a head-up display, laser ranger and marked-target seeker and other items to customer requirement, plus provision for a reconnaissance pod.

Current variants and operators

Hawk T.Mk 1: this is the baseline version of the Hawk for the RAF, and first flew as the HS.1182 prototype during August 1974. The type is powered by a single 5,200-lb (2359-kg) Rolls-Royce/Turboméca Adour Mk 151 non-afterburning turbofan, and is generally used with an 800-lb (363-kg) Aden cannon pod on the centreline hardpoint and with underwing stores limited to 1,500 lb (680 kg).

Hawk T.Mk 1A: designation of Hawk T.Mk 1s converted for the combat role with an armament of two AIM-9L Sidewinder air-to-air missiles and advanced drop loads.

Hawk Mk 50: export version of the T.Mk 1 sold to Finland, Indonesia and Kenya.

Hawk Mk 60: uprated export version with the 5,700-lb (2586-kg) Adour Mk 861 turbofan, and sold to Abu Dhabi, Dubai, Kuwait, Saudi Arabia, Switzerland and Zimbabwe.

Conceived as a trainer, the Hawk has matured into a potent multi-role type also able to undertake the light attack and interception roles. This is a Hawk T.Mk 1A of the RAF carrying a disposable armament of a Sea Eagle anti-ship missile and two AIM-9L Sidewinder AAMs.

Hawk Mk 200: first flown in May 1986, this is the single-seat dedicated combat derivative of the series, powered by the 6,500-lb (2948-kg) Adour Mk 871 and designed for the carriage of a wide assortment of weapons (including air-to-air, air-to-surface and anti-ship missiles) used in conjunction with a variety of avionics (including Ferranti Blue Fox or Thomson-CSF Agave radar, a head-up display, a laser-ranger and marked-target seeker, forward-looking infra-red, a radar-warning receiver, a tactical computer etc.)

T-45A Goshawk: trainer version for the US Navy with full carrier compatibility, twin-wheel nose unit, Adour Mk 861-46 turbofan downrated to 5,450 lb (2472 kg) for greater economy and life, revised cockpit and Martin-Baker NACES ejector seats and US Navy instrumentation.

Evidence of the Hawk T. Mk 1's versatility is provided by this quartet of aircraft: from top to bottom these are machines of the Red Arrows aerobatic team, of an unidentified 'shadow' squadron (probably of No 2 Tactical Weapons Unit), of No. 79 Squadron (a 'shadow' squadron of No 1 TWU) and of No. 4 Flying Training School.

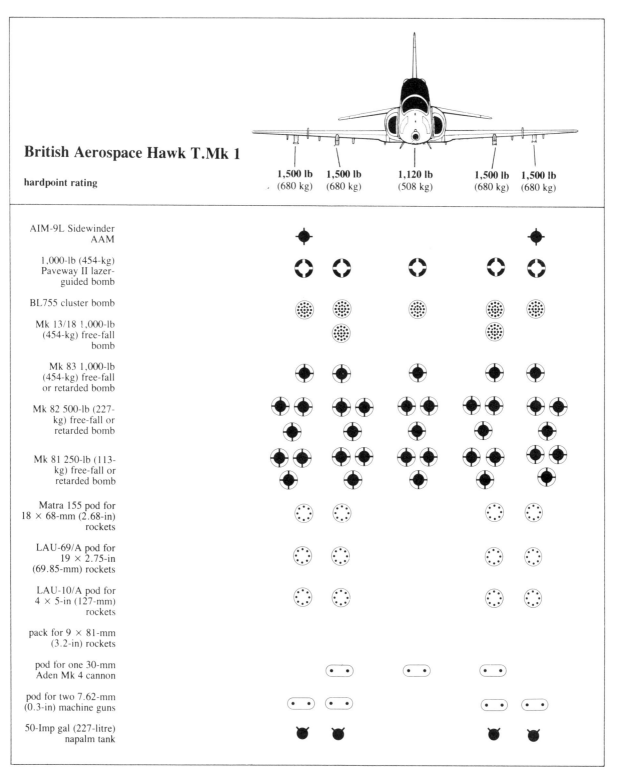

British Aerospace Hawk T.Mk 1

hardpoint rating

	1,500 lb (680 kg)	1,500 lb (680 kg)	1,120 lb (508 kg)	1,500 lb (680 kg)	1,500 lb (680 kg)
AIM-9L Sidewinder AAM	●				●
1,000-lb (454-kg) Paveway II lazer-guided bomb	◉	◉	◉	◉	◉
BL755 cluster bomb	◉	◉	◉	◉	◉
Mk 13/18 1,000-lb (454-kg) free-fall bomb		◉		◉	
Mk 83 1,000-lb (454-kg) free-fall or retarded bomb	●	●	●	●	●
Mk 82 500-lb (227-kg) free-fall or retarded bomb	●● ●	●● ●	●● ●	●● ●	●● ●
Mk 81 250-lb (113-kg) free-fall or retarded bomb	●● ●	●● ●	●● ●	●● ●	●● ●
Matra 155 pod for 18 × 68-mm (2.68-in) rockets	●	●		●	●
LAU-69/A pod for 19 × 2.75-in (69.85-mm) rockets	●	●		●	●
LAU-10/A pod for 4 × 5-in (127-mm) rockets	●	●		●	●
pack for 9 × 81-mm (3.2-in) rockets					
pod for one 30-mm Aden Mk 4 cannon		●	●	●	
pod for two 7.62-mm (0.3-in) machine guns	●	●		●	●
50-Imp gal (227-litre) napalm tank	●	●		●	●

British Aerospace (Hawker) Hunter FGA.Mk 9

Type: single-seat fighter/ground-attack aircraft.

Internal armament: four 30-mm Aden Mk 4 cannon plus 135 rounds per gun in a detachable ventral pack.

Disposable armament: up to 3,000 lb (1361 kg) of disposable stores carried on four hardpoints (two under each wing).

Electronics and operational equipment: normal communication and navigation equipment, plus ranging radar and a sight.

Current variants and operators

Hunter F.Mk 6: this was the definitive fighter variant of the Hunter, which first flew in July 1951 as the Hawker P.1067 prototype. The F.Mk 6 was introduced in June 1956 with the 10,150-lb (4604-kg) Rolls Royce Avon Mk 207, an all-moving tailplane and a number of detail improvements. Amongst current operators are India and Switzerland, the latter operating a potent upgraded version with a Saab bombing computer, AIM-9 Sidewinder air-to-air missiles and AGM-65 Maverick air-to-surface missiles.

Hunter T.Mk 7: side-by-side two-seat conversion trainer version of the Hunter T.Mk 4. Amongst current operators of this basic type are Abu Dhabi, India, Qatar and Singapore: an uprated version with the Avon Mk 203 was produced for India.

Hunter T.Mk 8: navalized version of the T.Mk 7 in several subvariants with different avionics.

Hunter FGA.Mk 9: dedicated ground-attack derivative of the F.Mk 6 used by Abu Dhabi, Chile, Kuwait, Lebanon, Qatar and Singapore.

Hunter FR.Mk 10: tactical reconnaissance version of the FGA.Mk 9 with a fan of three cameras in place of the ranging radar. The type is used by Singapore.

Hunter GA.Mk 11: attack trainer derivative of the F.Mk 4 for the Fleet Air Arm.

Hunter PR.Mk 11: photo-reconnaissance trainer of the F.Mk 4 for the Fleet Air Arm.

The Hunter family reached its combat peak as the Hunter FGA.Mk 9 ground-attack aircraft (seen here in the markings of No.9 Squadron, RAF) with full-bore Avon engine, four 30-mm cannon and the ability to carry a substantial load on the four underwing hardpoints.

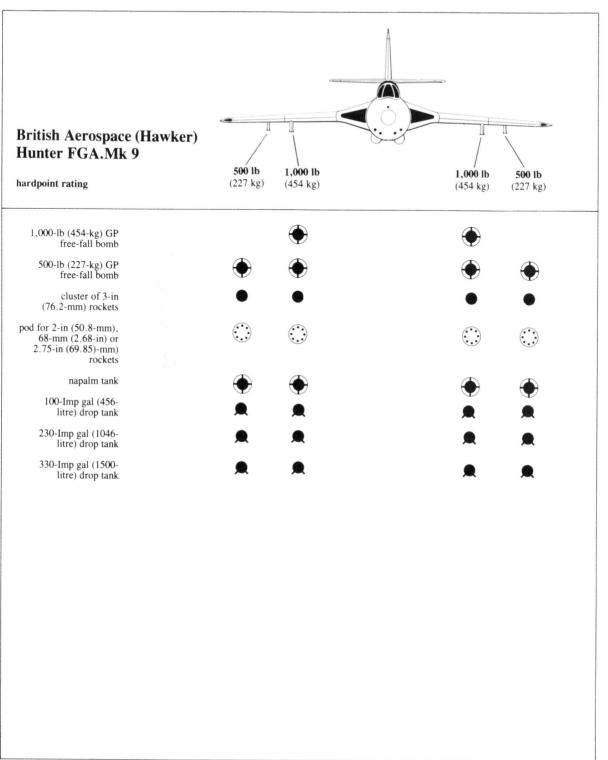

**British Aerospace (Hawker)
Hunter FGA.Mk 9**

hardpoint rating

	500 lb (227 kg)	1,000 lb (454 kg)	1,000 lb (454 kg)	500 lb (227 kg)
1,000-lb (454-kg) GP free-fall bomb		●	●	
500-lb (227-kg) GP free-fall bomb	●	●	●	●
cluster of 3-in (76.2-mm) rockets	●	●	●	●
pod for 2-in (50.8-mm), 68-mm (2.68-in) or 2.75-in (69.85)-mm rockets	⊙	⊙	⊙	⊙
napalm tank	●	●	●	●
100-Imp gal (456-litre) drop tank	●	●	●	●
230-Imp gal (1046-litre) drop tank	●	●	●	●
330-Imp gal (1500-litre) drop tank	●	●	●	●

British Aerospace (English Electric) Lightning F.Mk 53

Type: single-seat interceptor and ground-attack fighter.

Internal armament: two 30-mm Aden Mk 4 cannon plus 130 rounds per gun in the forward portion of the ventral fuel tank fairing.

Disposable armament: up to 6,000 lb (2722 kg) of disposable stores carried on four hardpoints (one above and one below each wing) plus provision for two air-to-air missiles or two retractable rocket-launcher packs in a lower fuselage installation.

Electronics and operational equipment: normal communication and navigation equipment, plus Ferranti AI-23S AIRPASS radar or (as an alternative to the air-to-air missile avionics) a reconnaissance package comprising five Vinten 360 cameras for daylight use or cameras and an infra-red linescan unit for nocturnal use.

Current variants and operators

Lightning F.Mk 3: the Lightning was conceived as the P.1 supersonic research aircraft but was then developed as a Mach 2 interceptor for the RAF, first flying in this form during October 1959. The Lightning F.Mk 3 appeared in June 1962 with a square-topped fin, two 16,360-lb (7421-kg) Rolls-Royce Avon Mk 301 afterburning turbojets, Red Top all-aspect rather than Firestreak pursuit-course air-to-air missiles (the whole AAM package being replaceable by two retractable Microcell packs, each containing 24 × 2-in/50.8-mm rockets), and the inbuilt armament of two 30-mm Aden cannon deleted. The Lightning F.Mk 3A introduced wings with reduced sweep on the outboard portions.

Lightning T.Mk 5: side-by-side two-seat armed operational conversion trainer based on the F.Mk 3.

Lightning F.Mk 6: improved F.Mk 3A with provision for a ventral fuel tank with two 30-mm cannon in its forward portion.

Lightning T.Mk 53: dual-role version for Saudi Arabia with a pair of overwing hardpoints.

Lightning T.Mk 55: side-by-side two-seat armed operational conversion trainer based on the F.Mk 53.

To the Royal Saudi air force range is a primary consideration, and aircraft such as these Lightning F.Mk 53 ground-attack fighters often train with little or no armament, though a retractable 48-cell rocket pack may be carried to supplement the two 30-mm cannon in the ventral tank.

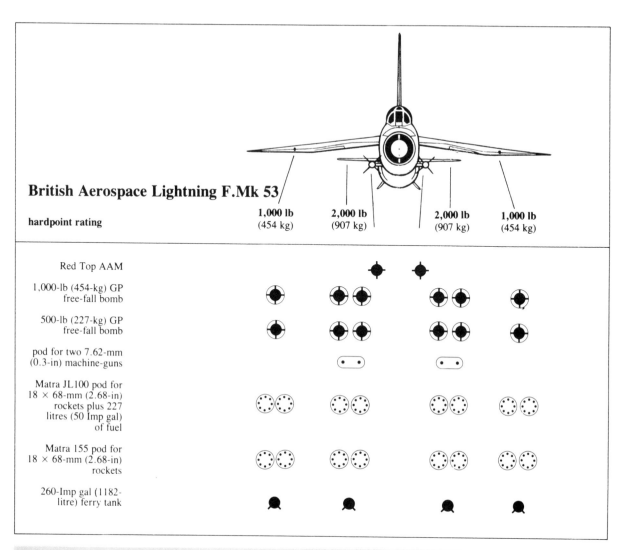

British Aerospace Lightning F.Mk 53

hardpoint rating

	1,000 lb (454 kg)	2,000 lb (907 kg)	2,000 lb (907 kg)	1,000 lb (454 kg)
Red Top AAM		●	●	
1,000-lb (454-kg) GP free-fall bomb	●	● ●	● ●	●
500-lb (227-kg) GP free-fall bomb	●	● ●	● ●	●
pod for two 7.62-mm (0.3-in) machine-guns		●	●	
Matra JL100 pod for 18 × 68-mm (2.68-in) rockets plus 227 litres (50 Imp gal) of fuel	● ●	● ●	● ●	● ●
Matra 155 pod for 18 × 68-mm (2.68-in) rockets	● ●	● ●	● ●	● ●
260-Imp gal (1182-litre) ferry tank	●	●	●	●

A Lightning F.Mk 6 of No. 5 Squadron, RAF Binbrook, sports a typical interception payload of two Red Top AAMs and two 30-mm Aden cannon on the forward part of the ventral tank. 67

British Aerospace (HS) Nimrod MR.Mk 2

Type: 12-seat maritime reconnaissance and anti-submarine aircraft.

Internal armament: none.

Disposable armament: up to 13,500 lb (6124 kg) of disposable stores carried in the 48.5-ft (14.78-m) lower-fuselage weapons bay in six lateral rows, plus provision for missiles on two hardpoints (one under each wing).

Electronics and operational equipment: normal communication and navigation equipment, plus Thorn EMI ARI.5980 Searchwater surveillance radar with attached data-processing system based on a Ferranti FM1600D digital computer; Marconi central tactical system based on a Marconi 920 ATC computer with inputs from the Ferranti inertial navigation system and radar; Emerson ASQ-10A magnetic system anomaly detection system; Loral ARI.18240/1 electronic support measures system and Marconi AQS-901 acoustic data-processing system based on two Marconi 920 ATC computers and using data from a variety of sonobuoy types such as the Australian BARRA, the Canadian TANDEM, the American SSQ-41 and SSQ-53, and the British Ultra X17255 CAMBS.

Current variants and operator

Nimrod R.Mk 1: the Nimrod series is used only by the RAF, and is derived aerodynamically from the de Havilland Comet 4 airliner with considerable structural revision and power provided by four 12,140-lb (5507-kg) Rolls-Royce Spey Mk 250 turbofans. The prototype of the series flew in May 1967, and the three Nimrod R.Mk 1s are highly classified electronic reconnaissance aircraft with Loral ESM pods at the wingtips, three spiral-helix receivers (one at the front of each wing tank and the third replacing the MAD 'sting' of the MR series) and a number of blade antennae.

Nimrod MR.Mk 2: current maritime patrol and anti-submarine version developed from the MR.Mk 1 to enter service from 1979 with a new tactical suite, a new radar, added inertial navigation and a general enhancement of operation capabilities, including provision for anti-ship and self-defence air-to-air missiles.

The Nimrod MR.Mk 2 provides the RAF with a magnificent long-range ocean patrol and anti-submarine platform that combines considerable dash speed with long on-station loiter. This is a fine example of the Nimrod MR.Mk 2P variant with an inflight-refuelling probe and several aerodynamic refinements in the tail area. Exterior views reveal little of the type's highly advanced avionics, though the various antennae, Emerson ASQ-10A MAD tail boom and Thomson-CSF ESM fintop fairing provide an indication. The aircraft is carrying self-defence AIM-9 Sidewinder AAMs, and a later addition is wingtip pods for Loral ARI.18240 ESM.

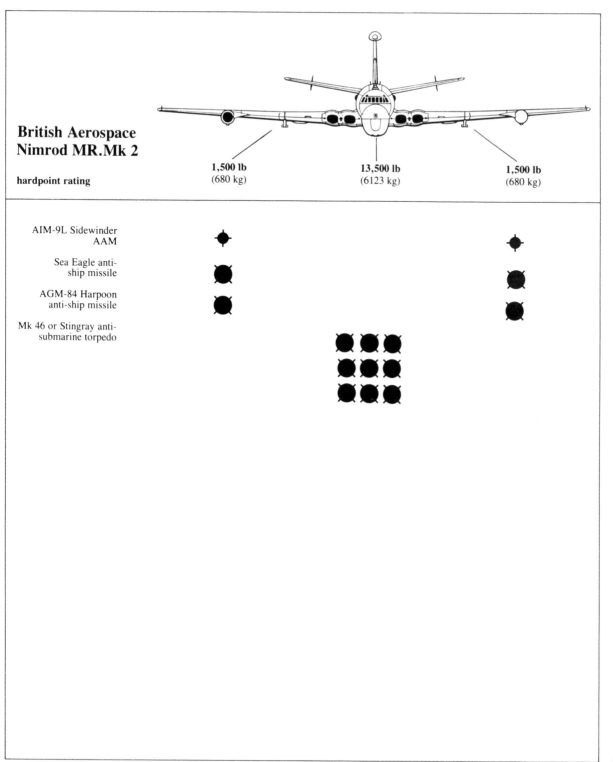

**British Aerospace
Nimrod MR.Mk 2**

hardpoint rating

1,500 lb	13,500 lb	1,500 lb
(680 kg)	(6123 kg)	(680 kg)

AIM-9L Sidewinder
AAM

Sea Eagle anti-
ship missile

AGM-84 Harpoon
anti-ship missile

Mk 46 or Stingray anti-
submarine torpedo

British Aerospace Sea Harrier FRS.Mk 1

Type: single-seat carrier-borne STOVL multi-role fighter.

Internal armament: (optional) two podded 30-mm Aden Mk 5 cannon plus 150 rounds per gun carried in place of the under-fuselage strakes.

Disposable armament: up to 8,000 lb (3269 kg) of disposable stores carried on five hardpoints (one under the fuselage and two under each wing), though the Sea Harrier is cleared for vertical take-off with only 5,000 lb (2268 kg) of stores.

Electronics and operational equipment: normal communication and navigation equipment, plus Ferranti Blue Fox multi-mode radar (search, attack, ranging and transponder modes); Ferranti heading and attitude reference system with twin gyros and Decca 72 Doppler navigation; Smiths head-up display and weapon-aiming system; Smiths air-data computer and Marconi ARI.18223 radar-warning receiver. A reconnaissance pod can be fitted on the centreline hardpoint.

Current variants and operators

Sea Harrier FRS.Mk 1: first flown in August 1978, the Sea Harrier is a much-improved development of the Harrier for British naval applications, the primary modifications being a new forward fuselage and revised avionics. The new forward fuselage accommodates the pilot in a higher, fighter-type cockpit with additional space for superior displays and provides volume for the Blue Fox radar, while the avionics are optimized for maritime nav/attack requirements.

The Royal Navy's Harrier FRS.Mk 1 proved itself a remarkably capable multi-role aircraft, especially in air-to-air combat, during the Falklands campaign of 1982, and is here seen flanked by two other types operated by 899 Squadron of the Fleet Air Arm, namely the Hunter T.Mk 8M and the Harrier T.Mk 4 (top).

Sea Harrier FRS.Mk 2: improved version under development with the more capable Blue Vixen pulse-Doppler radar (providing the Sea Harrier with a true look-down/shoot-down capability), superior electronic warfare equipment (including Marconi/Northrop Zeus active counter-measures), provision for the AIM-120A AMRAAM air-to-air missile, two additional underwing hardpoints, and the new 25-mm Aden high-velocity cannon.

Sea Harrier FRS.Mk 51: version of the FRS.Mk 1 for India with a different oxygen system and provision for Matra R550 Magic rather than Sidewinder air-to-air missiles.

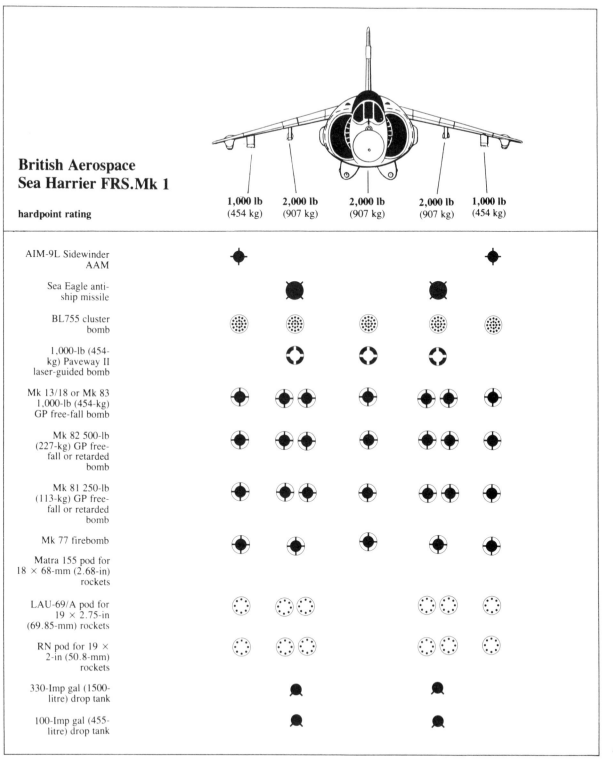

British Aerospace Sea Harrier FRS.Mk 1

hardpoint rating

	1,000 lb (454 kg)	2,000 lb (907 kg)	2,000 lb (907 kg)	2,000 lb (907 kg)	1,000 lb (454 kg)
AIM-9L Sidewinder AAM	●				●
Sea Eagle anti-ship missile		●		●	
BL755 cluster bomb	●	●	●	●	●
1,000-lb (454-kg) Paveway II laser-guided bomb		●	●	●	
Mk 13/18 or Mk 83 1,000-lb (454-kg) GP free-fall bomb	●	● ●	●	● ●	●
Mk 82 500-lb (227-kg) GP free-fall or retarded bomb	●	● ●	●	● ●	●
Mk 81 250-lb (113-kg) GP free-fall or retarded bomb	●	● ●	●	● ●	●
Mk 77 firebomb	●	●	●	●	●
Matra 155 pod for 18 × 68-mm (2.68-in) rockets					
LAU-69/A pod for 19 × 2.75-in (69.85-mm) rockets	●	● ●		● ●	●
RN pod for 19 × 2-in (50.8-mm) rockets	●	● ●		● ●	●
330-Imp gal (1500-litre) drop tank		●		●	
100-Imp gal (455-litre) drop tank		●		●	

71

UK

British Aerospace (BAC) Strikemaster Mk 80

Type: two-seat light attack and counter-insurgency aircraft.
Internal armament: two 7.62-mm (0.3-in) FN-Browning machine-guns plus 550 rounds per gun in the lower edges of the air inlets.
Disposable armament: up to 3,000 lb (1361 kg) of disposable stores carried on four hardpoints (two under each wing).
Electronics and operational equipment: normal communication and navigation equipment, plus a SFOM optical sight, or a GM2L reflector sight, or a Ferranti LFS Type 5 gyro sight. A five-camera reconnaissance pod can be carried on one of the underwing hardpoints.

Current variants and operators
Strikemaster Mk 50: this is essentially an armed version of the RAF's jet Provost T.Mk 5 trainer, which first flew in prototype form during June 1954. The Jet Provost T.Mk 5 and derived Strikemaster Mk 50 series (sold to Iraq, Sri Lanka, Sudan and Venezuela) introduced cockpit pressurization and the 2,500-lb (1134-kg) Rolls-Royce Viper Mk 201 turbojet.
Strikemaster Mk 80: strengthened version of the Mk 50 with better ejector seats and the 3,140-lb (1424-kg) Viper Mk 535 turbojet. Aircraft of this basic type were sold to Ecuador; Kenya; Kuwait; New Zealand; Oman; Saudi Arabia; Singapore and South Yemen.
Strikemaster Mk 90: updated version of the Mk 80 for Sudan.

The Strikemaster was developed from the Jet Provost as a light attack aircraft, and is seen here in the guise of a Strikemaster Mk 88 of the Royal New Zealand Air Force with an external load of two 75-Imp gal (341-litre) drop tanks and two Matra 155 rocket-launchers.

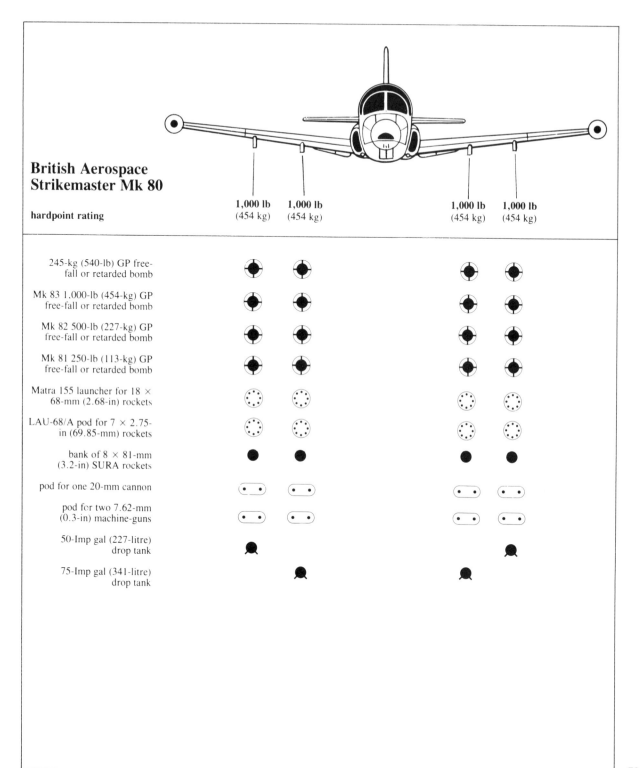

British Aerospace Strikemaster Mk 80

hardpoint rating

	1,000 lb (454 kg)	1,000 lb (454 kg)		1,000 lb (454 kg)	1,000 lb (454 kg)
245-kg (540-lb) GP free-fall or retarded bomb	●	●		●	●
Mk 83 1,000-lb (454-kg) GP free-fall or retarded bomb	●	●		●	●
Mk 82 500-lb (227-kg) GP free-fall or retarded bomb	●	●		●	●
Mk 81 250-lb (113-kg) GP free-fall or retarded bomb	●	●		●	●
Matra 155 launcher for 18 × 68-mm (2.68-in) rockets	◉	◉		◉	◉
LAU-68/A pod for 7 × 2.75-in (69.85-mm) rockets	◉	◉		◉	◉
bank of 8 × 81-mm (3.2-in) SURA rockets	●	●		●	●
pod for one 20-mm cannon	⊡	⊡		⊡	⊡
pod for two 7.62-mm (0.3-in) machine-guns	⊡	⊡		⊡	⊡
50-Imp gal (227-litre) drop tank	✹				✹
75-Imp gal (341-litre) drop tank		✹		✹	

Britten-Norman Defender

Type: variable-seat utility military aircraft.

Internal armament: none.

Disposable armament: up to 2,300 lb (1043 kg) carried on four hardpoints (two under each wing).

Electronics and operational equipment: normal communication and navigation equipment, plus customer-specified items such as a reconnaissance pod.

Current variants and operators

Defender: this is the military variant of the civil Islander light transport, which first flew in June 1965. Powered by two 300-hp 224-kW) Avco Lycoming IO-540-K1B5 piston engines, the Defender can carry a wide assortment of disposable stores on its underwing hardpoints and, most usefully for third-world operators, still provide unarmed accommodation for nine passengers, or eight paratroopers, or three litters plus two attendants, or 2,250 lb (1021 kg) of freight.

Maritime Defender: based on the Defender and intended for the resources protection and search-and-rescue roles, this has an enlarged nose for Bendix RDR 1400 search radar, the operator being located in the cabin together with two observers.

Turbine Defender: turbine-powered version of the Defender with two 320-shp (239-kW) Allison 250-B17C turboprops.

Trislander M: this is the military version of the Trislander civil transport, itself a derivative of the twin-engined Islander with three 260-hp (194-kW) O-540-E4C5 piston engines and able to carry 17 troops, or 16 paratroops or 3,700 lb (1678 kg) of freight. The type can also be used in the maritime role with optional search radar.

CASTOR Islander: designation of one Turbine Islander fitted with a nose-mounted Ferranti CASTOR (Corps Airborne STand-Off Radar) for battlefield surveillance with a two-man electronics crew to provide multi-mode data acquisition over the land

The Defender has proved popular with less affluent nations for its combination of versatility (transport and armed roles) with moderate field requirements and low purchase and operating costs. This Defender of the Mauritanian air force is seen here with the useful offensive load of twenty 81-mm (3.2 in) SURA rockets on the outboard underwing hardpoints.

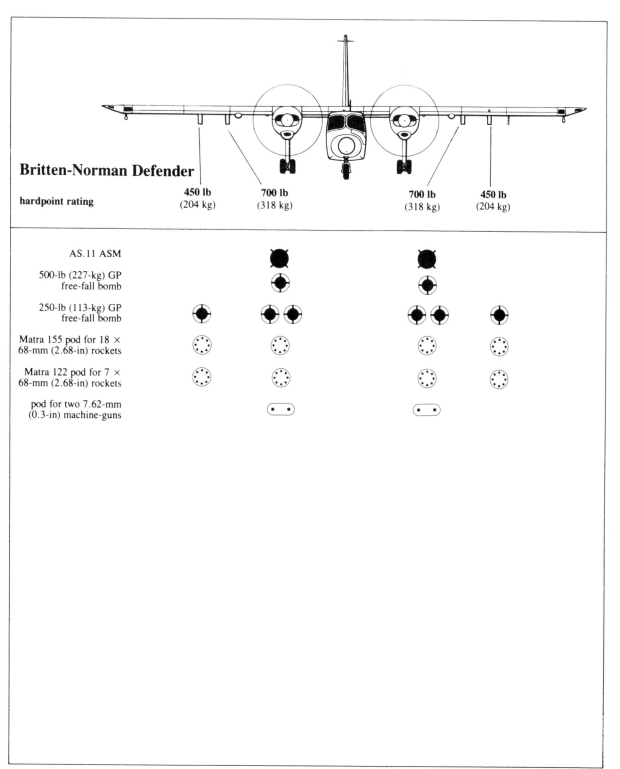

Britten-Norman Defender

hardpoint rating

	450 lb (204 kg)	700 lb (318 kg)	700 lb (318 kg)	450 lb (204 kg)

AS.11 ASM

500-lb (227-kg) GP
free-fall bomb

250-lb (113-kg) GP
free-fall bomb

Matra 155 pod for 18 × 68-mm (2.68-in) rockets

Matra 122 pod for 7 × 68-mm (2.68-in) rockets

pod for two 7.62-mm (0.3-in) machine-guns

battlefield, the data being passed to friendly forces by a data-link. The system is designed to operate in conjunction with the Phoenix stand-off radar fitted in remotely-piloted vehicles, targets of special interest being designated by the CASTOR system for closer investigation by the Phoenix-fitted RPV: the system is being evaluated against the CASTOR-C radar developed by Thorn EMI.

AEW Defender: private-venture development of the Turbine Islander with Thorn EMI Searchwater radar in a bulbous nose radome for the airborne early warning role: a version with additional capabilities is the AEW/MR Defender.

ASW/ASV Defender: version optimized for the maritime role with radar in a smaller radome and featuring provision for additional sensors such as forward-looking infra-red, magnetic anomaly detection and sonobuoys (plus the appropriate acoustic signal-processing equipment). This version can be fitted with four hardpoints for the carriage of anti-submarine and anti-ship weapons or electronic support measures and electronic countermeasures pods.

Offering much the same capabilities as the Islander series but with the added performance and operational advantages of a turbine powerplant, this is a Turbine Islander of the United Arab Emirates.

CASA C-101DD Aviojet

Spain

Type: two-seat advanced trainer with secondary light attack capability.

Internal armament: a pack with one 30-mm DEFA 553 cannon or two 0.5-in (12.7-mm) Colt-Browning M3 machine-guns can be accommodated in a bay under the rear cockpit.

Disposable armament: up to 2250 kg (4,960 lb) of disposable stores carried on six hardpoints (three under each wing).

Electronics and operational equipment: normal communication and navigation equipment, plus a Ferranti 4500 head-up display, Ferranti FIN1100 attitude and heading reference system, GEC Doppler navigation and a wide assortment of customer-specified avionics: the bay under the rear cockpit can accommodate (as alternatives to the weapon pack) a reconnaissance camera, an electronic countermeasures system or a laser designator.

Current variants and operators

C-101EB Aviojet: this is the baseline trainer and light attack model used by the Spanish air force. The type first flew in June 1977 and with the 3,500-lb (1588-kg) Garrett TFE331-2-2J turbofan the variant can carry only 1500 kg (3,311 lb) of disposable stores.

C-101BB Aviojet: improved version of the C-101EB for the export market (Chile and Honduras) with the 3,700-lb (1678-kg) TFE331-3-1J turbofan and Saab RGS2 sight.

CC-101CC Aviojet: further improved export model (Jordan) with the 4,700-lb (2132-kg) TFE331-5-1J and 2250 kg (4,690 lb) of disposable stores.

C-101DD Aviojet: 1985 model with considerably enhanced avionics adding capability for weapons such as the Sea Eagle anti-ship missile.

The C-101EB is an unsophisticated but capable trainer with useful secondary attack capability thanks to the provision of six underwing hardpoints and a gun pack beneath the fuselage.

77

A view of the C-101EB's underside shows off the type's weapon carriage capability: the underwing hardpoints are seen here with four rocket launchers and two practice bombs, while a gun pack is installed in the lower-fuselage bay that can alternatively accommodate a reconnaissance pack.

CASA C-101DD Aviojet

hardpoint rating

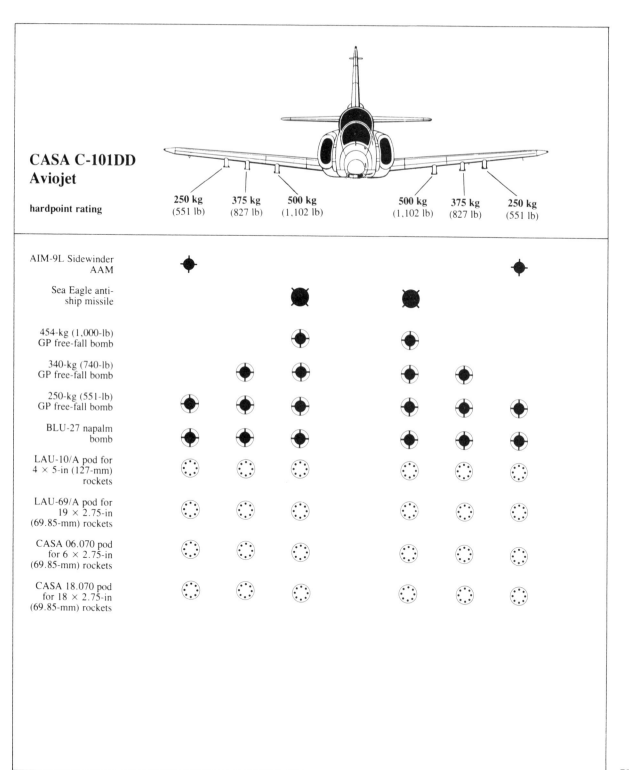

	250 kg (551 lb)	375 kg (827 lb)	500 kg (1,102 lb)		500 kg (1,102 lb)	375 kg (827 lb)	250 kg (551 lb)
AIM-9L Sidewinder AAM	●						●
Sea Eagle anti-ship missile			●		●		
454-kg (1,000-lb) GP free-fall bomb			●		●		
340-kg (740-lb) GP free-fall bomb		●	●		●	●	
250-kg (551-lb) GP free-fall bomb	●	●	●		●	●	●
BLU-27 napalm bomb	●	●	●		●	●	●
LAU-10/A pod for 4 × 5-in (127-mm) rockets	○	○	○		○	○	○
LAU-69/A pod for 19 × 2.75-in (69.85-mm) rockets	○	○	○		○	○	○
CASA 06.070 pod for 6 × 2.75-in (69.85-mm) rockets	○	○	○		○	○	○
CASA 18.070 pod for 18 × 2.75-in (69.85-mm) rockets	○	○	○		○	○	○

Cessna A-37B Dragonfly

Type: two-seat light attack and counter-insurgency aircraft.
Internal armament: one 7.62-mm (0.3-in) General Electric GAU-2B/A Minigun with 1,500 rounds in the nose.
Disposable armament: up to 5,680 lb (2576 kg) of disposable stores carried on eight hardpoints (four under each wing).
Electronics and operational equipment: normal communication and navigation equipment, plus Chicago Aerial CA-503 sight.

Current variants and operators

A-37B Dragonfly: this is the dedicated light attack derivative of the T-37 trainer series with beefed-up structure, a host of refinements, additional stores-carrying capability and power provided by two 2,850-lb (1293-kg) General Electric J85-GE-17A turbojets for considerably improved payload capability without loss of performance. The type first flew in October 1963 in the form of the YAT-37D prototype, followed by a few A-37A pre-production aircraft with the same basic airframe as the T-37 but fitted with downrated J85 engines. The A-37B currently serves with Chile; Colombia; Ecuador; El Salvador; Guatemala; Honduras; Peru; South Korea; Thailand and Uruguay.
OA-37B Dragonfly: designation of A-37Bs converted for the forward air control role with the US Air National Guard.
T-37B: this is the full-production version of the T-37A pre-production aircraft that first flew in October 1954 as the USAF's first custom-designed jet trainer. The type is powered by two 1,025-lb (465-kg) Teledyne CAE J69-T-25 turbojets and carries no armament. The type is used only by the USAF, which is to refurbish surviving aircraft for continued service after the cancellation of the Northrop T-46A that was to have succeeded it.
T-37C: export version of the T-37B with limited combat capability despite the provision of two underwing hardpoints for gun pods, rocket-launcher pods, light bombs and even AIM-9 Sidewinder air-to-air missiles. The variant is flown by Burma; Chile; Colombia; Greece; Jordan; Pakistan; Paraguay; Peru; Portugal; South Korea; Thailand; Turkey; West Germany.

The A-37B is remarkably rugged and, given its small size and comparative quietness, admirably suited to forward air control/light attack duties in areas where the latest air defences are absent.

Cessna A-37B Dragonfly

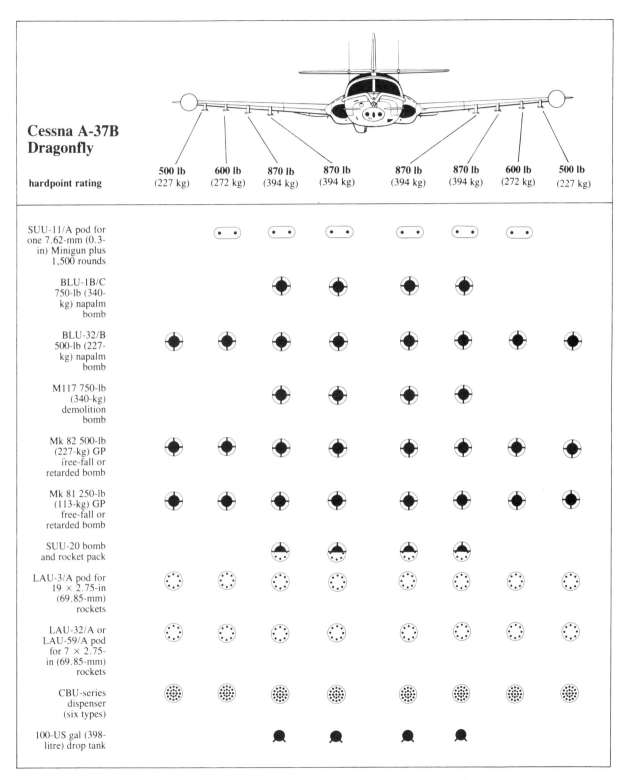

hardpoint rating	500 lb (227 kg)	600 lb (272 kg)	870 lb (394 kg)	870 lb (394 kg)	870 lb (394 kg)	870 lb (394 kg)	600 lb (272 kg)	500 lb (227 kg)
SUU-11/A pod for one 7.62-mm (0.3-in) Minigun plus 1,500 rounds		X	X	X	X	X	X	
BLU-1B/C 750-lb (340-kg) napalm bomb			X	X	X	X		
BLU-32/B 500-lb (227-kg) napalm bomb	X	X	X	X	X	X	X	X
M117 750-lb (340-kg) demolition bomb			X	X	X	X		
Mk 82 500-lb (227-kg) GP free-fall or retarded bomb	X	X	X	X	X	X	X	X
Mk 81 250-lb (113-kg) GP free-fall or retarded bomb	X	X	X	X	X	X	X	X
SUU-20 bomb and rocket pack			X	X	X	X		
LAU-3/A pod for 19 × 2.75-in (69.85-mm) rockets	X	X	X	X	X	X	X	X
LAU-32/A or LAU-59/A pod for 7 × 2.75-in (69.85-mm) rockets	X	X	X	X	X	X	X	X
CBU-series dispenser (six types)	X	X	X	X	X	X	X	X
100-US gal (398-litre) drop tank			X	X	X	X		

Dassault-Breguet Alizé

Type: three-seat carrier-borne anti-submarine aircraft.

Internal armament: none.

Disposable armament: up to 1,500 kg (3,307 lb) of disposable stores carried in a lower-fuselage weapons bay and on eight hardpoints (one under each inner wing panel and three under each outer wing panel).

Electronics and operational equipment: normal communication and navigation equipment, plus Thomson-CSF DRAA 2A or (in French aircraft) Thomson-CSF Iguane surveillance radar, electronic countermeasures and sonobuoys.

Current variant and operators

Alizé: first flown in October 1956 as the turboprop-powered anti-submarine derivative of the Breguet Br.960 Vultur turboprop/turbojet-powered carrier borne attack aircraft, the Alizé is an elderly type used by France and India, the capabilities of the French aircraft having been revived by the updating of the electronics and sensors.

For lack of a replacement the Alizé soldiers on as France's and India's sole carrier-based fixed-wing anti-submarine aircraft type, though its weapons capability is obsolescent and even its updated avionics suite limited.

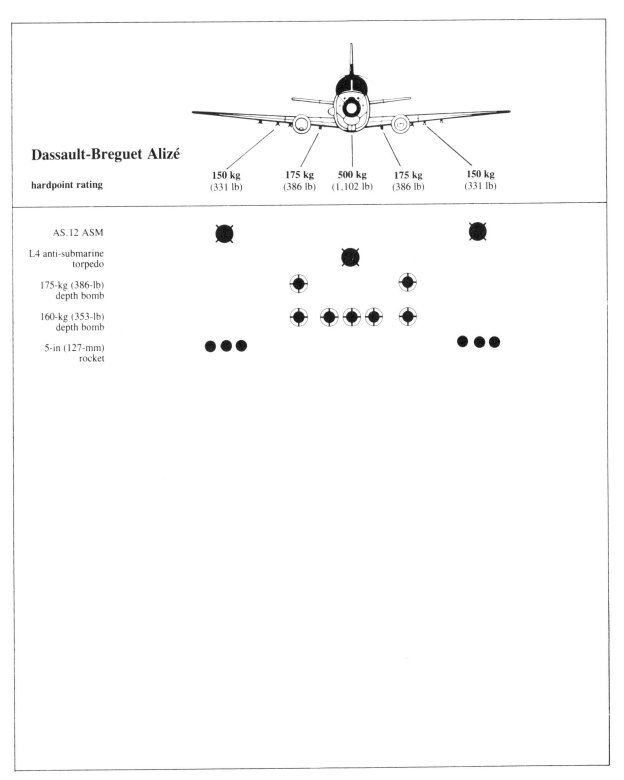

Dassault-Breguet Alizé

hardpoint rating

| | 150 kg
(331 lb) | 175 kg
(386 lb) | 500 kg
(1,102 lb) | 175 kg
(386 lb) | 150 kg
(331 lb) |

AS.12 ASM

L4 anti-submarine
torpedo

175-kg (386-lb)
depth bomb

160-kg (353-lb)
depth bomb

5-in (127-mm)
rocket

Dassault-Breguet Atlantique 2

Type: 12-seat maritime reconnaissance and anti-submarine aircraft.

Internal armament: none.

Disposable armament: up to 4,500 kg (9,921 lb) of disposable stores carried on three trusses in the lower-fuselage weapons bay and up to 3,500 kg (7,716 lb) of disposable stores carried on four hardpoints (two under each wing).

Electronics and operational equipment: normal communication and navigation equipment, plus ESD/Decca Doppler navigation, twin Sagem Uliss 53 inertial navigation systems and a Crouzet air-data computer, feeding navigational information to a Thomson-CSF tactical system which handles inputs from the Thomson-CSF Iguane surveillance radar (with a high-resolution side-looking synthetic-aperture mode for target identification); SAT/TRT forward-looking infra-red; Crouzet magnetic anomaly detection system; Thomson-CSF ARAR 13 electronic support measures system; plus Thomson-CSF Sadang acoustic signal-processing system used in conjunction with various sonobuoys carried in the rear fuselage.

Current variants and operators

Atlantic 1: designed to meet a NATO requirement, the Atlantic (redesignated Atlantic 1 after the development of the all-French Atlantique 2) first flew in October 1961 and is an extremely capable aircraft now suffering from increasing obsolesence in its avionics (Thomson-CSF DRAA 2A surveillance radar, Crouzet MAD and sonobuoys feeding a Plotac tatical system). The type is operated by France, Italy, Pakistan and West Germany. Italy is about to undertake a considerable update of its aircraft and West Germany has updated its aircraft with Loral electronic support measures equipment (five of the aircraft for the electronic intelligence role). The armament can include four L4 or Mk 44/46 torpedoes, nuclear depth bombs, unguided rockets and four AS.12 air-to-surface missiles.

Atlantique 2: French second-generation derivative of the Atlantic (hence the French spelling of the name) with an improved airframe (for longer fatique life and reduced corrosion) and a wholly revised avionics suite with modern sensors and data-processing (especially in the acoustic arena, for which more than 100 sonobuoys are carried). The type is slated to enter service in 1989.

The prototype of the Atlantique 2, then designated the Atlantic Nouvelle Génération, shows off its chin-mounted FLIR, retractable radome for the Iguane search radar, ARAR 13 electronic support measures in fintop and wingtip fairings, and Crouzet MAD in the large tail boom, as well as an underwing armament of four AS.30 air-to-surface missiles.

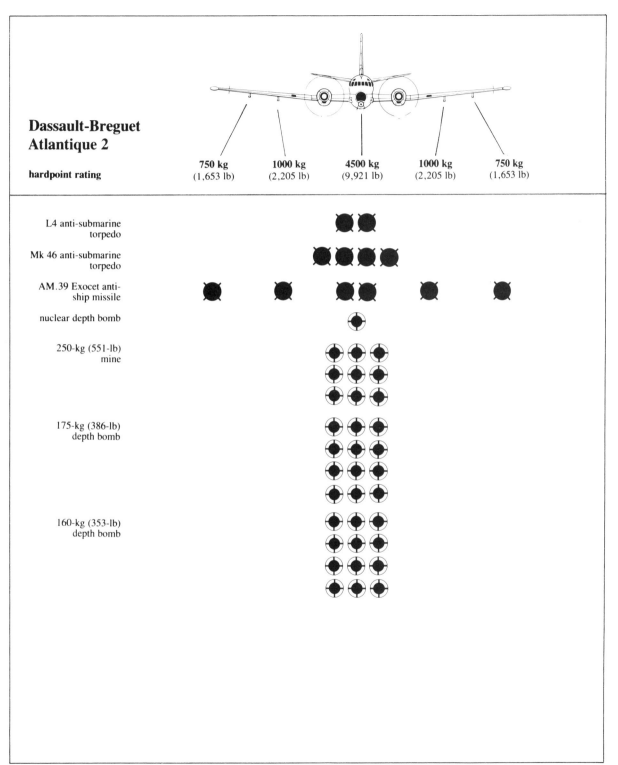

Dassault-Breguet
Atlantique 2

hardpoint rating

	750 kg (1,653 lb)	1000 kg (2,205 lb)	4500 kg (9,921 lb)	1000 kg (2,205 lb)	750 kg (1,653 lb)

L4 anti-submarine torpedo

Mk 46 anti-submarine torpedo

AM.39 Exocet anti-ship missile

nuclear depth bomb

250-kg (551-lb) mine

175-kg (386-lb) depth bomb

160-kg (353-lb) depth bomb

Dassault-Breguet Mirage IIIE

Type: single-seat intruder and fighter-bomber.

Internal armament: two 30-mm DEFA 552A cannon plus 125 rounds per gun in the lower fuselage (in the Mirage IIIC this installation cannot be carried in the rare instances where the SEPR booster rocket system is installed).

Disposable armament: up to 4000 kg (8,818 lb) of disposable stores carried on five hardpoints (one under the fuselage and two under each wing).

Electronics and operational equipment: normal communication and navigation equipment, plus Thomson-CSF Cyrano II search and fire-control radar, Thomson-CSF 97 sight; rudimentary head-up display; Marconi Doppler radar; Thomson-CSF BF radar-warning receiver and (on French aircraft) provision for a Bidon Cyclope (an under-fuselage tank containing fuel and electronic warfare equipment) or a Bidon Homing (an under-fuselage tank containing fuel plus electronic intelligence and homing equipment); plus provision for podded reconnaissance and electronic countermeasures systems such as the Thomson-CSF DB3163 Remora jammer and the Alkan chaff/flare dispenser. Many export customers have upgraded their aircraft with advanced systems such as inertial navigation, modern head-up display, state-of-the-art electronic warfare systems, laser ranger and digital computer.

Current variants and operators

Mirage IIIB: the Mirage III series has been one of France's great commercial and military successes in the period since World War 2, offering advanced and less-advanced customers alike a capable combat aircraft at modest cost. The type grew from the original Mirage III prototype which first flew in November 1956 with a 4500-kg (9,921-lb) SNECMA Atar 101G turbojet, via the pre-production Mirage IIIA with the 6000-kg (13,228-lb) Atar 09B. This latter aircraft first flew in May 1958 and was followed by the Mirage IIIB two-seat operational conversion trainer with the armament of the Mirage IIIC but lacking radar. The Mirage IIIB first flew in October 1959, and Mirage IIIs have been sold to Argentina; Australia; Brazil; Egypt; France; Israel; Lebanon; Pakistan; South Africa; Spain; Switzerland and Venezuela.

Mirage IIIBE: two-seat operational conversion trainer derived from the Mirage IIIE.

Mirage IIIC: initial all-weather interceptor and day attack aircraft with the Atar 09B turbojet, Cyrano II radar, Matra R530 air-to-air missiles and (in the absence of the optional SEPR booster rocket pack) two 30-mm cannon.

Mirage IIID: two-seat operational conversion trainer derived from the Mirage IIIO but with more advanced attack avionics. The Mirage IIID2Z is a version with the more powerful Atar 09K-50 turbojet for South Africa.

Mirage IIIE: optimized long-range intruder and fighter bomber with Cyrano IIbis radar, MEASL AD2300 Doppler navigation and the fuselage stretched by 30 cm (11.8 in), the French aircraft being nuclear-capable with one or two 15-kiloton AN52 free-fall weapons.

Mirage IIIO: version of the Mirage IIIE for Australia.

Mirage IIIR: tactical reconnaissance version of the Mirage IIIE with a length of 15.50 m (50.85 ft), a self-contained navigation system with Doppler and twin inertial platforms and five Omera 31 cameras in place of the nose radar. The Mirage IIIR2Z is a version with the more powerful Atar 09K-50 turbojet for South Africa.

Dassault-Breguet Mirage IIIE

hardpoint rating

168 kg (370 lb)	840 kg (1.852 lb)	1180 kg (2.601 lb)	840 kg (1.852 lb)	168 kg (370 lb)

Matra R550 Magic AAM

Matra R530 AAM

AS.30 ASM

AS.37 Martel or ARMAT anti-radiation missile

Durandal runway-cratering bomb

Beluga bomblet dispenser

Giboulee bomblet dispenser

Thomson-Brandt 400-kg (882-lb) modular cluster bomb

250-kg (551-lb) GP free-fall or retarded bomb

125-kg (276-lb) GP free-fall or retarded bomb

Alkan 530 grenade dispenser

Thomson-Brandt 100-6 pod for 6 × 103-mm (4.06-in) rockets

Matra F2 pod for 6 × 68-mm (2.68-in) rockets

CC420 pod for one 30-mm DEFA 553 cannon plus 400 rounds

87

Above *Here seen in the markings of the French EC2/5 'Ile de France', the Mirage IIIC is obsolescent by the latest operational standards, but in its time was a pioneer of supersonic high-altitude interception with limited radar and AAMs such as the Matra R530 and R550. The type was a great export success, and is still in valuable service with many third-world air arms.*

Below *The Mirage IIIE was developed as the standard multi-role and strike variant of the Mirage III series, this aircraft carrying an AS.37 Martel anti-radar missile on the centreline hardpoint on which it can also carry a 15-kiloton AN52 nuclear weapon. The fairing under the cockpit houses the Doppler navigation system.*

Mirage IIIRD: improved Mirage IIIR with modern Doppler navigation, Omera 33 and 40 automatic cameras, SAT Cyclope infra-red linescan and large drop tanks.

Mirage IIIS: much improved version for Switzerland with Hughes TARAN fire control and Falcon air-to-air missiles. The aircraft are being updated with small canard foreplanes and other items.

Dassault-Breguet Mirage IVA

Type: two-seat strategic penetration bomber.

Internal armament: none.

Disposable armament: up to 7200 kg (15,873 lb) of disposable stores carried as one semi-recessed nuclear weapon or as conventional weapons on four hardpoints (two under the fuselage and two under the wings).

Electronics and operational equipment: normal communication and navigation equipment, plus Thomson-CSF attack and mapping radar, Marconi Doppler navigation, EMD central computer and various electronic countermeasures systems.

Current variants and operator

Mirage IVA: the Mirage IV was designed for the strategic role and is used only by France. The aerodynamic origins of the type clearly lie with the Mirage III fighter and the first Mirage IV flew in June 1959. The type entered service as the carrier for the 60-kiloton AN 22 free-fall nuclear weapon, hardpoints being provided for the alternative carriage of conventional free-fall or missile armament.

Mirage IVP: designation of Mirage IVAs converted from 1985 for the carriage of the 100/150-kiloton ASMP stand-off missile in the theatre penetration role. The type has Thomson-CSF Arcana radar, an inertial navigation system, and new computer-generated cockpit displays. A reconnaissance pod can be carried in place of the missile.

Mirage IVR: dedicated reconnaissance variant with cameras, infra-red linescan and (probably) side-looking airborne radar.

Though on the verge of obsolescence, France's Mirage IV has been given a new lease of life as the Mirage IVP penetration bomber equipped with the ASMP 100/150-kiloton ASMP cruise missile carried under the fuselage.

Dassault-Breguet Mirage IVA

hardpoint rating

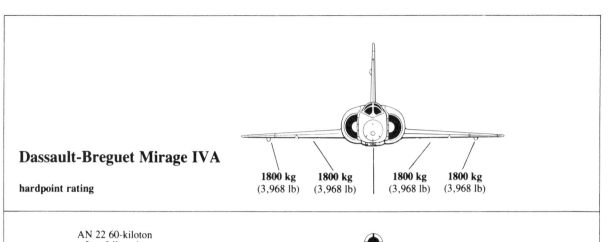

1800 kg
(3,968 lb)

1800 kg
(3,968 lb)

1800 kg
(3,968 lb)

1800 kg
(3,968 lb)

AN 22 60-kiloton
free-fall nuclear
weapon

AS.37 Martel or ARMAT anti-
radiation missile

450-kg (992-lb) GP
free-fall or
retarded bomb

2500-litre (550-Imp
gal) drop tank

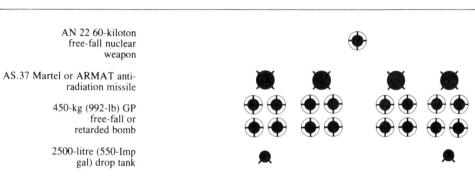

91

Dassault-Breguet Mirage 5

Type: single-seat ground-attack aircraft.

Internal armament: two 30-mm DEFA 552A cannon plus 125 rounds per gun in the lower fuselage.

Disposable armament: up to 4200 kg (9,259 lb) of disposable stores carried on seven hardpoints (one under the fuselage and three under each wing).

Electronics and operational equipment: normal communication and navigation equipment, plus either a Thomson-CSF Aida II fire-control radar (with a Thomson-CSF LT 102 or TAV 34 laser ranger) or a Thomson-CSF Agave multi-mode radar; Thomson-CSF 97 sight (rudimentary head-up display); Marconi Doppler radar; inertial navigation system and radar-warning receiver, plus provision for any podded reconnaissance and/or electronic countermeasures systems to customer requirement.

Current variants and operators

Mirage 5: this clear-weather ground-attack fighter was developed from the Mirage IIIE at the request of Israel, the bulky Cyrano II radar and associated avionics being unnecessary for clear-weather operations in the Middle East and removed (but later replaced by the miniaturized Aida type), the surplus volume and weight-carrying capability being used for extra fuel and armament. At the same time inner underwing hardpoints were revised into a tandem arrangement for double the carrying capacity. The Mirage 5 first flew in May 1967 and since that time the type has been sold to Abu Dhabi; Belgium; Colombia; Egypt; France; Gabon; Libya; Pakistan; Peru (some being passed to Argentina); Venezuela; Zaire. The French aircraft are nuclear capable with the 15-kiloton AN 52 free-fall weapon. Subsequent microminiaturization of electronics has made possible the development of small but highly capable radars, and many Mirage 5s are thus fitted with such equipment to make them more capable all-weather aircraft than the original Mirage IIIs but with the range and payload of the Mirage 5.

Mirage 5D: two-seat operational conversion and proficiency trainer based on the Mirage 5.

Mirage 5R: tactical reconnaissance aircraft with five cameras in the nose section.

Mirage 50: much improved aircraft for Chile with the Atar 09K-50 turbojet and the option of Thomson-CSF Agave (Magic missiles) or Cyrano IVM (R530 missiles) multi-mode radar. The type is also available in the same two-seat and reconnaissance options as the basic Mirage 5.

The Mirage 5 series was developed from the Mirage III at the behest of Israel, which required a clear-weather derivative that sacrificed radar and other avionics for greater fuel and ordnance loads. This is a French Mirage 5F of EC 3/13 'Auvergne', the store on the port inner underwing hard-point being a JL100 combined rocket-launcher (18 68-mm/ 2.68-mm rockets) and tank (250 litres/55 Imp gal).

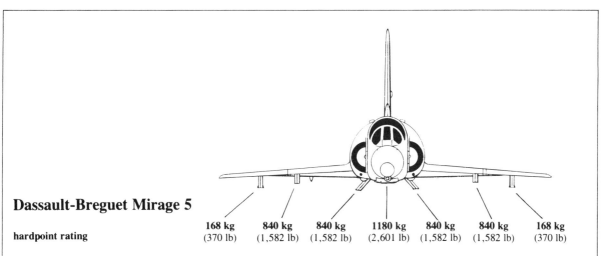

Dassault-Breguet Mirage 5

hardpoint rating

	168 kg (370 lb)	840 kg (1,582 lb)	840 kg (1,582 lb)	1180 kg (2,601 lb)	840 kg (1,582 lb)	840 kg (1,582 lb)	168 kg (370 lb)

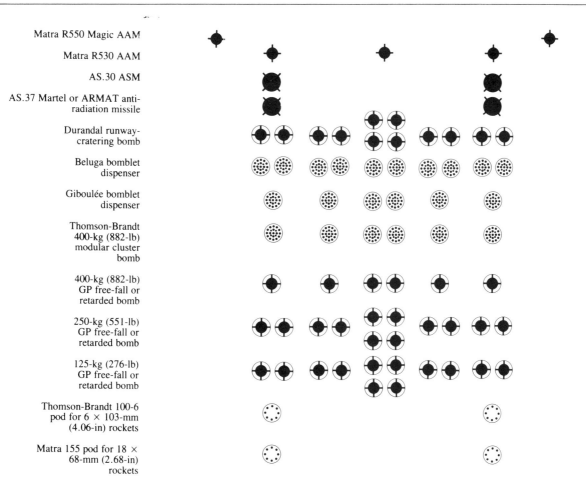

Weapon	1	2	3	4	5	6	7
Matra R550 Magic AAM	●						●
Matra R530 AAM		●		●		●	
AS.30 ASM		●				●	
AS.37 Martel or ARMAT anti-radiation missile		●				●	
Durandal runway-cratering bomb		●●	●●	●● / ●●	●●	●●	
Beluga bomblet dispenser		●●	●	●	●	●●	
Giboulée bomblet dispenser		●	●	●	●	●	
Thomson-Brandt 400-kg (882-lb) modular cluster bomb		●	●	●●	●	●	
400-kg (882-lb) GP free-fall or retarded bomb		●	●	●●	●	●	
250-kg (551-lb) GP free-fall or retarded bomb		●●	●●	●● / ●●	●●	●●	
125-kg (276-lb) GP free-fall or retarded bomb		●●	●●	●● / ●●	●●	●●	
Thomson-Brandt 100-6 pod for 6 × 103-mm (4.06-in) rockets		●				●	
Matra 155 pod for 18 × 68-mm (2.68-in) rockets		●				●	

Dassault-Breguet Mirage 2000C

Type: single-seat multi-role fighter optimized for interception and air superiority.

Internal armament: two 30-mm DEFA 554 cannon plus 125 rounds per gun in the underside of the forward fuselage.

Disposable armament: up to 6445 kg (14,209 lb) of disposable stores carried on nine hardpoints (one under the fuselage, two in tandem under each wing root, and two under each wing).

Electronics and operational equipment: normal communication and navigation equipment, plus Thomson-CSF RDM multi-role air-to-air and air-to-surface radar (to be succeeded in French and certain export aircraft by the Thomson-CSF/ESD RDI pulse-Doppler air-to-air radar); Thomson-CSF VE-130 head-up display; Thomson-CSF VMC-180 head-down display; Sagem Uliss 52 inertial navigation system; two ESD digital central computers; Thomson-CSF Serval-B radar-warning receiver; ESD internal electronic countermeasures; Thomson-CSF DB3163 Remora jammer pod and Thomson-CSF/Martin Marietta ATLIS 2 laser tracker, plus provision for a reconnaissance pod.

Current variants and operators

Mirage 2000B: though the Mirage 2000 series bears a marked aerodynamic similarity to the Mirage III it is a radically different aircraft with advanced structural features and construction, relaxed stability and 'fly-by-wire' system for the complex control surfaces, state-of-the-art electronics and an advanced propulsion system. The type was developed comparatively rapidly in the 1970s, the prototype flying in March 1978. The Mirage 2000B is the two-seat operational conversion trainer model with the ability to carry 6300 kg (13,889 lb) of disposable stores and with the fuselage lengthened by 19 cm (7.5 in) to facilitate the insertion of the second seat. The Mirage 2000 series has been ordered

The Mirage 2000-04 proto-type paved the way for the Mirage 2000C interceptor, and is seen here with a 1300-litre (286-Imp gal) drop tank and a disposable armament of two Super 530 semi-active radar-guided missiles and two R550 Magic IR-homing dogfighting missiles.

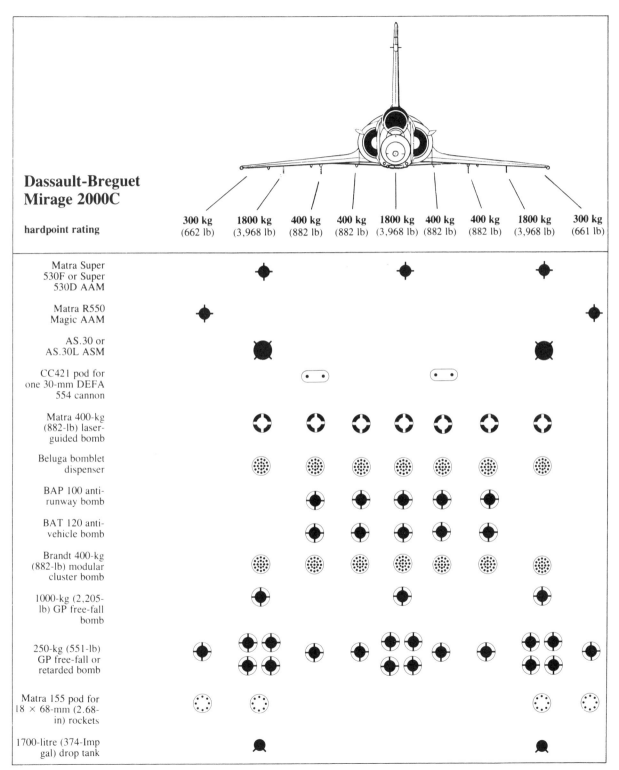

Dassault-Breguet Mirage 2000C

hardpoint rating

	300 kg (662 lb)	1800 kg (3,968 lb)	400 kg (882 lb)	400 kg (882 lb)	1800 kg (3,968 lb)	400 kg (882 lb)	400 kg (882 lb)	1800 kg (3,968 lb)	300 kg (661 lb)
Matra Super 530F or Super 530D AAM		●			●			●	
Matra R550 Magic AAM	●								●
AS.30 or AS.30L ASM		●						●	
CC421 pod for one 30-mm DEFA 554 cannon			●		●				
Matra 400-kg (882-lb) laser-guided bomb	●	●	●	●	●	●	●		
Beluga bomblet dispenser	●	●	●	●	●	●	●		
BAP 100 anti-runway bomb		●	●	●	●	●			
BAT 120 anti-vehicle bomb		●	●	●	●	●			
Brandt 400-kg (882-lb) modular cluster bomb	●	●	●	●	●	●	●		
1000-kg (2,205-lb) GP free-fall bomb		●			●			●	
250-kg (551-lb) GP free-fall or retarded bomb	●	●● ●●	●		●● ●●	●		●● ●●	●
Matra 155 pod for 18 × 68-mm (2.68-in) rockets	●	●						●	●
1700-litre (374-Imp gal) drop tank		●						●	

95

The use of the Mirage 2000's four underwing hardpoints for Super 530 and R550 Magic AAMs leaves five hardpoints under the fuselage free for other stores.

for Abu Dhabi, Egypt, France, Greece, India and Peru.

Mirage 2000C: baseline single-seat model with multi-role capability, though optimized for interception and air superiority. Despite its advanced control system, the Mirage 2000 is fundamentally unsuited to the long-range high-speed role at low level because of the high gust response of its large delta wing and is thus more suited to the medium/high-altitude role with the Super 530 (RDM radar) or Super 530D (RDI radar) missiles for engagement of targets flying at higher or lower altitudes.

Mirage 2000R: dedicated tactical/operational reconnaissance variant due for development later in the decade.

Mirage 2000N: dedicated low-level strike variant based on the Mirage 2000B and intended for the penetration role with the 100/150-kiloton ASMP missile. The avionics suite is revised to accommodate ESD/Thomson-CSF Antilope V radar (air-to-air, air-to-surface, terrain-following and navigation capabilities), twin Uliss 52 inertial navigation systems, an Omera camera, and other role-dedicated equipment.

Dassault-Breguet Mirage F1E   France

Type: single-seat multi-role fighter.

Internal armament: two 30-mm DEFA 553 cannon plus 135 rounds per gun in the underside of the forward fuselage.

Disposable armament: up to 4000 kg (8,818 lb) of disposable stores carried on five hardpoints (one under the fuselage and two under each wing) and two wingtip missile rails.

Electronics and operational equipment: normal commmunication and navigation equipment, plus Thomson-CSF Cyrano IVM radar (Cyrano IVM-0 without air-to-surface capability; Cyrano IVM-1 with limited look-down capability and Cyrano IVM-2 with beam-sharpening for improved air-to-surface capability); Thomson-CSF head-up display; Thomson-CSF head-down display; Doppler navigation; Sagem Uliss 47 inertial navigation system; laser ranger; terrain-avoidance radar and Thomson-CSF BF radar-warning receiver. In addition there is provision for podded systems such as Thomson-CSF DB3163 Remora electronic countermeasures and Alkan chaff/flare dispenser; for a reconnaissance pod with cameras; SAT Cyclope infra-red linescan and Thorn EMI side-looking airborne radar and for the Thomson-CSF/Martin Marietta ATLIS 2 laser target designation pod.

France uses its Mirage F1C fighters mainly for the air-defence role, but the type's versatility is attested by the armament on this aircraft: two Matra R550 Magic dogfighting AAMs on the wingtip rails, and an AS.37 Martel anti-radar missile on the centre-line. Also visible under the port inlet are the muzzle and blast trough of one DEFA 553 30-mm cannon.

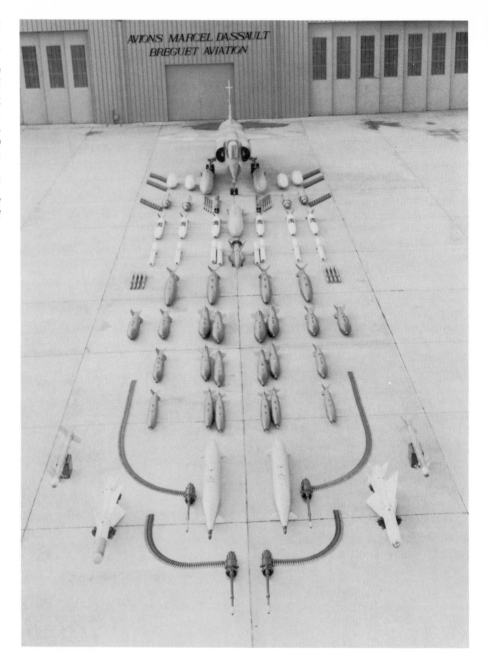

The genuine multi-role capability of the Mirage F1 series is attested by this impressive weapon layout, which includes Matra R530 and R550 AAMs, internal and podded DEFA 30-mm cannon; free-fall 'iron' bombs of various sizes; Durandal anti-runway bombs; BAP 100/BAT 120 anti-runway / anti-vehicle bombs; an AS.30 air-to-surface missile; a 1700-litre (347-Imp gal) drop tank, Beluga cluster bombs; and 100- and 68-mm (3.94- and 2.68-in) unguided rockets.

Current variants and operators

Mirage F1A: the Mirage F1 series was designed as a private-venture successor to the Mirage III family with reduced drag (and thus improved acceleration and sustained turning performance), better field performance and much greater internal fuel capacity. The type first flew in December 1966 and has proved highly successful in the domestic and export markets. The Mirage F1A bears the same relationship to the Mirage F1C as does the Mirage 5 to the Mirage III, being a simplified ground-attack derivative of the

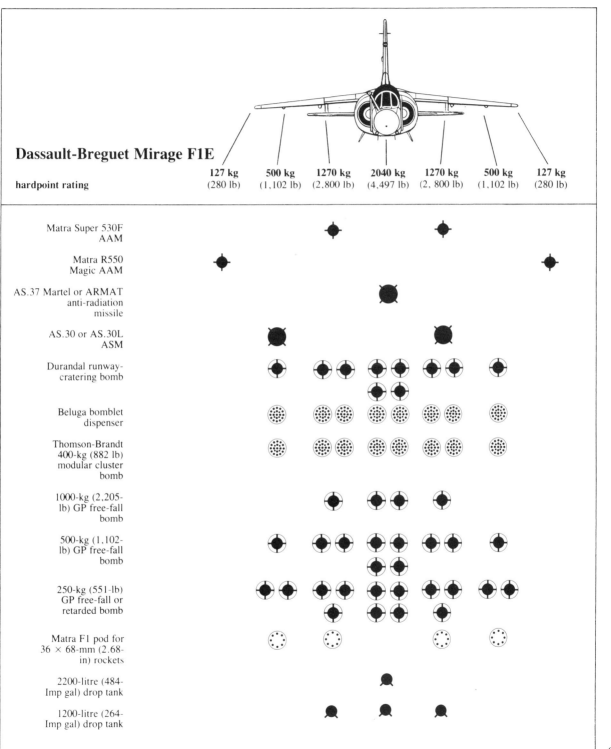

Dassault-Breguet Mirage F1E

hardpoint rating	127 kg (280 lb)	500 kg (1,102 lb)	1270 kg (2,800 lb)	2040 kg (4,497 lb)	1270 kg (2,800 lb)	500 kg (1,102 lb)	127 kg (280 lb)
Matra Super 530F AAM			●	●	●		
Matra R550 Magic AAM	●						●
AS.37 Martel or ARMAT anti-radiation missile				●			
AS.30 or AS.30L ASM		●			●		
Durandal runway-cratering bomb	●	● ●	● ● / ● ●	● ●	● ●	●	
Beluga bomblet dispenser	●	● ●	● ●	● ●	● ●	●	
Thomson-Brandt 400-kg (882 lb) modular cluster bomb	●	● ●	● ●	● ●	● ●	●	
1000-kg (2,205-lb) GP free-fall bomb		●	● ●	●			
500-kg (1,102-lb) GP free-fall bomb	●	● ●	● ● / ● ●	● ●	●		
250-kg (551-lb) GP free-fall or retarded bomb	● ●	● ● / ● ●	● ● / ● ●	● ● / ● ●	● ●		
Matra F1 pod for 36 × 68-mm (2.68-in) rockets	●	●		●	●		
2200-litre (484-Imp gal) drop tank				●			
1200-litre (264-Imp gal) drop tank			●	●	●		

99

The Mirage F1C generally carries a pair of R550 Magic AAMs for self-defence, and though optimized for the air-to-air role can serve in the counter-air role with a load such as that shown here: six Durandal runway-cratering munitions carried over a fair range with the aid of two 1700-litre (374-Imp gal) drop tanks.

multi-role type without the Cyrano IV radar and Super 530 missile. The Mirage F1A has optional Thomson-CSF Aida II radar and other avionics include SFIM inertial navigation, Doppler navigation and a Thomson-CSF laser ranger. Deliveries began in 1975 to Libya and South Africa.

Mirage F1B: two-seat operational conversion and proficiency trainer version of the Mirage F1C with the fuselage lengthened to facilitate the insertion of the second seat. The type retains full combat capability but has less fuel than the Mirage F1C and is operated by all countries that fly the single-seat versions.

Mirage F1C: multi-role fighter version with full avionics and flown by France, Greece, Jordan, Kuwait, Morocco, South Africa and Spain.

Mirage F1C-200: version of the Mirage F1C fitted with an inflight-refuelling probe for long-range deployments by the French air force.

Mirage F1CR-200: tactical reconnaissance version of the Mirage F1C-200 for the French air force, retaining radar and the basic avionics suite, but using the latest SNAR navigation system (using the Cyrano IVMR radar, an ESD digital computer and a Uliss 47 inertial navigation system) and fitted internally with at least two cameras (Omera 33 medium-altitude vertical and Omera 40 horizon-to-horizon panoramic), Thomson-CSF

Super Cyclope infra-red linescan and Thomson-CSF Raphael side-looking airborne radar. The type is also able to carry (on the centreline) any of France's latest reconnaissance pods, including the Harold multi-sensor, Nora optronic, Syrel electronic intelligence, and new SLAR types.

Mirage F1E: multi-role export attack model based on the Mirage F1C with the complete gamut of F1C avionics plus a Singer-Kearfott inertial navigation system, an EMD/Sagem 182 digital central computer, an improved VE-120C head-up display, and Crouzet air-data and stores-management systems. This variant is flown by Ecuador, Iraq, Jordan, Libya, Morocco, Qatar and Spain.

Dassault-Breguet Super Etendard

Type: single-seat land- and carrier-based strike and attack aircraft.

Internal armament: two 30-mm DEFA 552A cannon plus 125 rounds per gun in the underside of the forward fuselage.

Disposable armament: up to 2100 kg (4,630 lb) of disposable stores carried on five hardpoints (one under the fuselage and two under each wing).

Electronics and operational equipment: normal communication and navigation equipment, plus Thomson-CSF Agave (to be replaced by Thomson-CSF Anemone) multi-mode radar; Thomson-CSF VE-120 head-up display; Sagem-Kearfott 2602 inertial navigation system; Crouzet 66 air-data computer; Crouzet 97 navigation display and armament control system; and Thomson-CSF BF radar-warning receiver, as well as provision for a Thomson-CSF DB3161 Remora jammer pod.

Current variant and operators

Super Etendard: developed in the early 1970s on the basis of the subsonic Etendard IVM it was to replace, the transonic Super Etendard first flew in October 1974 and in comparison with its predecessor has much improved avionics (including search rather than ranging radar), a more powerful engine and considerably enhanced aerodynamics. The type has provision for a buddy refuelling pod and is used by Argentina, France and Iraq. The French aircraft have provision for one 15-kiloton AN 52 free-fall nuclear weapon and 50 of them are being fitted with provision for the 100/150-kiloton ASMP stand-off missile.

Jut about to be launched by a steam catapult on one of France's two aircraft-carriers, this Super Etendard of 11 Flottille carries two 1100-litre (242-Imp gal) drop tanks and two Matra 155 eighteen-tube rocket-launchers.

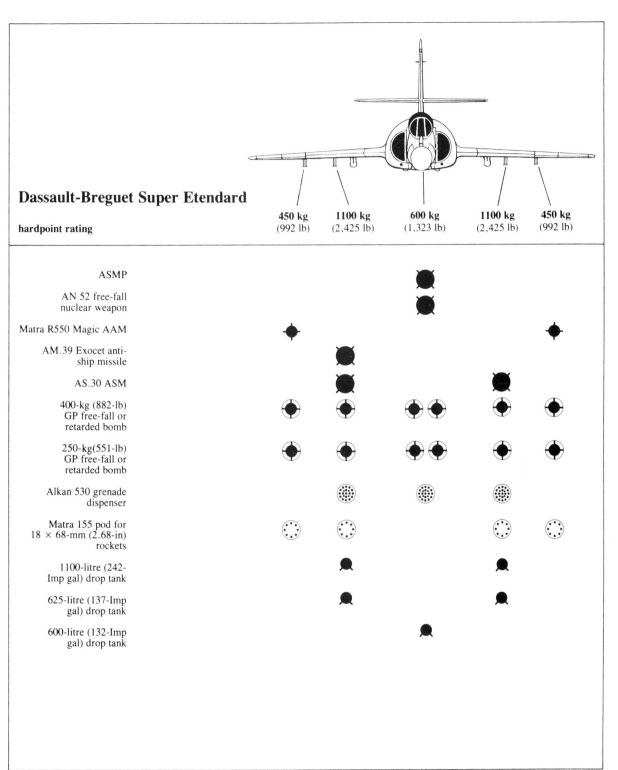

Dassault-Breguet Super Etendard

hardpoint rating

	450 kg (992 lb)	1100 kg (2,425 lb)	600 kg (1,323 lb)	1100 kg (2,425 lb)	450 kg (992 lb)
ASMP			●		
AN 52 free-fall nuclear weapon			●		
Matra R550 Magic AAM	●				●
AM.39 Exocet anti-ship missile		●			
AS.30 ASM		●		●	
400-kg (882-lb) GP free-fall or retarded bomb	●	●	● ●	●	●
250-kg (551-lb) GP free-fall or retarded bomb	●	●	● ●	●	●
Alkan 530 grenade dispenser		●	●	●	
Matra 155 pod for 18 × 68-mm (2.68-in) rockets	●	●		●	●
1100-litre (242-Imp gal) drop tank		●		●	
625-litre (137-Imp gal) drop tank		●		●	
600-litre (132-Imp gal) drop tank			●		

France/West Germany

Dassault-Breguet/Dornier Alpha Jet A

Type: two-seat trainer and light attack aircraft.

Internal armament: none.

Disposable armament: up to 2500 kg (5,511 lb) of disposable stores carried on five hardpoints (one under the fuselage and two under each wing).

Electronics and operational equipment: normal communication and navigation equipment, plus Kaiser/VDO KM808 head-up display; Litef Doppler navigation; attitude and heading reference system and pods for reconnaissance equipment or for electronic countermeasures such as the Elettronica ELT/460 or ELT/555 and the Selenia ALQ-234.

Though in fact a company-owned demonstrator, this Alpha Jet resembles the proposed Lancier model apart from its lack of Agave nose radar, improved head-up display and FLIR. The AM.39 Exocet anti-ship missile under the starboard wing is balanced by a drop tank under the port wing, and the aircraft also carries a pair of self-defence Matra R550 Magic AAMs.

Current variants and operators

Alpha Jet A: the Alpha Jet was developed jointly in France and West Germany for the trainer and battlefield close-support/reconnaissance roles and first flew in French trainer form during October 1973. First flown in April 1978, the Alpha Jet A is the light attack model used only by West Germany and is distinguishable from the French model by its pointed nose with probe for air-data sensors, Stencel S-III-S3AJ ejector seats and under-fuselage pod for one 27-mm IKWA-Mauser cannon plus 150 rounds. The Alpha Jet can also carry a Super Cyclope reconnaissance pod with one Omera 40 and three Omera 31

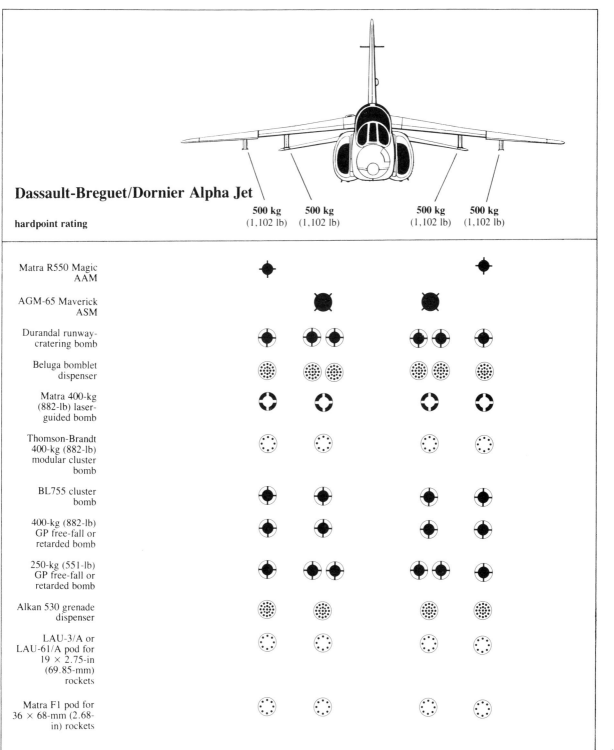

Dassault-Breguet/Dornier Alpha Jet

hardpoint rating	500 kg (1,102 lb)	500 kg (1,102 lb)	500 kg (1,102 lb)	500 kg (1,102 lb)
Matra R550 Magic AAM	●		●	
AGM-65 Maverick ASM		●	●	
Durandal runway-cratering bomb	●	● ●	● ●	●
Beluga bomblet dispenser	●	● ●	● ●	●
Matra 400-kg (882-lb) laser-guided bomb	●	●	●	●
Thomson-Brandt 400-kg (882-lb) modular cluster bomb	●	●	●	●
BL755 cluster bomb	●	●	●	●
400-kg (882-lb) GP free-fall or retarded bomb	●	●	●	●
250-kg (551-lb) GP free-fall or retarded bomb	●	● ●	● ●	●
Alkan 530 grenade dispenser	●	●	●	●
LAU-3/A or LAU-61/A pod for 19 × 2.75-in (69.85-mm) rockets	●	●	●	●
Matra F1 pod for 36 × 68-mm (2.68-in) rockets	●	●	●	●

cameras. The aircraft are currently slated for updating (between 1990 and 1995) with 1440-kg (3,175-lb) SNECMA/Turboméca Larzac 04-C20 turbofans in place of the present 1350-kg (2,976-lb) Larzac 04-C5 engines; improved electronic counter-measures; updated head-up display; better attitude and heading reference system; new nav/attack system for night and adverse-weather operations; enhanced armament in the form of AIM-9L Sidewinder and AIM-132 ASRAAM air-to-air missiles, AGM-88 HARM anti-radiation missiles, CVR-7 rockets and Verbal/Syndrom vertically-pro-jected anti-armour weapons.

Alpha Jet E: French trainer model with rounded nose, Martin-Baker AJRM4 (or AJRM10 in export aircraft) ejector seats and under-fuselage pod for one 30-mm DEFA 553 cannon plus 150 rounds. The type has a simple weapon system comprising the Thomson-CSF 902 sight and computer. This variant is flown by Belgium, Egypt, France, Ivory Coast, Morocco, Nigeria, Qatar and Togo.

Alpha Jet NGEA: this is an improved model developed in France with superior attack capability. The type is distinguishable by its blunted nose (containing a Thomson-CSF TMV 630 laser ranger), Sagem Uliss 81 inertial navigation system, Thomson-CSF VE-110C head-up display and ESD Digibus multiplex digital databus. This variant has been bought by Cameroun and Egypt.

Lancier: much improved French single-seat model developed in the first part of the 1980s for the dedicated attack role with Thomson-CSF Agave radar, forward-looking infra-red, advanced cockpit displays, active and passive electronic countermeasures, and diverse combat capability with weapons such as the AM.39 Exocet anti-ship missile and Matra R550 Magic air-to-air missile.

Fairchild Republic
A-10A Thunderbolt II

Type: single-seat anti-tank, close-support and attack aircraft.

Internal armament: one 30-mm General Electric GAU-8/A Avenger cannon plus 1,174 rounds in the nose.

Disposable armament: up to 16,000 lb (7258 kg) of disposable stores carried on 11 hardpoints (three under the fuselage and four under each wing).

Electronics and operational equipment: normal communication and navigation equipment, plus Kaiser head-up display; Martin Marietta AAS-35 'Pave Penny' laser pod; Itek ALR-46(V) radar-warning receiver; and Martin Marietta/Hughes LANTIRN (Low-Altitude Navigation and Targeting Infra-Red for Night) system with two pods (one for navigation with forward-looking infra-red and terrain-following radar, and the other for targeting with forward looking infra-red and a laser designator); plus provision for electronic warfare pods such as the Westinghouse ALQ-119 and ALQ-131 electronic countermeasures, ALE-37 chaff dispenser and other systems.

Current variant and operator

A-10A Thunderbolt II: used only by the USAF, the Thunderbolt II is a remarkable close-support and anti-tank aircraft intended for long loiters over the battlefield with exceptionally potent armament, relying on manoeuvrability, armour and redundant systems/structures for survival against anti-aircraft artillery and surface-to-air missiles. The type first flew in May 1972 and entered service as an 'austere' aircraft with few avionics systems other than the radar-warning receiver, head-up display and 'Pave Penny' system. This has proved a distinct limitation in the European and South Korean environments, so the addition of the LANTIRN system is much improving the situation.

The A-10A carries the most powerful gun ever fitted to an operational aircraft, namely the General Electric GAU-8/A Avenger, a seven-barrel 30-mm weapon fitted with a 1,174-round ammunition drum. The gun has an overall length of 21.0 ft (6.4 m) and a weight of 3,800 lb (1,724 kg), and fires an exceptional anti-tank round with a sub-calibre penetrator of depleted uranium.

107

A-10As of the 354th Tactical Fighter Wing are prepared for a sortie. Each aircraft carries an ALQ-119(V) jammer pod under its starboard wing. Attached to the starboard side of the fuselage under the cockpit is the 'Pave Penny' laser pod essential for the effective use of laser-homing missiles. Projecting from the underside of the nose is the muzzle assembly of the massive and extremely powerful GAU-8/A Avenger 30-mm cannon.

The tactical utility of the A-10A is its ability to loiter over the battlefield for long periods with a substantial weapons load, and to this end the US Air Forces in Europe practise the FOL (Forward Operating Location) technique, in which A-10As operate from austere strips close to the front line, returning to their main base in eastern England only for major repairs and servicing.

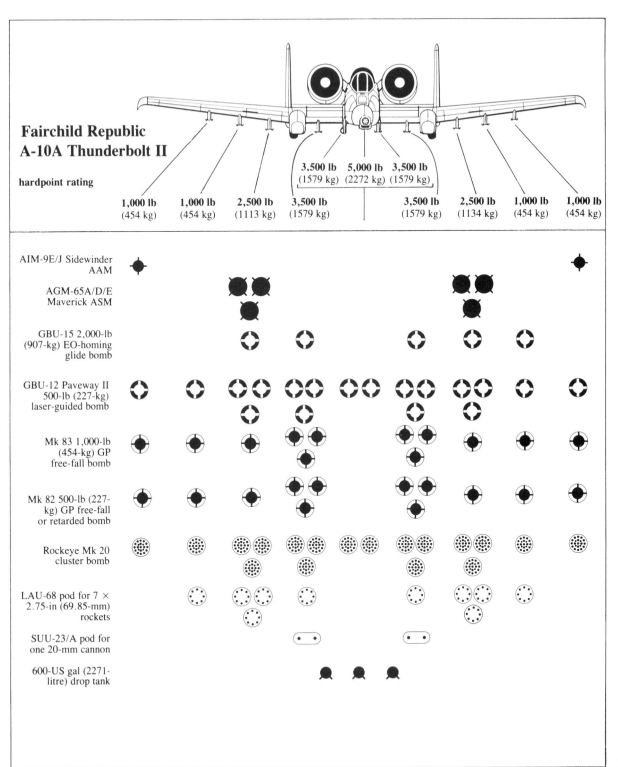

**Fairchild Republic
A-10A Thunderbolt II**

hardpoint rating

| | 1,000 lb (454 kg) | 1,000 lb (454 kg) | 2,500 lb (1113 kg) | 3,500 lb (1579 kg) | 3,500 lb (1579 kg) 5,000 lb (2272 kg) 3,500 lb (1579 kg) | 3,500 lb (1579 kg) | 2,500 lb (1134 kg) | 1,000 lb (454 kg) | 1,000 lb (454 kg) |

AIM-9E/J Sidewinder AAM

AGM-65A/D/E Maverick ASM

GBU-15 2,000-lb (907-kg) EO-homing glide bomb

GBU-12 Paveway II 500-lb (227-kg) laser-guided bomb

Mk 83 1,000-lb (454-kg) GP free-fall bomb

Mk 82 500-lb (227-kg) GP free-fall or retarded bomb

Rockeye Mk 20 cluster bomb

LAU-68 pod for 7 × 2.75-in (69.85-mm) rockets

SUU-23/A pod for one 20-mm cannon

600-US gal (2271-litre) drop tank

FMA IA-58A Pucará

Type: two-seat light attack and counter-insurgency aircraft.

Internal armament: two 20-mm Hispano-Suiza HS-2804 cannon plus 270 rounds per gun (in some aircraft replaced by two 30-mm DEFA 553 cannon plus 140 rounds per gun) and four 7.62-mm (0.3-in) FN-Browning machine-guns plus 900 rounds per gun, all located in the nose.

Disposable armament: up to 1620 kg (3,571 lb) of disposable stores carried on three hardpoints (one under the fuselage and one under each wing).

Electronics and operational equipment: normal communication and navigation equipment, plus a Matra 83-4-3 reflector sight and Bendix stores-management system.

Current variants and operators

IA-58A Pucará: the Pucará was first flown in August 1969 as a moderate-performance counter-insurgency aircraft designed for the accurate delivery of substantial warloads against low-intensity opposition. The type began to enter service in 1974 and is operated by Argentina, Iraq, Uruguay and Venezuela.

IA-66 Pucará: due to enter service in the second half of the 1980s, the IA 66 features 1,000-shp (746-kW) Garrett TPE331-11-601W turboprops instead of the 737-kW (988-shp) Turboméca Astazou XVIG turboprops of the IA-58A and will probably be developed with an armament of one 30-mm DEFA cannon plus 250 rounds in addition to the two 20-mm cannon and two/four 7.62-mm (0.3-in) machine guns. The type has a Saab RGS2 sight suitable for use with conventional air-to-surface weapons and also with the Martin Pescador air-to-surface missile.

Pucara FMA IA-58A of the Argentine Air Force.

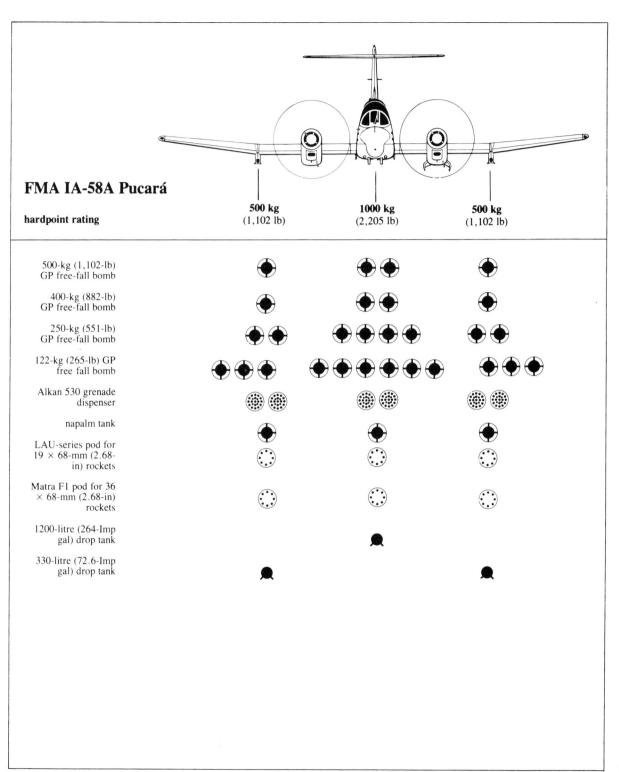

FMA IA-58A Pucará

hardpoint rating

	500 kg (1,102 lb)	1000 kg (2,205 lb)	500 kg (1,102 lb)

500-kg (1,102-lb) GP free-fall bomb

400-kg (882-lb) GP free-fall bomb

250-kg (551-lb) GP free-fall bomb

122-kg (265-lb) GP free fall bomb

Alkan 530 grenade dispenser

napalm tank

LAU-series pod for 19 × 68-mm (2.68-in) rockets

Matra F1 pod for 36 × 68-mm (2.68-in) rockets

1200-litre (264-Imp gal) drop tank

330-litre (72.6-Imp gal) drop tank

General Dynamics
F-16A Fighting Falcon

Type: air-combat and multi-role fighter with advanced attack capability.

Internal armament: one 20-mm General Electric M61A1 Vulcan six-barrel rotary cannon with 500 rounds in the port leading-edge root extension.

Disposable armament: up to 20,450 lb (9276 kg) of disposable stores at up to 5.5 g or 11,950 lb (5420 kg) of disposable stores at up to 9 g, carried on seven hardpoints (one under the fuselage and three under each wing) and two wingtip missile rails.

Electronics and operational equipment: normal communication and navigation equipment, plus Westinghouse APG-66 pulse-Doppler multi-role radar (air-to-air search and track-while-scan and air-to-surface ground mapping); Marconi head-up display; Kaiser head-down display; Singer-Kearfott SKN-2400 inertial navigation system; Delco fire-control system; Magnavox KY-58 secure voice communications; Dalmo-Victor ALR-69 radar-warning receiver; and provision for the Martin Marietta AAS-35 'Pave Penny' laser pod and electronic countermeasures systems such as the podded Westinghouse ALQ-119 and Westinghouse ALQ-131 or (Belgian aircraft) internal Loral Rapport III.

Current variants and operators

F-16A Fighting Falcon: derived for the YF-16 contender (first flown in February 1974) in the USAF's Lightweight Fighter competition of the early 1970s, the Fighting Falcon is a highly capable air-combat fighter with only moderately high performance but excellent manoeuvrability (using relaxed stability and 'fly-by-wire' controls for a pilot using a Hands On Throttle And Stick control system in a superbly designed cockpit) and also a potent attack platform with a wide assortment of weapons and a tactical reconnaissance aircraft with the Oldelft Orpheus or similar pod. The type is in service with or on order for Bahrain; Belgium; Denmark; Egypt; Greece; Indonesia; Israel; Netherlands; Norway; Singapore; South Korea; Thailand; USA and Venezuela.

An F-16B two-seater of US Air Force Systems Command's Armament Development and Test Center at Eglin AFB, Florida shows off part of the Fighting Falcon's remarkable warload, in this instance an AIM-9 Sidewinder AAM and Mk 82 Snakeye 500-lb (227-kg) high-drag bombs.

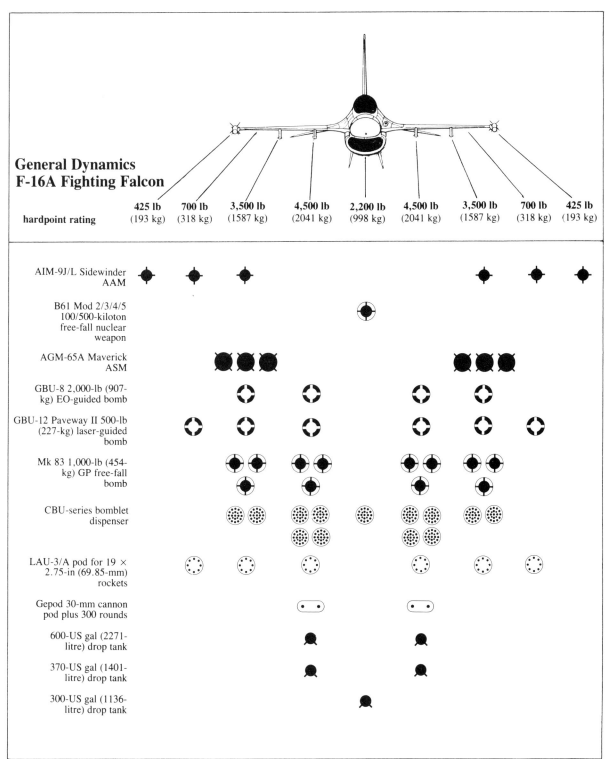

General Dynamics F-16A Fighting Falcon

Right *Development launch of an AIM-20 AMRAAM advanced medium-range air-to-air-missile from an F-16A single-seater of the US Air Force Systems Command.*

Below *The flight line at Hill AFB, Utah as a crewman prepares to load a 500-lb (227-kg) Mk 82 concrete-filled practice bomb on to one of the waiting F-16A single-seaters of the 388th Tactical Fighter Wing.*

F-16B Fighting Falcon: two-seat combat-capable conversion trainer version of the F-16A, used by the same countries.

F-16C Fighting Falcon: improved F-16A resulting from the Multi-national Staged Improvement Program with maximum take-off weight increased from 35,400 lb (16057 kg) to 37,500 lb (17010 kg); greater weapon-carrying capability (on the standard hardpoints, supplemented by an additional pair on the sides of the inlet duct); a larger tailplane and (successively in later aircraft) much enhanced combat avionics such as the APG-68 radar (based on the APG-66 but with a digital signal processor and Doppler beam sharpening for greater range and resolution in the look-down mode); a Marconi holographic head-up display; multi-function head-down displays and provision for systems such as Martin Marietta LANTIRN (Low-Altitude Navigation and Targeting Infra-Red for Night); Westinghouse ALQ-165 Airborne Self-Protection Jammer; Joint Tactical Information Distribution System and Global Positioning System. The F-16C is compatible with weapons such as the AIM-120 AMRAAM and AIM-132 ASRAAM air-to-air missiles; the AGM-65D Maverick imaging infra-red air-to-surface missile; the 30-mm Gepod cannon pod; low-altitude dispenser weapons and other types currently under development. This version is slated for service with Egypt, Greece, Israel, Turkey and USA. The type is planned with a choice of two powerplants in a common engine bay, namely the Pratt & Whitney F100 and General Electric F110 afterburning turbofans. There have already been several fascinating developments of the basic type (the F-16/79 turbojet-powered reduced-cost model, the F-16/AFTI control-configured aircraft, the F-16/101 with the F101 Derivative Fighter Engine paving the way for the F-16C, and the F-16XL cranked-arrow wing development with much greater payload and range combined with reduced field requirements), so there seems every possibility that further operational models will be developed, one probability being an advanced 'Wild Weasel' defence-suppression type with the appropriate electronics and AGM-88 HARM missiles.

F-16D Fighting Falcon: two-seat combat-capable operational conversion trainer derivative of the F-16C.

The Fighting Falcon was developed as a lightweight air-combat fighter proto-type, but has matured in development and service into a remarkable multi-role fighter, as indicated by this layout of weapon combina-tions, which are too numerous for full exposition but include the ALQ-131 jammer pod (front); two tactical nuclear weapons (behind the ALQ-131); Mk 82 Snakeye 500-lb (227-kg) high-drag bombs (arrow-head from front nuclear weapon); other 'iron' and cluster bombs; rocket-launchers; Paveway laser-guided bombs; Maverick air-to-surface missiles on triple racks; and AIM-9 Sidewinder AAMs on the aircraft.

The US contribution to the air
defence of South Korea rests
mainly on the 8th Tactical
Fighter Wing, which is based
at Kunsan AB and operates
aircraft such as this F-16A
carrying two AIM-9 Side-
winder AAMs and two Mk 84
2,000-lb (907-kg) 'iron'
bombs in addition to the
internal M61A1 cannon with
its muzzle in the port wing root
extension.

Launch sequence for one of the three AGM-65 Maverick air-to-surface missiles that can be carried on the innermost hardpoint under each wing of a Fighting Falcon, in this instance the first F-16B two-seater.

F-16N Fighting Falcon: derivative of the basic model for US Navy aggressor training with revised avionics and other modifications.

General Dynamics F-111F

Type: two-seat variable-geometry all-weather strike and attack aircraft.

Internal armament: (optional) one 20-mm General Electric M61A1 Vulcan six-barrel rotary cannon plus 2,084 rounds in the weapons bay at the cost of reduced accommodation for other stores (one instead of two 2,100-lb/953-kg B43 free-fall nuclear weapons).

Disposable armament: up to 31,500 lb (14288 kg) of disposable stores carried in an internal weapons bay and on six hardpoints (two swivelling and one optional fixed under each wing).

Electronics and operational equipment: normal communication and navigation equipment, plus General Electric APQ-144 attack and navigation radar; Texas Instruments APQ-110 terrain-following radar; Litton inertial navigation system, GPL Doppler navigation; IBM ASQ-133 digital fire-control system; General Electric ASG-25 optical display sight; Sanders ALQ-94 (being replaced by the same company's ALQ-137) deception noise jammer; ALR-41 radar-warning receiver; Dalmo-Victor ALR62(V) radar-warning receiver; Cincinnati Electronics AAR-44 infra-red warning receiver; Textron radar homing and warning receiver and Avco passive electronic countermeasures receiver; plus provision for the Ford AVQ-26 'Pave Tack' laser designator and marked-target seeker/forward-looking infra-red turret under the fuselage, and pod-mounted Westinghouse ALQ-119(V) or ALQ-131 electronic countermeasures. The Westinghouse ALQ-165 Airborne Self-Protection Jammer is to be retrofitted when available.

Current variants and operators

F-111A: this was the initial production variant of the F-111, the world's first operational variable-geometry aircraft. The type was designed as a single airframe able to accommodate the avionics and weapons suiting it to the USAF's tactical attack and US Navy's fleet defence fighter roles, the latter proving impossible of attainment for reasons of drastic weight escalation. The F-111 first flew in December 1964, and suffered a lengthy development process in terms of airframe, avionics and inlet fixes before entering inauspicious service late in 1967. Since then the type has been built in a number

In terms of payload and range, the most impressive of the 'Aardvark' family is the FB-111A operated by Strategic Air Command, in this instance the 509th Bomb Wing at Pease AFB, New Hampshire. The FB-111A can carry a substantial external load (though only at the expense of range) and strategic tasks are best accomplished with two nuclear weapons carried internally and perhaps complemented by two or four AGM-69A SRAMs carried externally.

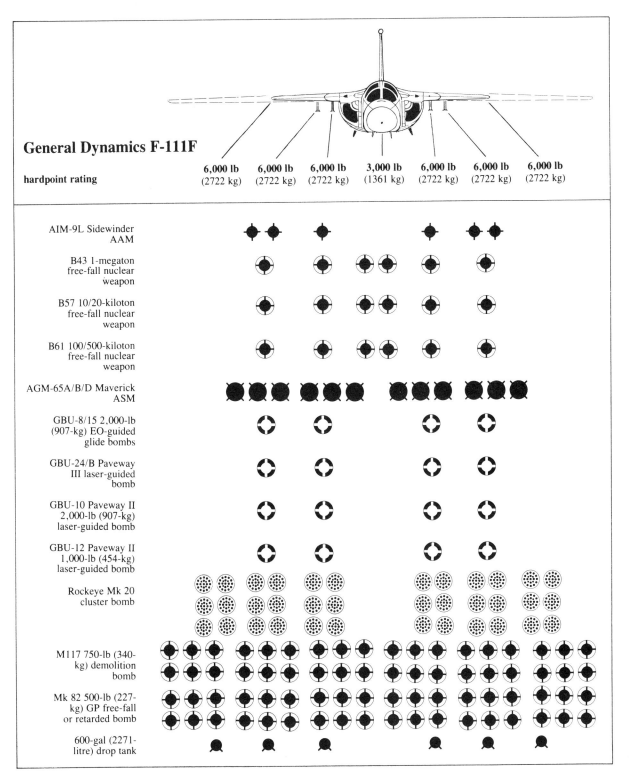

General Dynamics F-111F

hardpoint rating

	6,000 lb (2722 kg)	6,000 lb (2722 kg)	6,000 lb (2722 kg)	3,000 lb (1361 kg)	6,000 lb (2722 kg)	6,000 lb (2722 kg)	6,000 lb (2722 kg)
AIM-9L Sidewinder AAM							
B43 1-megaton free-fall nuclear weapon							
B57 10/20-kiloton free-fall nuclear weapon							
B61 100/500-kiloton free-fall nuclear weapon							
AGM-65A/B/D Maverick ASM							
GBU-8/15 2,000-lb (907-kg) EO-guided glide bombs							
GBU-24/B Paveway III laser-guided bomb							
GBU-10 Paveway II 2,000-lb (907-kg) laser-guided bomb							
GBU-12 Paveway II 1,000-lb (454-kg) laser-guided bomb							
Rockeye Mk 20 cluster bomb							
M117 750-lb (340-kg) demolition bomb							
Mk 82 500-lb (227-kg) GP free-fall or retarded bomb							
600-gal (2271-litre) drop tank							

119

Above *Undoubtedly the most effective tactical interdiction version of the F-111 series is the F-111F, seen here in the form of an aircraft of the 48th Tactical Fighter Wing, US Air Forces in Europe, and based at RAF Lakenheath. In the lowered position under the fuselage is the AVO-26 'Pave Tack' laser/FLIR system pack for adverse-weather nav/attack and guidance of laser-guided weapons such as the four Paveway II bombs carried by this aircraft. An ALQ-119(V) ECM jammer pod is carried under the rear fuselage between the ventral fins.*

Below *Though the F-111 series lacks the weapons versatility of other US combat aircraft, it more than balances this 'failing' by the sheer weight of conventional and nuclear weapons it can carry over long ranges at high speed, and then deliver with pinpoint accuracy under all weather conditions.*

of variants for the USAF and has matured into an exceptionally capable all-weather interdiction aircraft. The F-111A has Mk I avionics (General Electric APQ-113 radar and the AJQ-20A nav/attack system, the latter slated for updating to digital standard for use in conjunction with the new USAF inertial navigation and display systems) and 18,500-lb (8930-kg) Pratt & Whitney TF30-P-3 afterburning turbofans. The F-111A airframe has been used as the basis for the General Dynamics/Grumman EF-111A Raven stand-off electronic warfare aircraft fitted with the Raytheon ALQ-99E automated electronic countermeasures system.

F-111C: version of the F-111A with Mk I avionics and the long-span wings of the FB-111A for Australia. Four have been converted as RF-111C multi-sensor reconnaissance aircraft with a General Dynamics pallet of optical TV and infra-red line-scan sensors.

F-111D: updated F-111A with Mk II digital avionics (APQ-189 Doppler navigation and APQ-130 main radar with moving target indication, Doppler beam sharpening and improved air-to-air capability including target illumination), head-up displays for both crew members and 19,600-lb (8891-kg) TF30-P-9 afterburning turbofans.

F-111E: improved F-111A with larger inlets and TF30-P-9 afterburning turbofans, plus refinements to the avionics.

F-111F: definitive tactical version based on the F-111D with Mk II avionics large inlets and 25,100-lb (11385-kg) TF30-P-100 afterburning turbofans, later fitted with the 'Pave Tack' system allowing day/night operations in all weather conditions for the accurate delivery of weapons with electro-optical, infra-red and laser guidance.

FB-111A: medium-range strategic version for the USAF's Strategic Air Command, and fitted with Mk IIB avionics (derived from those of the F-111D but with APQ-114 main radar) and the long-span wings (with eight hardpoints) designed for the abortive naval F-111B. The type is powered by two 20,350-lb (9231-k) TF30-P-7 afterburning turbofans and can carry a maximum weapon load of 41,250 lb (18711 kg), including six 1-megaton B43 or megaton-range B61 Mod 1 free-fall nuclear weapons; or six 170-kiloton AGM-69A Short-Range Attack Missiles; or four SRAMs and two bombs; or a maximum of 50,825-lb (374-kg) free-fall conventional bombs, each having the nominal weight of 750 lb (340 kg).

The F-111 series suffered many problems (associated mainly with the powerplant and avionics) during a chequered early career, but has since built up an impressive record in the long-range interdiction role.

Grumman A-6E/TRAM Intruder

Type: two-seat carrier-borne all-weather strike and attack aircraft.

Internal armament: none.

Disposable armament: up to 18,000 lb (8165 kg) of disposable stores carried on five hardpoints (one under the fuselage and two under each wing).

Electronics and operational equipment: normal communication and navigation equipment, plus Norden APQ-148 multi-mode radar (navigation, target identification, moving target indication, and terrain following/avoidance modes); Kaiser AVA-1 multi-mode head-down displays; Litton ASN-92 CAINS (Carrier Aircraft Inertial Navigation System); APN-153 Doppler navigation; IBM/ Fairchild ASQ-133 digital nav/attack system; CNI (Communication, Navigation and Identification) system; Sanders ALQ-41 or ALQ-100 forward-emitting deception jammer; Hughes AAS-33 TRAM (Target Recognition and Attack Multi-sensor) package with forward-looking infra-red and laser designator/marked-target seeker, and Chicago Aerial MX 3146A/A optical sight, plus provision for podded systems such as Sanders ALQ-126 electronic countermeasures, Eaton-AIL ALQ-130 electronic countermeasures, Tracor ALE-39 chaff/flare dispenser and Xerox ALQ-123 infra-red countermeasures.

Current variants and operators

EA-6A Intruder: the Intruder first flew in April 1960 and provided the US Navy and US Marine Corps (the type's sole operators) with their first genuinely all-weather strike (nuclear) and attack (conventional weapons) aircraft capable of effective operations in all climatic and weather conditions. The early models had analog thermionic electronics, reducing reliability and involving considerable maintenance to ensure the type's great attack potential, but the older attack aircraft have now been phased out. The EA-6A is the strike and attack support aircraft version of the A-6A with ALH-6 signals recording, ALQ-31 noise jammer, ALQ-53 track breaking jammer, ALQ-76 noise jammer and ALQ-86 electronic support measures systems (supported by some 30 antennae) for the location, classification and jamming of radars targeting any Intruder attack force: the type also carries the Lundy ALE-32 chaff dispenser.

EA-6B Prowler: highly advanced derivative of the EA-6A with the fuselage lengthened by 4.5 ft (1.37 m) to accommodate the additional two crew members required to operate the Raytheon ALQ-99 tactical jamming system, which has receivers in the fintop pod to provide raw information to the central digital computer which then controls the operation of ten jammers built into five self-powered pods.

An A-6E of VA-176, part of USS Independence's Carrier Wing 6, transits at comparatively high speed and low level while carrying 12 250-lb (113-kg) Mk 81 bombs as tandem triplets on each outer hardpoint. The TRAM turret is just visible under the nose.

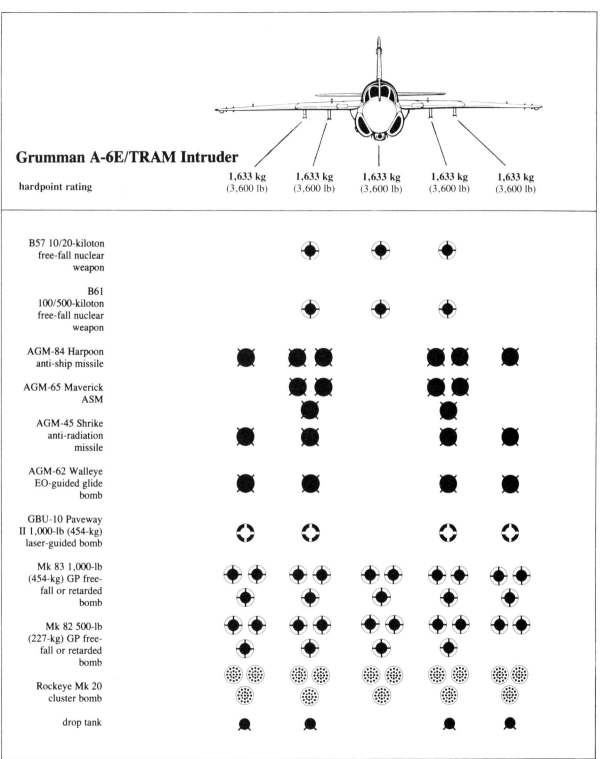

Grumman A-6E/TRAM Intruder

hardpoint rating	1,633 kg (3,600 lb)	1,633 kg (3,600 lb)	1,633 kg (3,600 lb)	1,633 kg (3,600 lb)	1,633 kg (3,600 lb)

B57 10/20-kiloton free-fall nuclear weapon

B61 100/500-kiloton free-fall nuclear weapon

AGM-84 Harpoon anti-ship missile

AGM-65 Maverick ASM

AGM-45 Shrike anti-radiation missile

AGM-62 Walleye EO-guided glide bomb

GBU-10 Paveway II 1,000-lb (454-kg) laser-guided bomb

Mk 83 1,000-lb (454-kg) GP free-fall or retarded bomb

Mk 82 500-lb (227-kg) GP free-fall or retarded bomb

Rockeye Mk 20 cluster bomb

drop tank

123

Designed for all-weather attack with nuclear and conventional munitions, the A-6E has the under-nose TRAM turret for adverse-weather location and designation of targets for weapons such as the Paveway II laser-guided bomb carried by this Intruder of VA-65 from the USS Dwight D. Eisenhower's Carrier Air Wing 7.

An A-6A rebuilt to A-6E standard (and operated by the Naval Weapons Center) carries a mixed underwing load of Mk 82 500-lb (227-kg) 'iron' bombs on the inboard hardpoints and AGM-88 HARM anti-radar missiles on the outer hard-points.

A non-TRAM A-6E of VA-85 of USS John F. Kennedy's Carrier Air Wing 3 unloads Mk 82 retarded bombs in a low-level pass over decidedly inhospitable terrain.

KA-6D Intruder: buddy refuelling conversion of A-6A aircraft, able to transfer 3150 US gal (11924 litres) of fuel immediately after take-off or 2,250 US gal (8517 litres) at a radius of 288 miles (463 km).

A-6E/TRAM: the A-6E was the definitive attack version with solid-state micro-electronics for greater capability and reliability with much reduced maintenance requirements; TRAM has been retrofitted to all older A-6Es.

A-6F Intruder: much improved version due for service in the early 1990s with the AWSACS (All-Weather Stand-Off Attack Control System) for beyond-visual-range air-to-air and air-to-surface missile capability, high-resolution synthetic-aperture radar, head-down displays and General Electric F404 non-afterburning turbofans for greater fuel economy.

Grumman F-14A Tomcat

Type: two-seat variable-geometry carrier-borne multi-role fighter.

Internal armament: one 20-mm General Electric M61A1 Vulcan cannon plus 675 rounds in the port side of the forward fuselage.

Disposable armament: up to 14,500 lb (6577 kg) of disposable stores carried on six hardpoints (four under the fuselage in two tandem pairs and one under the fixed inner portion of each wing).

Electronics and operational equipment: normal communication and nagivation equipment, plus Hughes AWG-9 coherent pulse-Doppler fire-control radar (with good look-down and track-while-scan capabilities); Northrop TCS (Television Camera Set, for the long-range identification of possible targets) gradually replacing the original forward-looking infra-red pod carried under the nose; Kaiser AVG-12 head-up and vertical situation display system; AYK-14 central digital computer; Honeywell laser ring-gyro inertial navigation system; Itek ALR-45 radar-warning receiver; Tracor ALE-39 chaff dispenser, and on 49 aircraft the TARPS (Tactical Air Reconnaissance Pod System) with KS-87B and KA-99 cameras plus AAD-5 infra-red linescan. Aircraft are also to be retrofitted with a programmable digital signal-processor for the main radar, improved displays in the rear cockpit and, as it becomes available, the Westinghouse APQ-165 ASPJ (Airborne Self-Protection Jammer) and the Hughes/ITT JTIDS (Joint Tactical Information Distribution System) integrated with the Itek ALR-67 threat-warning system.

Current variants and operators

F-14A Tomcat: first flown in December 1970 as the US Navy's new and highly capable fleet defence fighter (and later sold to Iran), this can fairly claim to be the world's most powerful fighter, combining good performance with an excellent match of radar and the whole range of air-to-air weapons. The type was developed after the failure of the General Dynamics F-111B, using the same combination of AWG-9 fire-control system (whose radar can detect targets at a range of more than 195 miles/315 km, track 24 of them simultaneously and control six simultaneous engagements) and AIM-54 Phoenix long-range missiles in a new airframe with variable-gemeotry wings incorporating

Undoubtedly the world's premier air-superiority fighter, the F-14A can carry a wide assortment of short-, medium- and long-range AAMs in addition to its close-in gun armament of one M61A1 20-mm cannon. Seen here is a Tomcat (of VF-1 from USS Ranger) sporting a pair of drop tanks under the engine trunks. Visible under the fuselage (with a large fairing bulged downward under the rear cockpit, is one of the two special pallets each carrying interface units and able to accommodate two AIM-54 Phoenix long-range AAMs.

The ultimate in long-range air-superiority firepower: an F-14A of VF-32 (at the time part of the USS America's *Carrier Air Wing 1) shows off its maximum load of six AIM-54 Phoenix AAMs, with which it can engage six separate targets at ranges of over 115 miles (185 km) once designated by the AWG-9 fire-control radar.*

Grumman's experience as prime contractor for the F-111B. The type is designed mainly as a fleet defence fighter, but can be used in the attack role (though no details of the weapons carried in this role have been officially promulgated). The type's most important disadvantages are lack of reliable power from the two 20,900-lb (9480-kg) Pratt & Whitney TF30-P-412A afterburning turbofans, shortages of the TCS, and the growing limitations of the current analog avionics.

F-14A(Plus) Tomcat: designation of F-14A aircraft with the 29,000-lb (13154-kg) General Electric F110 afterburning turbofan and most of the avionics improvements described above.

F-14D Tomcat: version due for service in 1990 with a full suite of digital avionics (matched by the AIM-54C Phoenix long-range and AIM-120 AMRAAM medium-range air-to-air missiles), General Electric F110-GE-401 afterburning turbofans and features such as a new cockpit with improved displays and Martin-Baker NACES in place of the original Martin-Baker GRU7A ejector seats, an infra-red search and tracking system, ASPJ and JTIDS.

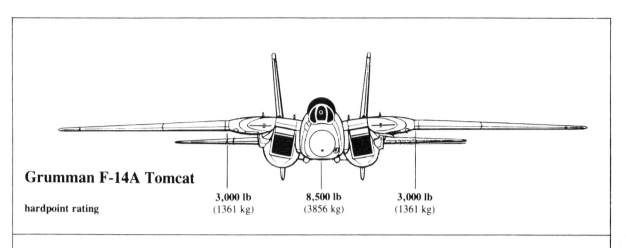

Grumman F-14A Tomcat

hardpoint rating

| **3,000 lb**
(1361 kg) | **8,500 lb**
(3856 kg) | **3,000 lb**
(1361 kg) |

AIM-54A Phoenix AAM

AIM-7F/M Sparrow AAM

AIM-9J/L Sidewinder AAM

267-US gal (1011-litre) drop tank

India

HAL Ajeet

Type: single-seat interceptor and light attack aircraft.

Internal armament: two 30-mm Aden Mk 4 cannon plus 130 rounds per gun in the sides of the inlets.

Disposable armament: up to 1,500 lb (680 kg) of disposable stores carried on four hardpoints (two under each wing).

Electronics and operational equipment: normal communication and navigation equipment, plus a Ferranti F195R/3 ISIS sight.

Current variants and operator

Ajeet: this neat fighter and light attack aircraft is an Indian development of the Folland Gnat lightweight fighter, and first flew in March 1975. The type differs from the Gnat primarily in having a more effective longitudinal-control system and integral wing tanks to free the hardpoints for offensive stores: the Ajeet is used only by India.

Ajeet Trainer: combat-capable two-seat operational conversion trainer with the fuselage lengthened by 3.75 ft (1.14 m) to allow the insertion of the second seat and with the 30-mm cannon optionally replaceable by additional fuel.

The Ajeet was derived from the Gnat lightweight fighter, the adoption of integral wing tankage allowing all four underwing hardpoints to be used for weapons without any sacrifice in combat radius.

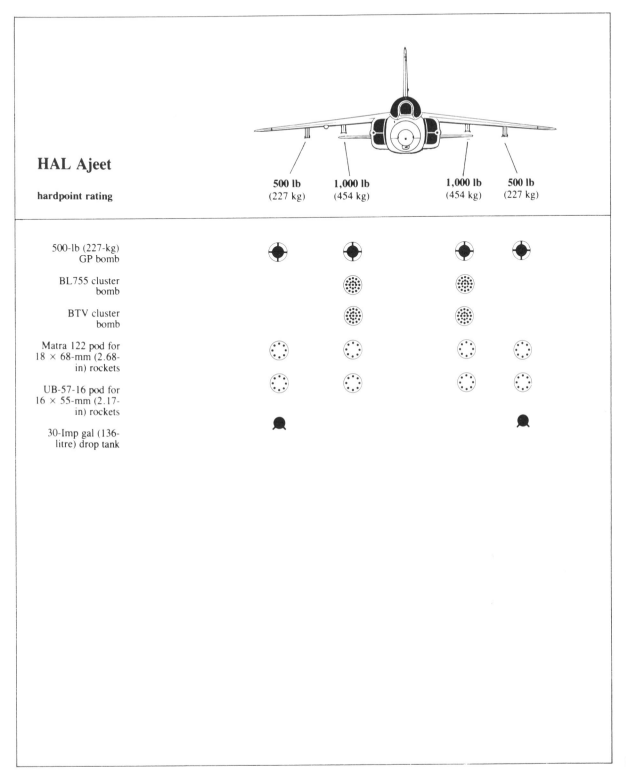

HAL Ajeet

hardpoint rating

	500 lb (227 kg)	**1,000 lb** (454 kg)	**1,000 lb** (454 kg)	**500 lb** (227 kg)
500-lb (227-kg) GP bomb	●	●	●	●
BL755 cluster bomb		●	●	
BTV cluster bomb		●	●	
Matra 122 pod for 18 × 68-mm (2.68-in) rockets	●	●	●	●
UB-57-16 pod for 16 × 55-mm (2.17-in) rockets	●	●	●	●
30-Imp gal (136-litre) drop tank	●			●

Hughes (McDonnell Douglas) AH-64A Apache

Type: two-seat battlefield close-support and anti-tank helicopter.

Internal armament: one 30-mm Hughes M230E1 cannon plus 1,200 rounds in an under-fuselage turret.

Disposable armament: up to 3,880 lb (1760 kg) of disposable stores carried on four hardpoints (two under each stub wing).

Electronics and operational equipment: normal communication and navigation equipment, plus Singer-Kearfott Doppler navigation, Martin Marietta TADS (Target Acquisition and Designation System) and PNVS (Pilot's Night Vision System); Honeywell IHADSS (Integrated Helmet And Display Sighting System); Teledyne fire-control system; CPG stabilized sight with forward-looking infra-red and laser ranger/designator/tracker; radar-warning receiver; laser-warning receiver; infra-red warning receiver; radar jammer; infra-red jammer and chaff/ flare dispenser.

Variant and operator

AH-64A Apache: used only by the US Army, this is an exceptionally capable battlefield helicopter, though large and extremely expensive. The type first flew in September 1974 but was delayed considerably by rising costs so that service deliveries began only in 1984.

Located in the front (lower) seat, the co-pilot/gunner of the AH-64A has basic flight instruments but also the primary weapon controls and sensors, dominated in the centre by the sight control and viewing console associated with the FLIR and TV optics in the lower part of the nose-mounted sensor system.

130

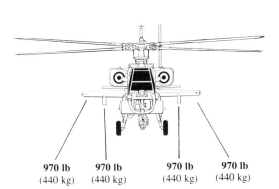

Hughes AH-64A Apache

hardpoint rating

970 lb (440 kg)   **970 lb** (440 kg)   **970 lb** (440 kg)   **970 lb** (440 kg)

AGM-114A Hellfire
anti-tank missile

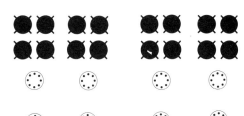

Hughes M260 pod for
19 × 2.75-in (69.85-
mm) rockets

LAU-61/A pod for
19 × 2.75-in
(69.85-in)
rockets

Right *Seated above and behind the gunner/co-pilot, the pilot of the AH-64A has a central CRT for the display of attitude, speed, altitude and hover data; basic analog flight instrumentation; vertical strip instrumentation for dynamic system data; and (bottom left of vertical panel) integrated weapons controls for the Apache's weapons (Hellfire missiles, 2.75-in/69.85-mm rockets and 30-mm cannon) as well as the sight system.*

Opposite *In classic attack configuration, the AH-64A carries an under-fuselage 30-mm cannon, eight AGM-114A Hellfire anti-tank missiles on the inner hardpoints, and 38 unguided rockets on the outer hardpoints.*

Below *The AH-64A is an attack helicopter of impressive capability and performance, but is extremely expensive and suffers the tactical limitations of sensors located low in the nose rather than high above the main rotor.*

Hughes (McDonnell Douglas) Model 500MD/TOW Defender

Type: two-seat scout and anti-tank helicopter.

Internal armament: none.

Disposable armament: up to 500 lb (227 kg) of disposable stores carried on two hardpoints (one on each side of the fuselage).

Electronics and operational equipment: normal communication and navigation equipment, plus Hughes M65 TOW sight in a stabilized nose position, and provision for customer-specified items.

Current variants and operators

OH-6A Cayuse: developed from the Model 369 prototype, this light scout helicopter was developed for the US Army in the early 1960s, and first flew in February 1963. The type possessed admirable flight and performance qualities, and was thus ordered into widespread production. However, the programme was halted after the delivery of 1,434 units because of rising costs and slow deliveries. This variant can carry an armament

The diminutive but speedy and highly agile OH-6A can carry light armament, but is generally used in the unarmed scout role to provide reconnaissance and targetting information for heavily armed attack helicopters.

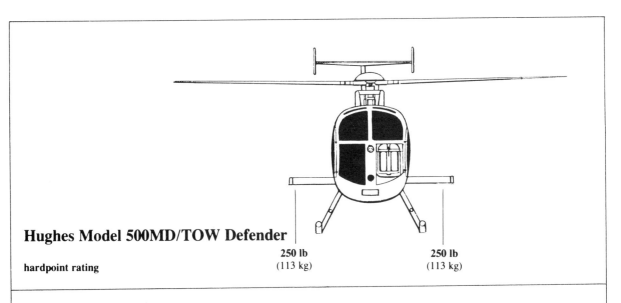

Hughes Model 500MD/TOW Defender

hardpoint rating

	250 lb (113 kg)	**250 lb** (113 kg)

BGM-71 TOW anti-tank
missile

Developed from the OH-6A via the Model 500 series, the McDonnell Douglas (Hughes) Nightfox is essentially a low-cost derivative of the Model 530MG for nocturnal surveillance and attack. The pilots wear night-vision goggles and have an image of the terrain ahead through use of the chin-mounted trainable FLIR pod, while offensive armament comprises two externally-mounted 7.62-mm (0.3-in) EX-34 Chain Guns.

package on the port side of the fuselage, comprising one M134 7.62-mm (0.3-in) 40-mm grenade-launcher.

Model 500M: designation of the export version of the OH-6A, Spanish aircraft being fitted for anti-submarine operations with Texas Instruments ASQ-81 magnetic anomaly detection and two Mk 46 torpedoes.

Model 500 MD Defender: uprated model with its Allison 250 turboshaft generally flat-rated at 375 shp (280 kW) and available with options such as infra-red suppression, armour and self-sealing fuel tanks. Subvariants are the Model 500MD Scout Defender (provision for machine-guns, two seven-tube 2.75-in/69.85-mm rocket-launchers, and four TOW anti-tank missiles); the Model 500MD/TOW Defender (optimized for the anti-tank role with TOW missiles); the Model 500MD/ MMS-TOW (with a mast-mounted sight for low-level operations); the Model 500MD/ASW (optimized for the anti-submarine role with two torpedoes and specialist avionics) and the Defender II (multi-mission version with more power, APR-39 radar-warning receiver, laser ranger and designator, and other updated features). The Model 500 series is used by Israel, Jordan, Kenya, Morocco, South Korea and Taiwan.

Model 530F: upgraded model with the 650-shp (485-kW) Allison 250-C30 turboshaft, and being developed with the same options as the Model 500.

Left *Offering better performance than the Model 500MD Defender series, the Model 530MG series has a fully integrated avionics and weapon-control system (including an optical mast-mounted sight and chin-mounted FLIR) as well as weapons such as four BGM-71 TOW heavyweight anti-tank missiles, two gun pods, two rocket-launchers, or a mix of these weapons.*

Below *McDonnell Douglas is pioneering the future for attack helicopters with an experimental version of the Model 500MG with a mast-mounted sight. Located in a trainable mounting above the main rotor, this allows the crew to maintain surveillance of potentially hostile territory while remaining concealed (and thus comparatively invulnerable) behind natural cover such as a hilltop or trees.*

Ilyushin Il-28 'Beagle'

Type: three-seat light bomber.
Internal armament: two 23-mm NR-23 cannon plus 200 rounds per gun in a fixed nose installation and two 23-mm NR-23 cannon plus 450 rounds per gun in the tail turret.
Disposable armament: up to 3000 kg (6,614 lb) of disposable stores carried in a lower-fuselage weapons bay.
Electronics and operational equipment: normal communication and navigation equipment, plus navigation and bombing radar with its antenna in a ventral radome, a tail-warning radar and a gyro sight for the pilot.

Current variants and operators
Il-28 'Beagle': first flown in July 1948, this elderly light bomber entered service in 1951 and continues in fairly widespread service with a number of Soviet client states, notably Afghanistan, North Korea, Poland and Romania.
Il-28R 'Beagle': three-seat tactical reconnaissance version with four or five cameras and (sometimes) a second radar in the weapons bay. The type is also used for electronic intelligence gathering with a revised electronic fit.
Il-28U 'Beagle': operational conversion trainer lacking radar and armament but fitted with a second cockpit in the nose.

An Ilyushin Il-28 of the Finnish Air Force.

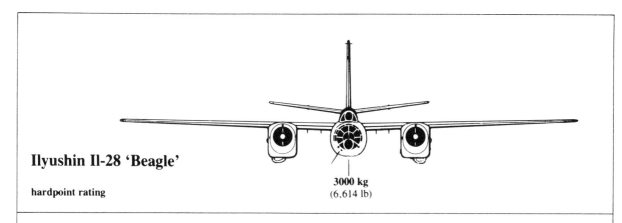

Ilyushin Il-28 'Beagle'

hardpoint rating

3000 kg
(6,614 lb)

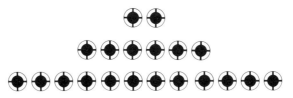

FAB-3000 3,000-kg (6,614-lb)
    GP free-fall bomb

FAB-1000 1000-kg (2,205-lb)
    GP free-fall bomb

FAB-500 500-kg (1,102-lb)
    GP free-fall bomb

Israel

IAI Kfir-C2

Though based aerodynamically and structurally on the Mirage 5 series, the Kfir offers greater power, a far more advanced electronic suite of Israeli origin, greater weapons capability and, in the later models, the added agility and field performance bestowed by fixed canard foreplanes. This Kfir-C7 carries an air-combat load of four AIM-9 Sidewinder AAMs (usually replaced by Shafrir 2 or Python 3 missiles) and a centreline 500-litre (110-Imp gal) supersonic drop tank.

Type: single-seat multi-role fighter.

Internal armament: two 30-mm DEFA 552 cannon plus 150 rounds per gun in the underside of the forward fuselage.

Disposable armament: up to 4295 kg (9,469 lb) of disposable stores carried on nine hardpoints (one on the centreline, two tandem pairs under the fuselage and two under each wing).

Electronics and operational equpment: normal communication and navigation equipment, plus Elta EL/M-2001B ranging radar (the Israelis claim that the larger EL/M-2021B pulse-Doppler air-to-air and air-to-surface radar is fitted); Israel Electro-Optics head-up display; Elbit head-down display; Tamam central computer; Elbit (Singer-Kearfott) S-8600 multi-mode navigation system; Rafael Mahat or IAI WDNS-141 weapon-delivery system; radar-warning receiver and internal electronic countermeasures systems (possibly the Elta EL/L-8230 noise and repeater jammer), plus provision for podded ECM systems such as the Elta L-8202.

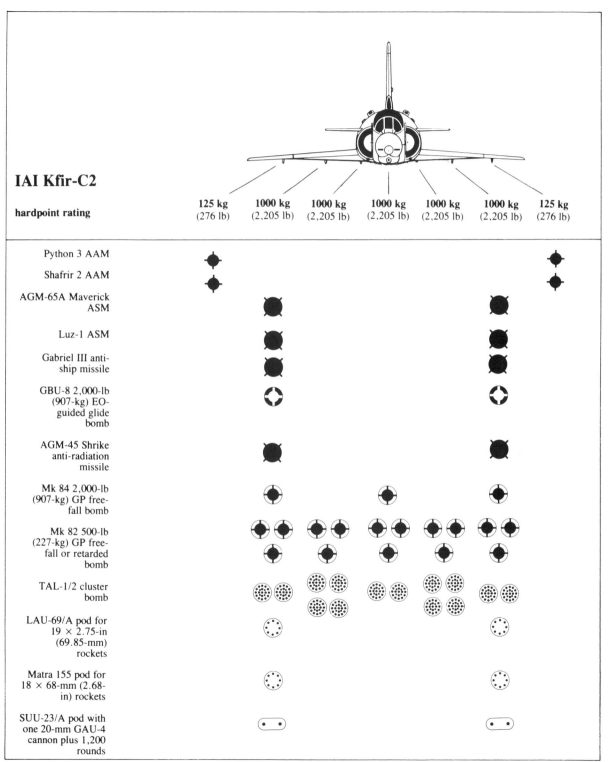

IAI Kfir-C2

hardpoint rating

	125 kg (276 lb)	1000 kg (2,205 lb)	1000 kg (2,205 lb)	1000 kg (2,205 lb)	1000 kg (2,205 lb)	1000 kg (2,205 lb)	125 kg (276 lb)
Python 3 AAM	●						●
Shafrir 2 AAM	●						●
AGM-65A Maverick ASM		●				●	
Luz-1 ASM		●				●	
Gabriel III anti-ship missile		●				●	
GBU-8 2,000-lb (907-kg) EO-guided glide bomb		◉				◉	
AGM-45 Shrike anti-radiation missile		●				●	
Mk 84 2,000-lb (907-kg) GP free-fall bomb		●		●		●	
Mk 82 500-lb (227-kg) GP free-fall or retarded bomb		● ● ●	● ● ●	● ● ●	● ● ●	● ● ●	
TAL-1/2 cluster bomb		● ● ●	● ●	●	● ● ●	●	
LAU-69/A pod for 19 × 2.75-in (69.85-mm) rockets		●				●	
Matra 155 pod for 18 × 68-mm (2.68-in) rockets		●				●	
SUU-23/A pod with one 20-mm GAU-4 cannon plus 1,200 rounds		⬭				⬭	

A picture of the IAI Kfir C2 showing a variety of possible weapons carried by the type (IAI via MARS).

Current variants and operators

Kfir-C1: given the French refusal to continue arms sales to Israel after the 1973 'Yom Kippur' War, Israel's decision as early as 1969 to produce its own combat aircraft was a most prudent move, and the first result was the IAI Nesher (exported as the Dagger), essentially an unlicensed copy of the Dassault-Breguet Mirage 5 with the SNECMA Atar 09C turbojet but using Israeli avionics. This led to the Kfir-C1, essentially the airframe of the Mirage IIICJ married to a 17,900-lb (8119-kg) General Electric J79-IAI-J1E. The larger diameter but reduced length of this afterburning turbojet (in comparison with the SNECMA Atar) required a revision of the rear fuselage, which thus became shorter and wider. Other developments included Israeli avionics and a flat undersurface to the nose. The type first flew in 1972, and only limited production was undertaken.

Kfir-C2: much improved development that first appeared in 1976 with fixed canard foreplanes on the inlet ducts (to improve field performance and combat manoeuvrability), dogtoothed outer panels to the wings, and strakes under the nose. Israel is modifying Colombian Mirage 5s to this standard. Some of the type have been leased by the US Navy under the designation F-21A for dissimilar air combat training.

Kfir-TC2: combat-capable operational conversion trainer and electronic warfare aircraft with a longer but drooped nose increasing length from 15.65 to 16.36 m (51.35 to 53.67 ft). This aircraft is fitted internally with the highly capable Elta L-8230 jamming system as well as other systems.

Kfir-C7: introduced in 1983, this is a further refined version with an additional 1,000 lb (454 kg) of afterburning thrust tweaked from the J79-IAI-J1E to permit a 1540-kg (3,395-lb) increase in take-off weight without loss of performance. The Kfir-C7 has a HOTAS (Hands On Throttle And Stick) control system, the digital WDNS-341 navigation and weapon-delivery system allowing the carriage and delivery of 'smart' weapons, inflight-refuelling capability, increased internal fuel capacity and, as an option, the definitive EL/M-2021 radar.

Kfir-TC7: two-seat parallel to the Kfir-TC2 but based on the Kfir-C7 and probably optimized for the electronic warfare role with systems as yet not revealed.

Israel Aircraft Industries/ McDonnell Douglas Phantom 2000

Type: two-seat all-weather multi-role fighter.

Internal armament: one 20-mm General Electric M61A1 Vulcan rotary-barrel cannon with 640 rounds.

Disposable armament: up to 16,000 lb (7257 kg) of disposable stores carried in four semi-recessed lower-fuselage missile stations and on five hardpoints (one under the fuselage and two under each wing).

Electronics and operational equipment: communication and navigation equipment, plus Elta pulse-Doppler multi-role fire-control radar, Israel Electro-Optics head-up display, Elbit head-down display, Tamam central computer, upgraded Elbit (Singer-Kearfott) S-8600 multi-mode navigation system, AJB-7 bombing system, weapon-release system, General Electric ASG-26A computing sight, Northrop ASX-1 TISEO (Target Identification System Electro-Optical), Itek APR-36 radar-warning receiver, plus provision for podded electronic countermeasures (usually Israeli systems such as the Elta L-8202, but with systems such as the ALQ-101, ALQ-119, ALQ-130 and ALQ-131 possible) and for the Sanders ALQ-140 infra-red countermeasures system.

Current variants and operators

IAI/McDonnell Douglas Phantom 2000: Israel operates a substantial fleet of Phantom aircraft, all of the basic F-4E variant for the ground-attack role, and 140 of these are being upgraded locally to Phantom 2000 (otherwise known as **Super Phantom**) standard in order to meet the threat of advanced Soviet anti-aircraft weapons supplied to the Arab nations by the USSR. Several nations have given thought to such an upgrade, for the Phantom II is still potentially a capable combat aircraft with considerable airframe life still available for effective use if the electronics and certain other features are upgraded. The Israeli programme is the most advanced currently envisaged, and additional impetus was given to the programme by the cancellation of the IAI Lavi multi-role fighter in mid-1987, and though it has now been decided not to re-engine the aircraft with Pratt & Whitney PW1120 afterburning turbofans in place of the standard General Electric J79-GE-17 afterburning turbofans (a saving of $10 million per aircraft), each will be structurally strengthened and refurbished, and additionally fitted with fixed canard foreplanes in the inlet trunks to increase agility, stronger landing gear, a 2728-litre (600-Imp gal) external belly tank and an improved cockpit featuring HOTAS (Hands-On-Throttle-And-Stick) controls and advanced avionics. The last are an Elbit responsibility that includes a new Elta pulse-Doppler radar with Elbit ACE-3 data processor, wide-angle head-up display and head-down cathode ray tube displays, and a new nav/attack system. Israel also operates a small number of F-4E(S) special reconnaissance aircraft of the type modified by General Electric with the HIAC-1 photo-reconnaissance system in a drastically revised nose. The converted aircraft have been further revised in the powerplant for high-altitude high-speed flight for long-range strategic and operational reconnaissance.

IAI/McDonnell Douglas Phantom 2000

hardpoint rating

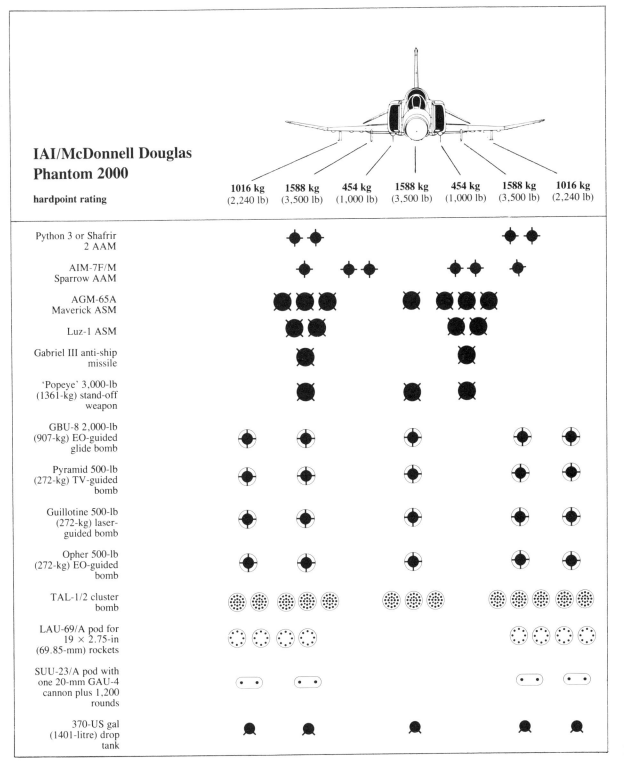

	1016 kg (2,240 lb)	1588 kg (3,500 lb)	454 kg (1,000 lb)	1588 kg (3,500 lb)	454 kg (1,000 lb)	1588 kg (3,500 lb)	1016 kg (2,240 lb)
Python 3 or Shafrir 2 AAM		● ●				● ●	
AIM-7F/M Sparrow AAM		●	● ●		● ●	●	
AGM-65A Maverick ASM		● ● ●		●	● ● ●		
Luz-1 ASM		● ●			● ●		
Gabriel III anti-ship missile		●			●		
'Popeye' 3,000-lb (1361-kg) stand-off weapon		●		●	●		
GBU-8 2,000-lb (907-kg) EO-guided glide bomb	●	●		●		●	●
Pyramid 500-lb (272-kg) TV-guided bomb	●	●		●		●	●
Guillotine 500-lb (272-kg) laser-guided bomb	●	●		●		●	●
Opher 500-lb (272-kg) EO-guided bomb	●	●		●		●	●
TAL-1/2 cluster bomb	● ● ●	● ● ●		● ●		● ● ●	● ● ●
LAU-69/A pod for 19 × 2.75-in (69.85-mm) rockets	● ●	● ●				● ●	● ●
SUU-23/A pod with one 20-mm GAU-4 cannon plus 1,200 rounds	●	●				●	●
370-US gal (1401-litre) drop tank	●	●		●		●	●

145

Lockheed F-104G Starfighter

Type: single-seat multi-role strike and attack fighter.

Internal armament: one 20-mm General Electric M61A1 Vulcan six-barrel rotary cannon plus 725 rounds in the port side of the forward fuselage.

Disposable armament: up to 4,310 lb (1955 kg) of disposable stores carried on five hardpoints (one under the fuselage and two under each wing) and on two wingtip missile rails.

Electronics and operational equipment: normal communication and navigation equipment, plus Autonetics F-15A NASARR (North American Search And Ranging Radar used primarily for the air-to-surface, ground mapping and terrain-avoidance roles); General Electric ASG-14 sight; Litton LN-3 inertial navigation; Minneapolis-Honeywell MH-97 automatic flight-control system; Mergenthaler Linotype bombing computer and various radar-warning and electronic countermeasures systems such as the Sanders ALQ-126 or any one of four Elettronica noise jammer systems.

Current variants and operators

F-104A Starfighter: now in only very limited service with Taiwan, the F-104A was the initial production version of the Starfighter, schemed towards the end of the Korean War as an uncompromised interceptor possessing unmatched speed and rate of climb. The type first flew in February 1954 and the F-104A is remarkably short-ranged—at the same time possessing the highly limited armament of but one 20-mm M61A1 cannon and two AIM-9 Sidewinder air-to-air missiles.

F-104G Starfighter: radically transformed multi-role version developed for European air arms in the strike and attack roles now generally being replaced by the Panavia Tornado and General Dynamics F-16 Fighting Falcon. The type is still used in limited numbers by Denmark, Taiwan, Turkey and West Germany. The F-104Gs of the NATO air arms can be fitted for the carriage of a single nuclear weapon in the strike role, the possibilities being the B28 (with a variable yield of 70 kilotons, or 350 kilotons or 1.1

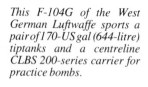

This F-104G of the West German Luftwaffe sports a pair of 170-US gal (644-litre) tiptanks and a centreline CLBS 200-series carrier for practice bombs.

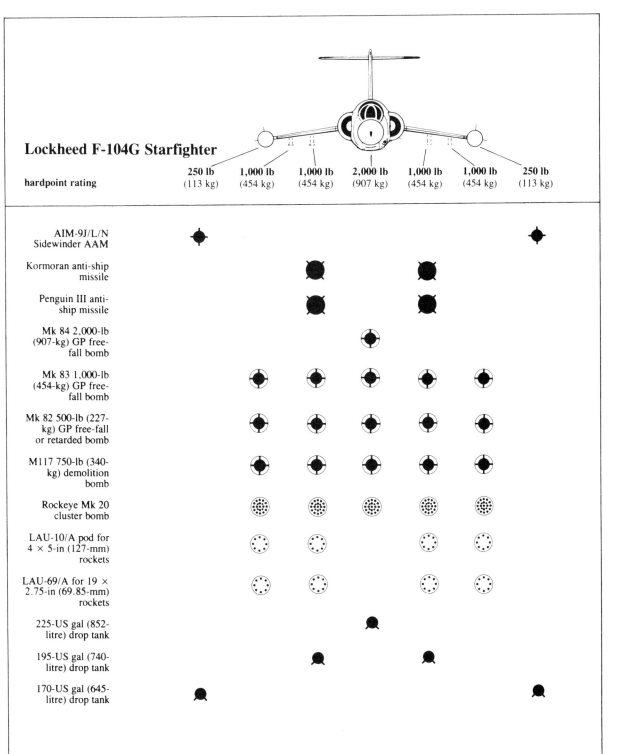

Lockheed F-104G Starfighter

hardpoint rating	250 lb (113 kg)	1,000 lb (454 kg)	1,000 lb (454 kg)	2,000 lb (907 kg)	1,000 lb (454 kg)	1,000 lb (454 kg)	250 lb (113 kg)
AIM-9J/L/N Sidewinder AAM	✦						✦
Kormoran anti-ship missile		●			●		
Penguin III anti-ship missile		●			●		
Mk 84 2,000-lb (907-kg) GP free-fall bomb				●			
Mk 83 1,000-lb (454-kg) GP free-fall bomb		●	●	●	●	●	
Mk 82 500-lb (227-kg) GP free-fall or retarded bomb		●	●	●	●	●	
M117 750-lb (340-kg) demolition bomb		●	●	●	●	●	
Rockeye Mk 20 cluster bomb		⊛	⊛	⊛	⊛	⊛	
LAU-10/A pod for 4 × 5-in (127-mm) rockets		⊙	⊙		⊙	⊙	
LAU-69/A for 19 × 2.75-in (69.85-mm) rockets		⊙	⊙		⊙	⊙	
225-US gal (852-litre) drop tank				●			
195-US gal (740-litre) drop tank			●		●		
170-US gal (645-litre) drop tank	●						●

147

megatons), the B57 (with yields from below 1 kiloton to 20 kilotons) and the B61 Mod 2/3/4/5 (with yields between 100 and 500 kilotons).

RF-104G Starfighter: tactical reconnaissance version of the F-104G with three cameras.

TF-104G Starfighter: combat-capable two-seat operational conversion and proficiency trainer variant of the F-104G.

CF-104 Starfighter: Canadian-built version of the F-104G.

CF-104D Starfighter: Canadian-built version of the TF-104G.

F-104J Starfighter: version of the F-104G for Japan, mostly built under licence by Mitsubishi.

F-104S Starfighter: Italian-developed version optimized for the all-weather air-to-air role with R-21G/H radar with continuous-wave target illumination for the primary armament of AIM-7 Sparrow or Selenia Aspide air-to-air missiles. This version is used by Italy and Turkey and has a 7,500-lb (3402-kg) weapon-carrying capability, the centreline hardpoint being rated at 2,000 lb (907 kg), the two lateral hardpoints on the fuselage at 250 kg (113 lb) each for air-to-air missiles, the two inboard underwing hardpoints at 1,000 lb (454 kg) each, the two outer underwing hardpoints at 500 lb (227 kg) each, and the two wingtip hardpoints at 1,000 lb (454 kg) each.

Lockheed P-3C Orion Update III

Type: ten-seat maritime patrol and anti-submarine aircraft.

Internal armament: none.

Disposable armament: up to 19,250 lb (8732 kg) of disposable stores carried in the lower-fuselage weapons bay and on ten hardpoints (five under each wing).

Electronics and operational equipment: normal communication and navigation equipment, plus Texas Instruments APS-125 surveillance radar; ASQ-84 magnetic anomaly detection; Loral ALQ-78 electronic support measures; Texas Instruments AAS-36 chin-mounted forward-looking infra-red; AQA-7 DIFAR sonobuoy indicator sets and sonar receivers (used in conjunction with the IBM AYS-1 Proteus acoustic signal processing system for the 87 air-dropped sonobuoys carried) feeding data to the Univac ASQ-114 central digital computer and AYA-8 data processor (which also receive inputs from two Litton LN-72 inertial navigation systems and APN-227 Doppler navigation to generate information for ASA-66 tactical consoles). Other electronic items are being added as and when they become available, the most important being the new Eaton-AIL electronic support measures to be added in wingtip fairings.

Current variants and operators

P-3A Orion: derived from the Lockheed L-188 Electra four-turboprop airliner, the Orion is the Western world's most important land-based maritime patrol and anti-submarine aircraft, and first flew in August 1958. The original P-3A has an avionics suite derived from that of the preceding Lockheed P-2 Neptune and the type survives now only with Spain and in subvariants such as the CP-3A freighter, VP-3A staff transport and WP-3A weather reconnaissance aircraft.

The airframe and powerplant of the P-3C differ only insignificantly from those of the P-3B, but the revised sensor and tactical system make the aircraft radically more effective than its predecessor. This is a P-3C Update II with provision for AGM-84 Harpoon anti-ship missiles under the wings and retractable FLIR under the nose. Also visible are the MAD tail boom, the 48 sonobuoy chutes discharging under the rear fuselage and, under the port wing root, the fairing for the ALQ-78 ESM system.

P-3B Orion: improved production version with Avco Lycoming T56-A-14 turboprops rather than the water-injected T56-A-10Ws of the P-3A. The type serves with New Zealand, Norway and the reserve forces of the US Navy, most having been upgraded with the aid of a US Navy/Lear Siegler navaid and sensor improvement package. New Zealand's aircraft have in addition the Boeing UDACS display system.

P-3C Orion: retaining the airframe/powerplant combination of the P-3B, the P-3C is a much improved variant with the A-NEW avionics suite using new sensors and displays based on the Univac digital computer. The type has been bought by Australia, Japan, the Netherlands and the USA, and has been evolved rapidly through a number of Update programmes. In 1975 production of the P-3C Orion Update I began with increased computer memory, more accurate navigation and increased sensitivity for the acoustic signal processors. In 1976 the P-3C Orion Update II added an infra-red detection system and provision for the AGM-84 Harpoon anti-ship missile. In 1978 the P-3C Orion Update III introduced the IBM Proteus acoustic signal processor and a new sonobuoy receiver system obviating the need to overfly the buoys for position fixing and in the late 1980s the P-3C Update IV will add yet further enhanced capabilities.

EP-3E Orion: electronic intelligence conversions of earlier aircraft with GTE Sylvania ALR-60 communications interception and analysis equipment, Loral ALQ-78 electronic support measures system, ARGO Systems ALR-52 electronic frequency measuring system, ASQ-171 electronic intelligence system and ALQ-110 radar signals collection system.

P-3F Orion: longer-range version of the P-3C for Iran, now of doubtful serviceability in anything but the patrol role.

P-3 Orion AEW&C: under this designation Lockheed is offering a conversion of older airframes to the airborne early warning and control system configuration with an above-fuselage rotodome for General Electric APS-138 surveillance radar and role equipment in the fuselage.

CP-140 Aurora: this is a version of the P-3C for Canada with the avionics suite of the Lockheed S-3A Viking (including the Texas Instruments APS-116 radar and AYK-10 tactical computer system). The type also has provision for ice reconnaissance, search-and-rescue, fishery protection and resources survey.

L-188 Electra: several ex-airline transports are operated by air arms, and some of these have been modified for electronic intelligence and comparable roles.

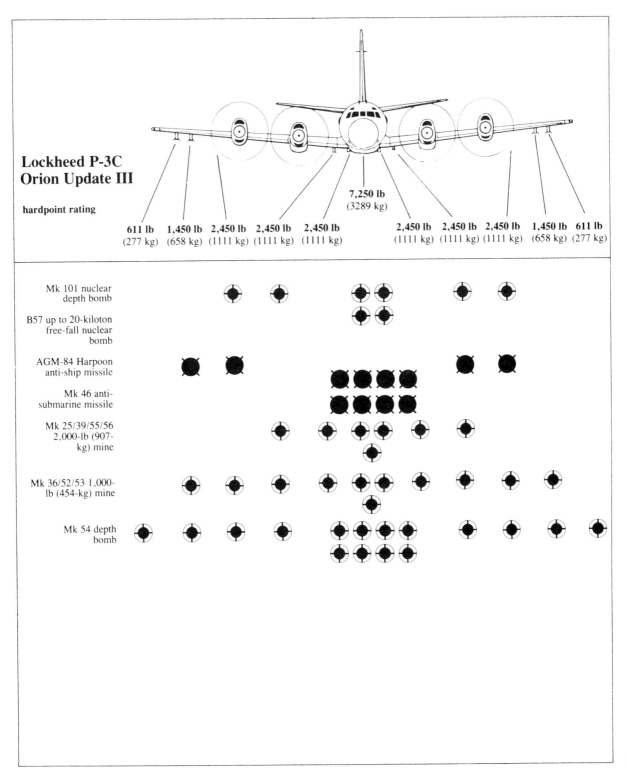

**Lockheed P-3C
Orion Update III**

hardpoint rating

| 611 lb
(277 kg) | 1,450 lb
(658 kg) | 2,450 lb
(1111 kg) | 2,450 lb
(1111 kg) | 2,450 lb
(1111 kg) | 7,250 lb
(3289 kg) | 2,450 lb
(1111 kg) | 2,450 lb
(1111 kg) | 2,450 lb
(1111 kg) | 1,450 lb
(658 kg) | 611 lb
(277 kg) |

Mk 101 nuclear depth bomb

B57 up to 20-kiloton free-fall nuclear bomb

AGM-84 Harpoon anti-ship missile

Mk 46 anti-submarine missile

Mk 25/39/55/56 2,000-lb (907-kg) mine

Mk 36/52/53 1,000-lb (454-kg) mine

Mk 54 depth bomb

Lockheed S-3A Viking

USA

Type: four-seat carrier-borne anti-submarine aircraft.

Internal armament: none.

Disposable armament: up to 6,000 lb (2722 kg) of disposable stores carried in the lower-fuselage weapons bay and on two hardpoints (one under each wing).

Electronics and operational equipment: normal communication and navigation equipment, plus Texas Instruments APS-116 search radar; Texas Instruments ASQ-81 magnetic anomaly detection; Texas Instruments OR-89/AA forward-looking infra-red; ASN-92(V) inertial navigation system; APN-200 Doppler navigation; IBM ALR-47 radar-warning receiver; sonobuoy receiver and reference systems used in conjunction with 60 sonobuoys, and other items feeding data to the Univac AYK-10 digital central computer and tactical system.

Current variants and operator

S-3A Viking: used only by the US Navy as its primary carrier-based anti-submarine aircraft, the Viking is an enormous achievement in aeronautical and systems terms, an extremely capable anti-submarine system having been built into a compact but long-ranged airframe able to operate from current US Navy carriers with ease. The type was designed to replace the Grumman S-2 Tracker series, and first flew in January 1972.

US-3A Viking: carrier onboard delivery variant to supplement the Grumman C-2A Greyhound. The type has a crew of two and can carry six passengers and 4,600 lb (2087 kg) of freight, including some 3,000 lb (1361 kg) in two underwing pods: the all-freight load is 7,500 lb (3402 kg).

S-2B Viking: improved version of the S-3A to be procured by conversion of earlier aircraft; this variant has the IBM AYS-1 Proteus acoustic signal processing system, a new sonobuoy receiver, improved electronic support measures and provision for the AGM-84 Harpoon anti-ship missile on the underwing hardpoints.

The S-3A is in no way an elegant aeroplane, but it is a classic example of packing maximum capability into minimum airframe, and thus a truly formidable warplane within its carrier-based anti-submarine speciality. Seen here is a Viking of VS-22 of USS Saratoga carrying an atypical load of six Mk 82 500-lb (227-kg) bombs. Notable electronic features are the retracted tail 'sting' for the Texas Instruments ASQ-81 MAD, the 60 under-fuselage launch tubes for sonobuoys and the wingtip fairings for the IBM ALR-47 ESM system.

152

Lockheed S-3A Viking

hardpoint rating

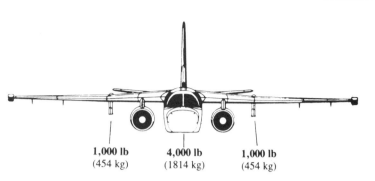

	1,000 lb (454 kg)	**4,000 lb** (1814 kg)	**1,000 lb** (454 kg)

Mk 46 anti-submarine torpedo		⬤⬤⬤⬤	
B57 up to 20-kiloton free-fall nuclear bomb		⬤⬤	
1,000-lb (454-kg) destructor	⬤	⬤⬤⬤	⬤
Mk 82 500-lb (227-kg) GP free-fall bomb	⬤⬤	⬤⬤⬤	⬤⬤
Mk 54 depth bomb	⬤	⬤⬤⬤	⬤
Mk 55/56 2,000-lb (907-kg) mine		⬤⬤	
Mk 36/52/53 1,000-lb (454-kg) mine	⬤	⬤⬤⬤	⬤
Rockeye Mk 20 cluster bomb	⬤		⬤
LAU-10/A pod for 4 × 5-in (127-mm) rockets	⬤		⬤
LAU-61/69 pod for 19 × 2.75-in (69.85-mm) rockets	⬤		⬤
300-US gal (1137-litre) drop tank	⬤		⬤

153

McDonnell Douglas A-4M Skyhawk II

Type: single-seat carrier-borne and land-based light attack aircraft.

Internal armament: two 20-mm Mk 12 cannon plus 200 rounds per gun in the wing roots.

Disposable armament: up to 9,155 lb (4153 kg) of disposable stores carried on five hardpoints (one under the fuselage and two under each wing).

Electronics and operational equipment: normal communication and navigation equipment, plus APN-153(V) ground mapping, terrain avoidance and ranging radar used in conjunction with the ASN-41 navigation system; Marconi AVQ-24 head-up display; Texas Instruments AJB-3 LABS loft-bombing system; Hughes ASB-19 ARBS (Angle-Rate Bombing System); Itek ALR-45 radar-warning receiver; Magnavox ALR-50 SAM-warning system and various electronic countermeasures including the Tracor ALE-39 chaff/flare dispenser and the Sanders ALQ-100 deception electronic countermeasures and Sanders ALQ-130 tactical communications jamming systems.

Current variants and operators

A-4E Skyhawk: one of the most successful aircraft ever designed, the A-4 resulted from a US Navy requirement of 1950 for a turbojet-powered successor to the piston-engined Douglas AD (later A-1) Skyraider, the design team achieving wonders of weight reduction to meet the US Navy's requirement at little over half the 30,000-lb (13607-kg) weight specified. The XA4D-1 prototype first flew in June 1954 with a 7,200-lb (3266-kg) Wright J65-W-2 turbojet and demonstrated the ability to carry a 5,000-lb (2722-kg) warload. The oldest version still in service is the A-4E powered by an 8,500-lb (3855-kg) Pratt & Whitney J52-P-6A non-afterburning turbojet in place of the Wright engine. The type also introduced a better ejector seat and increased weapon-carriage capability: it remains in service with Indonesia.

The TA-4F is a two-seat operational conversion and proficiency trainer of the Skyhawk family, serving mainly with the US Marine Corps, and is seen here with two 400-US gal (1,514-litre) droptanks, two AGM-12 Bullpup air-to-surface missiles and two triplets of 'iron' bombs.

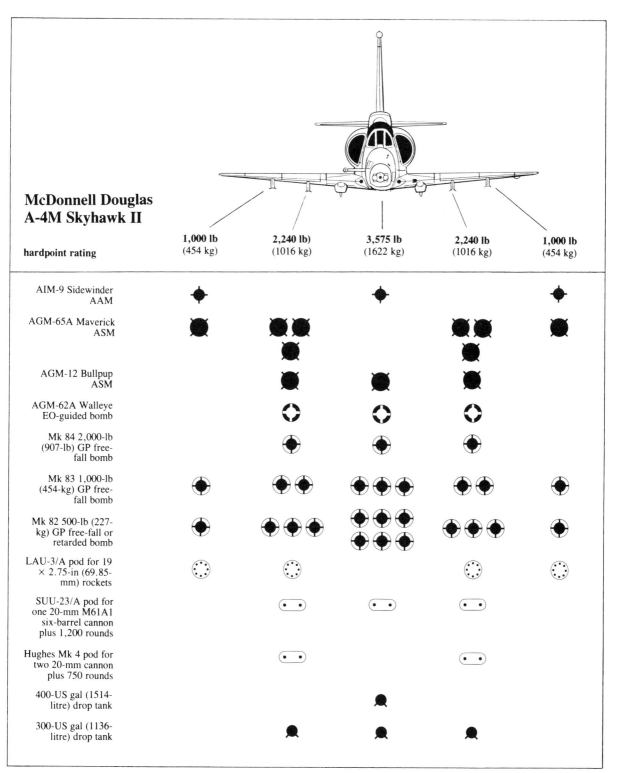

McDonnell Douglas A-4M Skyhawk II

hardpoint rating

	1,000 lb (454 kg)	2,240 lb) (1016 kg)	3,575 lb (1622 kg)	2,240 lb (1016 kg)	1,000 lb (454 kg)
AIM-9 Sidewinder AAM	●		●		●
AGM-65A Maverick ASM	●	● ● ●		● ● ●	●
AGM-12 Bullpup ASM		●	●	●	
AGM-62A Walleye EO-guided bomb		●	●	●	
Mk 84 2,000-lb (907-lb) GP free-fall bomb		●	●	●	
Mk 83 1,000-lb (454-kg) GP free-fall bomb	●	● ●	● ● ●	● ●	●
Mk 82 500-lb (227-kg) GP free-fall or retarded bomb	●	● ● ●	● ● ● ● ● ●	● ● ●	●
LAU-3/A pod for 19 × 2.75-in (69.85-mm) rockets	●	●		●	●
SUU-23/A pod for one 20-mm M61A1 six-barrel cannon plus 1,200 rounds		●	●	●	
Hughes Mk 4 pod for two 20-mm cannon plus 750 rounds		●		●	
400-US gal (1514-litre) drop tank			●		
300-US gal (1136-litre) drop tank		●	●	●	

A-4F Skyhawk: improved A-4E powered by the 9,200-lb (4218-kg) Pratt & Whitney J52-P-8A and featuring a zero/zero ejector seat and a humped dorsal spine for the additional avionics raising the standard well above the 'austere' level of earlier models. The type can carry an 8,200-lb (3720-kg) ordnance load over comparatively short ranges.

T-4F Skyhawk: two-seat operational conversion and proficiency trainer variant of the A-4F.

A-4H Skyhawk: version of the A-4F for Israel, but featuring a square-topped fin, two 30-mm DEFA 552 cannon plus 150 rounds per gun and an increasing measure of Israeli avionics: most aircraft have been upgraded to a standard comparable to that of the A-4N.

TA-4H Skyhawk: two-seat operational conversion and proficiency trainer variant of the A-4H.

TA-4J Skyhawk: simplified and unarmed version of the TA-4F for the US Navy with the J52-P-6 or J52-P-8A engine.

A-4K Skyhawk: equivalent of the A-4F for New Zealand.

TA-4K Skyhawk: two-seat operational conversion trainer variant of the A-4K.

A-4KU Skyhawk II: equivalent of the A-4M for Kuwait.

TA-4KU Skyhhawk II: two-seat operational conversion trainer variant of the A-4KU.

A-4M Skyhawk II: much improved variant for the US Marine Corps with the fin of the A-4H, upgraded avionics and an increase in disposable load.

OA-4M Skyhawk II: forward air control conversion of TA-4F aircraft to A-4M standard.

A-4N Skyhawk II: version of the A-4M for Israeli with a larger nose (containing improved avionics including a new weapon-delivery system); advanced defensive avionics (including the Elta EL/L-8202 and EL/L-8230 pods); extended jetpipes to reduce infra-red signature; chaff and flare dispensers; two additional underwing hardpoints; two 30-mm DEFA cannon, provision for Shafir 2 AAMs and Gabriel III anti-ship missiles, and other detail improvements.

A-4P Skyhawk: refurbished and uprated A-4B for the Argentine air force fitted with the Ferranti ISIS sight.

A-4PTM Skyhawk: refurbished and upgraded aircraft of earlier variants for Malaysia.

A-4Q Skyhawk: refurbished and uprated A-4B for the Argentine navy fitted with the Ferranti F195 ISIS sight.

A-4S Skyhawk: much improved refurbishment of the A-4B for Singapore with new avionics and weapons (including 30-mm Aden Mk 4 cannon) and fitted with the General Electric F404 non-afterburning turbofan.

TA-4S Skyhawk: two-seat operational conversion trainer variant of the A-4S with separate cockpits.

McDonnell Douglas F-4E Phantom II

Type: two-seat multi-role fighter.

Internal armament: one 20-mm General Electric M61A1 Vulcan six-barrel rotary cannon plus 639 rounds in the lower nose.

Disposable armament: up to 16,000 (7257 kg) of disposable stores carried in four lower-fuselage missile stations and on five hardpoints (one under the fuselage and two under each wing).

Electronics and operational equipment: normal communication and navigation equipment, plus Hughes APQ-120 fire-control radar; AJB-7 bombing system; ASQ-91 weapon-release system; General Electric ASG-26A lead-computing optical sight; Northrop ASX-1 TISEO (Target Identification System, Electro-Optical); ASN-63 inertial navigation system; CPK-92A central computer; ASA-32 flight-control system and Itek APR-36 radar-warning receiver plus an assortment of podded countermeasures such as the ALQ-101, ALQ-119, ALQ-130 and ALQ-131 electronic systems, and the Sanders ALQ-140 infra-red system.

Current variants and operators

RF-4B Phantom II: oldest surviving in-service model, the RF-4B is the US Marine Corps' tactical reconnaissance version of the F-4B naval fighter with 17,000-lb (7711-kg) General Electric J79-GE-8 afterburning turbojets. It carries no armament but has its nose lengthened by 4.75 ft (1.44 m) for the accommodation of Texas Instruments APQ-99 radar and forward/oblique cameras (or a mapping camera) and is also fitted with

Now somewhat long in the tooth but still valuable on the US Navy's smaller carriers, the F-4 Phantom is a useful multi-role type. Seen in the markings of VF-121 during 1967, this is an F-4B of the initial fighter production model, a type later upgraded to F-4N standard for the US Naval Air Reserve.

infra-red linescan and Goodyear UPD-4 (in some aircraft more advanced UPD-8) side-looking airborne radar. The F-4 series was planned as a heavy strike and attack fighter but developed as a fleet defence fighter for a first flight in May 1958.

F-4C Phantom II: minimum-change version of the F-4B for the US Air Force with dual controls, low-pressure tyres, J79-GE-15 engines, revised inflight-refuelling arrangements, and a different avionics suite including Westinghouse APQ-100 radar, AJB-7 bombing system, ASN-48 inertial navigation system and ASN-46 navigation computer. The variant is also used by Spain.

RF-4C Phantom II: tactical reconnaissance version of the F-4C for the USAF with APQ-99 radar in a lengthened nose also accommodating forward and oblique cameras. Other equipment of this unarmed version includes fuselage-located APQ-102 (UPD-8) side-looking airborne radar; AAS-18A infra-red linescan and, most recently, the Litton ALQ-125 TEREC (Tactical Electronic REConnaissance) system. The type is also used by Spain.

F-4D Phantom II: improved version of the F-4C for the USAF with Westinghouse APQ-109A radar, other avionics revisions and reduced fuselage fuel; the type is also used by Iran and South Korea.

F-4E Phantom II: definitive USAF model with an inbuilt 20-mm M61A1 cannon, revised avionics and powerplant, leading-edge slots on the tailplane, automatic manoeuvring slats on the leading edges of the outer wing panels, and additional fuel capacity. The type is also flown by Greece, Iran, Israel, Japan (the F-4EJ licence-built by Mitsubishi and scheduled for considerable updating in the later 1980s), South Korea, Turkey and West Germany. Some Israeli aircraft have been modified to the F-4E(S) standard as extremely high altitude stand-off reconnaissance aircraft with a much revised nose for the special HIAC-1 photo-reconnaissance system.

RF-4E Phantom II: tactical reconnaissance version of the F-4E with the revisions and equipment of the RF-4C. The type is also used by Greece, Iran, Israel, Japan (as the

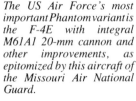

The US Air Force's most important Phantom variant is the F-4E with integral M61A1 20-mm cannon and other improvements, as epitomized by this aircraft of the Missouri Air National Guard.

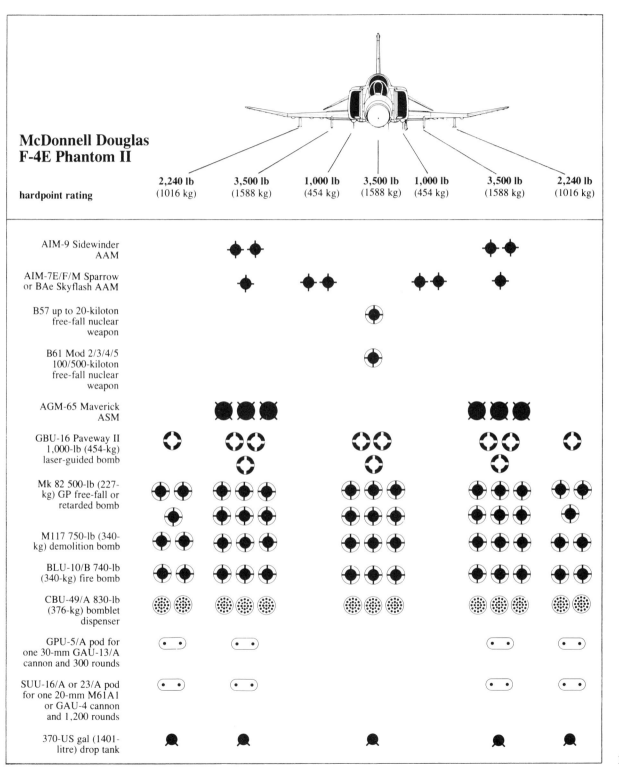

McDonnell Douglas F-4E Phantom II

hardpoint rating

	2,240 lb (1016 kg)	3,500 lb (1588 kg)	1,000 lb (454 kg)	3,500 lb (1588 kg)	1,000 lb (454 kg)	3,500 lb (1588 kg)	2,240 lb (1016 kg)
AIM-9 Sidewinder AAM	●●					●●	
AIM-7E/F/M Sparrow or BAe Skyflash AAM	●	●●			●●	●	
B57 up to 20-kiloton free-fall nuclear weapon				●			
B61 Mod 2/3/4/5 100/500-kiloton free-fall nuclear weapon				●			
AGM-65 Maverick ASM		●●●				●●●	
GBU-16 Paveway II 1,000-lb (454-kg) laser-guided bomb	●	●● ●		●● ●		●● ●	●
Mk 82 500-lb (227-kg) GP free-fall or retarded bomb	●● ●●	●●● ●●●		●●● ●●●		●●● ●●●	●● ●
M117 750-lb (340-kg) demolition bomb	●●	●●●		●●●		●●●	●●
BLU-10/B 740-lb (340-kg) fire bomb	●●	●●●		●●●		●●●	●●
CBU-49/A 830-lb (376-kg) bomblet dispenser	●●	●●●		●●●		●●●	●●
GPU-5/A pod for one 30-mm GAU-13/A cannon and 300 rounds	●	●				●	●
SUU-16/A or 23/A pod for one 20-mm M61A1 or GAU-4 cannon and 1,200 rounds	●	●				●	●
370-US gal (1401-litre) drop tank	●	●		●		●	●

RF-4EJ), Turkey and West Germany. Improvements to in-service aircraft include augmented target acquisition capability through the retrofit of items such as the Ford AVQ-26 'Pave Tack' system with forward-looking infra-red (for the acquisition), and a laser (for the designation) of targets.

F-4F Phantom II: air-superiority version of the F-4E for West Germany with weight reduced by the elimination of all air-to-surface capability. The aircraft are being upgraded in the late 1980s for continued viability.

F-4G Advanced Wild Weasel: dedicated defence-suppression version for the USAF produced as conversions of F-4E airframes with the Loral APR-38 emitter locater system; Itek APR-36 and Itek APR-37 radar-warning and homing systems; Westinghouse ALQ-101(V)-10, Westinghouse ALQ-119-12/14 or Westinghouse ALQ-131 defensive jammer pods; plus an all-missile armament of AMG-45 Shrike, AGM-78 Standard ARM and AGM-88 HARM anti-radiation missiles, and AGM-65 Maverick air-to-surface missiles.

F-4J Phantom II: second-generation fighter for the US Navy and US MarineCorps with J79-GE-8 or J79-GE-10 turbojets, larger wheels, slotted tailplane, drooping ailerons and Westinghouse AWG-10 fire-control radar (later upgraded to AWG-10A standard with greater maintainability and added air-to-air and air-to-surface modes). A small number of aircraft transferred to the UK have the designation F-4J(UK). In common with other variants not fitted with an internal cannon, this type is generally fitted with one SUU-23/A pod (containing a 20-mm M61A1 cannon plus 1,200 rounds) on the centreline hardpoint.

F-4K Phantom II: version of the F-4J for the Royal Navy with Rolls-Royce Spey afterburning turbofans, double-extending nosewheel leg, folding radome as Westinghouse AWG-11 fire-control radar plus British avionics. The type is designated Phantom FG.Mk 1 in British service, the aircraft passing to the RAF as the Royal Navy's carriers were phased out.

F-4M Phantom II: version of the F-4K for the Royal Air Force with unslotted tailplane, standard nosewheel leg, Ferranti inertial navigation system, electronic countermeasures pod at the top of the fin and AWG-12 fire-control radar. The type is designated Phantom FGR.Mk 2 in British service.

F-4N Phantom II: designation of F-4B aircraft modified to considerably higher structural, aerodynamic and avionics standards for service into the 1990s.

F-4S Phantom II: designation of F-4J aircraft modified to the same basic standard as the F-4N with features of the F-4E and F-4F (leading-edge slats and J79-GE-10B engines) and AWG-10A fire-control radar.

McDonnell Douglas F-15C Eagle   USA

Type: single-seat air-superiority fighter with advanced attack capability.

Internal armament: one 20-mm General Electric M61A1 Vulcan six-barrel rotary cannon plus 940 rounds in the upper edge of the starboard inlet.

Disposable armament: up to 16,000 lb (7258 kg) of disposable stores carried on two tandem pairs of missile ejectors (one pair on each fuselage flank) and five hardpoints (one under the fuselage and two under each wing).

Electronics and operational equipment: normal communication and navigation equipment, plus Hughes APG-63 pulse-Doppler multi-mode search and tracking radar; McDonnell Douglas head-up display; Sperry Rand head-down display; IBM central digital computer; Sperry Rand air-data computer; Litton inertial navigation system; Northrop ALQ-135 internal electronic countermeasures system; Loral ALR-56 radar-warning receiver and Magnavox ALR-50 SAM-warning receiver; plus podded countermeasures such as the Westinghouse ALQ-119(V) and Westinghouse ALQ-131 systems and electro-optical sensors such as the Ford AVQ-26 'Pave Tack' pod. A retrofit may add the Westinghouse ALQ-153 tail warning and automatic countermeasures set.

Carrying the embellished markings of Air Defense Tactical Air Command on its tail, a Sparrow- and Side-winder-armed F-15A of the 318th Fighter Interceptor Squadron cruises over Washington State after take-off from its base at McChord AFB. The large nose radome is occupied by the antenna for the highly capable APG-63 multi-mode pulse-Doppler radar which is optimized for the air-to-air role suited to the Eagle's air-superiority and continental air defence taskings.

The F-15E is entering US Air Force service in the later 1980s as a two-seat long-range interdiction aircraft with features such as synthetic-aperture radar and up to 24,000 lb (10,885 kg) of disposable weapons. Elements of this new version are seen here under evaluation, including FAST packs with additional fuel and tangential carriage of twelve 'iron' bombs, four AIM-9 Sidewinder self-defence AAMs, and the navigation and targetting pods for the LANTIRN nav/attack system.

Current variants and operators

F-15A Eagle: designed in response to the threat supposedly posed by the USSR's Mikoyan-Gurevich MiG-25 'Foxbat', the F-15 first flew in July 1972 as US Air Force successor to the McDonnell Douglas F-4 Phantom II and though used now as a potent multi-role fighter, was at first schemed as a dedicated air-superiority fighter with equal short- and medium-range armament capability in an airframe capable of remarkable performance and agility with a HOTAS (Hands On Throttle And Stick) cockpit. The only other operator of this initial model is Israel.

F-15B Eagle: combat-capable two-seat operational conversion and proficiency trainer variant of the F-15A.

F-15C Eagle: improved single-seat version with some 1,820 lb (826 kg) more internal fuel and various MSIP (Multi-Stage Improvement Program) updates such as a programmable signal processor (allowing the radar to switch from one locked-on target to another, to search while locked onto one or more targets and to switch between air and surface targets); greater radar computer memory; an upgraded central computer; a new head-up display processor; new software in the flight and fire-control systems; a coupler linking the flight and fire-control systems and provision for the Martin Marietta ATLIS 2 optical and laser tracking pod in the forward port Sparrow AAM recess. The type also has provision for FAST (Fuel And Sensor Tactical) conformal packs on the sides of the inlet trunks for 9,750 lb (4423 kg) more fuel and/or volume for optional sensors and electronic warfare equipment. The FAST packs also have provision for tangential carriage of armament in the form of 12 1,000-lb (454-kg) Mk 83 or four 2,000-lb (907-kg) Mk 84 bombs, so leaving the airframe hardpoints free for additional armament and/or drop tanks. Aircraft based in the USA are also to be provided with capability for the Vought ASAT anti-satellite missile and the type could also be converted for the carriage of a tactical nuclear weapon in emergencies. The F-15C is operated by Israel, Japan (licence-built by Mitsubishi as the F-15J) and Saudi Arabia.

F-15D Eagle: combat-capable two-seat operational conversion and proficiency trainer variant of the F-15C and used by the same countries (including licence-built F-15DJ aircraft by Japan).

F-15E Eagle: due to enter service in 1987, this two-seat all-weather attack derivative is based on the airframe of the F-15D and incorporates all MSIP improvements as well as the upgraded Hughes APG-70 radar (with a synthetic-aperture mode for very high resolution ground mapping); forward-looking infra-red; wide-angle head-up display in

McDonnell Douglas F-15C Eagle

hardpoint rating

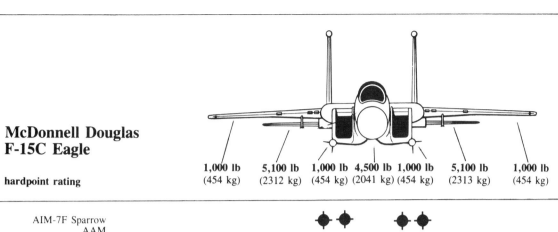

	1,000 lb (454 kg)	5,100 lb (2312 kg)	1,000 lb (454 kg)	4,500 lb (2041 kg)	1,000 lb (454 kg)	5,100 lb (2313 kg)	1,000 lb (454 kg)
AIM-7F Sparrow AAM		✦✦		✦✦			
AIM-9J/L Sidewinder AAM		✦✦				✦✦	
AGM-84 Harpoon anti-ship missile		⬤				⬤	
AGM-65 Maverick ASM		⬤⬤⬤				⬤⬤⬤	
GBU-15(V) 2,000-lb (907-kg) EO-guided glide bomb		✪		✪		✪	
GBU-10 Paveway II 2,000-lb (907-kg) laser-guided bomb		✪		✪		✪	
GBU-16 Paveway II 1,000-lb (454-kg) laser-guided bomb	✪	✪✪		✪✪		✪✪	✪
GBU-12 Paveway II 500-lb (227-kg) laser-guided bomb	✪	✪✪		✪✪		✪✪	✪
Mk 84 2,000-lb (907-kg) GP free-fall bomb		◉		◉		◉	
Mk 83 1,000-lb (454-kg) GP free-fall bomb	◉	◉◉◉		◉◉◉		◉◉◉	◉
Mk 82 500-lb (227-kg) free-fall or retarded bomb	◉	◉◉◉ ◉◉◉		◉◉◉ ◉◉◉		◉◉◉ ◉◉◉	◉
Rockeye Mk 20 cluster bomb	◉	◉◉◉ ◉◉◉		◉◉◉ ◉◉◉		◉◉◉ ◉◉◉	◉
BLU-27 860-lb (390-kg) napalm bomb	◉	◉◉◉ ◉◉◉		◉◉◉ ◉◉◉		◉◉◉ ◉◉◉	◉
600-US gal (2271-litre) drop tank		⬤		⬤		⬤	

An F-15A of the 5th Fighter Interceptor Squadron, Minot AFB, North Dakota shows off an air-to-air armament of four AIM-7 Sparrow and four AIM-9 Sidewinder AAMs.

the front cockpit; head-down displays in the rear cockpit (for radar, FLIR, digital map and threat warning information); Martin Marietta LANTIRN (Low-Altitude Navigation and Targeting Infra-Red for Night) all-weather navigation and targeting system; Westinghouse APQ-165 ASPJ (Airborne Self-Protection Jammer); programmable stores-management system; provision for AIM-120 AMRAAM air-to-air missiles and 24,500-lb (11113-kg) stores-carriage capability on hardpoints and FAST packs.

McDonnell Douglas F/A-18A Hornet

Type: single-seat carrier-borne and land-based multi-role fighter and attack aircraft.

Internal armament: one 20-mm General Electric M61A1 Vulcan six-barrel rotary cannon plus 570 rounds in the upper side of the nose.

Disposable armament: up to 17,000 lb (7711 kg) of disposable stores carried on seven hardpoints (one under the fuselage, one under each wing root and two under each wing) and two wingtip missile rails.

Electronics and operational equipment: normal communication and navigation equipment, plus Hughes APG-65 pulse-Doppler multi-mode radar, Kaiser head-up display, three Kaiser head-down displays, General Electric flight-control system, two AYK-14 digital computers, Litton inertial navigation system, Itek ALR-67 radar-warning receiver and infra-red sensor, plus provision for Martin Marietta ASQ-173 laser spot tracker on the side of the starboard inlet and the Ford AAS-38 forward-looking infra-red on the side of the port inlet.

Current variants and operators

F/A-18A Hornet: derived with some extensive modifications from the Northrop YF-17 contender which lost to the General Dynamics YF-16 in the US Air Force's Light-Weight Fighter competition of 1974, the Hornet first flew in November 1978 and is maturing into a highly capable dual-role fighter and attack aircraft designed to replace the McDonnell Douglas F-4 multi-role fighter and Vought A-7 medium attack aircraft in US Navy and US Marine Corps service. The type's entry into service has been marred by a number of structural and training problems (the latter associated largely with the complex cockpit and its advanced systems), but the Hornet is proving highly popular and adaptable; it is to be provided with extra range with a McDonnell Douglas-developed conformal dorsal tank, which will add only 300 lb (136 kg) to empty weight yet add

Successor to the legendary F-4 Phantom in the general-purpose role and to the classic A-7 Corsair II in the attack role, the F/A-18 Hornet is a potent fighter and attack aircraft. Seen here are F/A-18A single-seaters of VFA-125, the US Pacific Fleet's USN/USMC Hornet readiness squadron based at NAS Lemoore.

provision for another 3,000 lb (1361 kg) of fuel.

RF-18A Hornet: designation of the dedicated tactical and operational reconnaissance variant of the F/A-18A with a pallet for cameras (including the KA-99) and AAD-5 infrared linescan equipment in a bulged nose no longer fitted with the 20-mm cannon.

F/A-18B Hornet: designation of the combat-capable two-seat operational conversion trainer variant of the F/18A, originally designated TF/A-18A and possessing 6 per cent less internal fuel capacity.

F/A-18C Hornet: improved tactical version first flown in 1986 with internal ASPJ (Airborne Self-Protection Jammer) a Martin-Baker NACES ejector seat, databus-linked small computers rather than one large mission computer, and provision for reconnaissance equipment and for the AIM-120 AMRAAM air-to-air missile and AGM-65F IIR Maverick air-to-surface missile.

F/A-18D Hornet: two-seat version of the F/A-18C equivalent to the F/A-18B operational conversion and proficiency trainer.

CF-18A Hornet: designation of the F/A-18A version for Canada with a different instrument landing system and intended for land-based operations. A basically similar aircraft is being bought by Australia.

CF-18B Hornet: designation of the F/A-18B version for Canada with a different instrument landing system and intended for land-based operations. A basically similar aircraft is being bought by Australia.

EF-18A: designation of the F/A-18A for Spain.

EF-18B: designation of the F/A-18B for Spain.

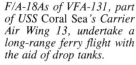

F/A-18As of VFA-131, part of USS Coral Sea*'s Carrier Air Wing 13, undertake a long-range ferry flight with the aid of drop tanks.*

McDonnell Douglas
F/A-18A Hornet

hardpoint rating

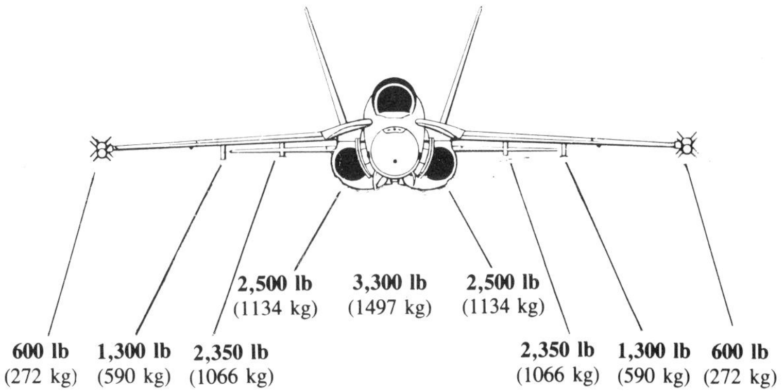

Hardpoint ratings (left to right):

600 lb (272 kg)	1,300 lb (590 kg)	2,350 lb (1066 kg)	2,500 lb (1134 kg)	3,300 lb (1497 kg)	2,500 lb (1134 kg)	2,350 lb (1066 kg)	1,300 lb (590 kg)	600 lb (272 kg)

Weapon	HP1	HP2	HP3	HP4	HP5	HP6	HP7	HP8	HP9
AIM-9J/L Sidewinder AAM	●	●	●				●	●	●
AIM-7 Sparrow AAM	●	●	●					●	●
B57 ?/20-kiloton free-fall nuclear weapon		●						●	
B61 Mod 2/3/4/5 100/500-kiloton free-fall nuclear weapon		●						●	
AGM-88 HARM anti-radiation missile			●				●		
AGM-84 Harpoon anti-ship missile			●				●		
AGM-65 Maverick ASM	●	●●	●●				●●	●●	●
AGM-62 Walleye 2,000-lb (907-kg) EO-guided glide bomb		◉	◉				◉	◉	
GBU-12 Paveway II 500-lb (227-kg) laser-guided bomb		◉	◉◉	◉◉			◉	◉◉	◉
Mk 83 1,000-lb (454-kg) GP free-fall bomb	●	●●	●●				●●	●●	●
Rockeye Mk 20 cluster bomb	⊛	⊛⊛	⊛⊛				⊛⊛	⊛⊛	⊛

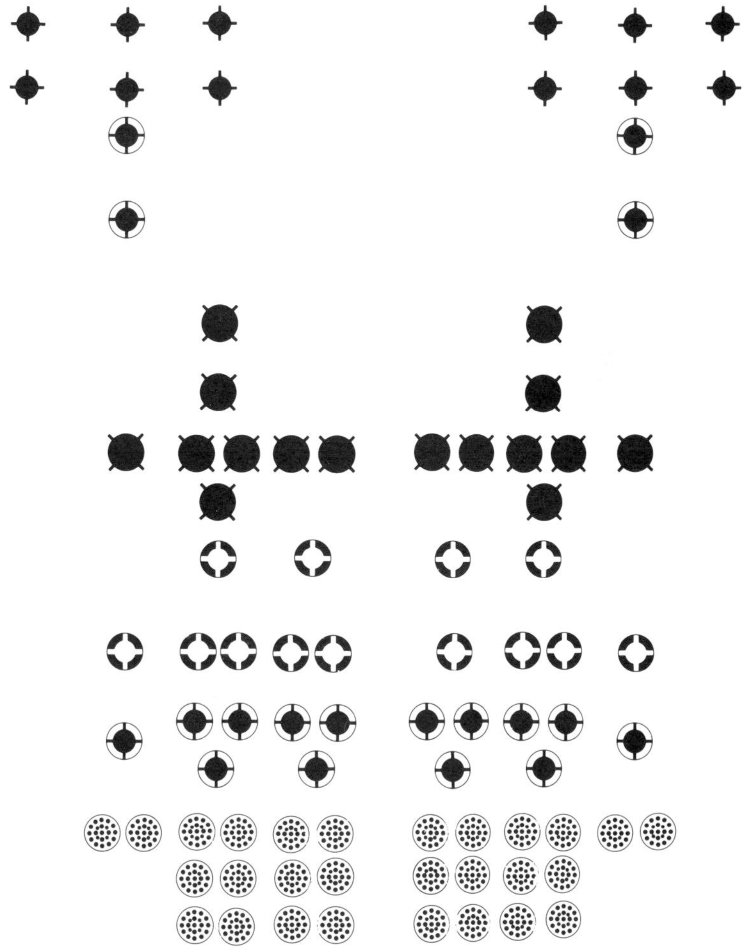

167

Above *An F/A-18A of VFA-125 operates in the A/Gavionics mode for ground attack. The Hornet has three avionics modes (Navigation, Air/Air and Air/Ground), the A/G mode optimizing the APG-65 radar with Doppler beam sharpening for clarity in the search for, definition of and locking on to targets. In this tactical situation the pilot is greatly aided by the Hornet's standard ability to carry FLIR and a laser tracker/strike camera on the unused Sparrow missile points.*

Left *Seen here with a pair of AGM-84 Harpoon medium-range anti-ship missiles, this F/A-18A reveals its considerable stores-carrying capability: one centreline and four underwing hardpoints, plus two engine trunk mountings (for AIM-7 Sparrow medium-range AAMs, or a FLIR pod on the port side and a laser tracker and strike camera on the starboard side) in addition to two wingtip rails (for AIM-9 Sidewinder short-range AAMs).*

McDonnell Douglas/British Aerospace AV-8B Harrier II

Type: single-seat STOVL ship- and land-based multi-role attack aircraft
Internal armament: one 25-mm General Electric GAU-12/U cannon plus 300 rounds in two under-fuselage pods.
Disposable armament: up to 17,000 lb (7711 kg) or 7,000 lb (3175 kg) of disposable stores (for short take-off or vertical take-off respectively) carried on seven hardpoints (one under the fuselage and three under each wing).
Electronics and operational equipment: normal communication and navigation equipment, plus Hughes ASB-19 ARBS (Angle-Rate Bombing System) with TV and laser target seeker/trackers tied into the Smiths head-up display via the IBM weapon-delivery computer; head-down display; Litton ASN-130A inertial navigation system; Garrett air-data computer; radar-warning receiver and Tracor ALE-39 chaff/flare dispenser; plus provision for electronic countermeasures such as the ALQ-164 jammer and the Westinghouse/ITT ALQ-165 ASPJ (Airborne Self-Protection Jammer) system, in this instance fitted in a converted ALQ-131 pod.

Current variants and operators
AV-8B Harrier II: developed by McDonnell Douglas and BAe on the basis of the latter's Harrier close support aircraft, the Harrier II first flew in November 1981 and is a much improved aircraft intended primarily for the US Marine Corps. The whole design has been revised, the most important modifications being the new composite-structure wing (with reduced sweep, greater area, supercritical section, more fuel capacity and additional stores-carrying capability), slotted flaps, leading-edge root extensions, zero-scarf nozzles for the 21,550-lb (9775-kg) Rolls-Royce Pegasus F402-RR-406 non-afterburning turbofan, under-fuselage lift-improvement devices, a higher cockpit and revised avionics and armament. This type is also used by Spain.
TAV-8B Harrier II: combat-capable two-seat operational conversion trainer variant with the fuselage lengthened by 4 ft (1.2 m) to allow the insertion of the second seat.

Though seen here without external armament, the AV-8B can lift substantially greater warloads than the baseline Harrier series as a result of its more powerful engine, larger and lighter wing with bigger flaps, lift-improvement devices and two additional hardpoints.

170

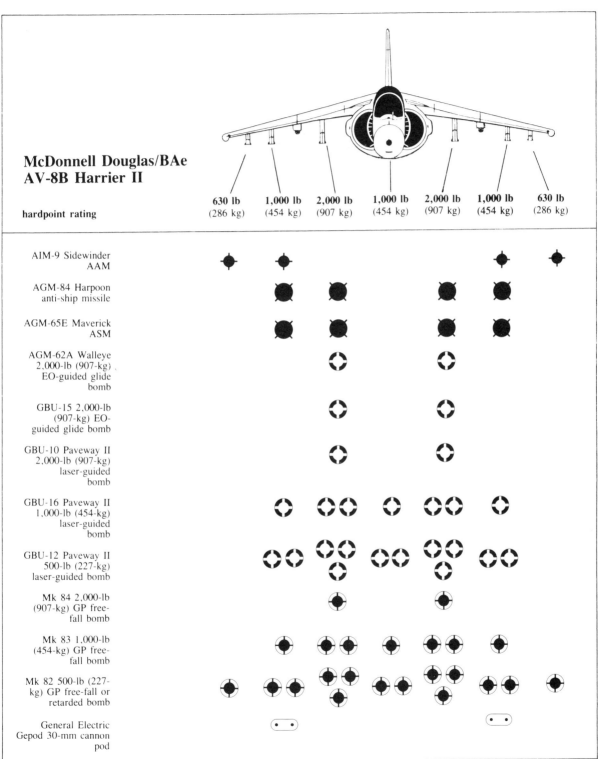

McDonnell Douglas/BAe AV-8B Harrier II

hardpoint rating

	630 lb (286 kg)	1,000 lb (454 kg)	2,000 lb (907 kg)	1,000 lb (454 kg)	2,000 lb (907 kg)	1,000 lb (454 kg)	630 lb (286 kg)
AIM-9 Sidewinder AAM							
AGM-84 Harpoon anti-ship missile							
AGM-65E Maverick ASM							
AGM-62A Walleye 2,000-lb (907-kg) EO-guided glide bomb							
GBU-15 2,000-lb (907-kg) EO-guided glide bomb							
GBU-10 Paveway II 2,000-lb (907-kg) laser-guided bomb							
GBU-16 Paveway II 1,000-lb (454-kg) laser-guided bomb							
GBU-12 Paveway II 500-lb (227-kg) laser-guided bomb							
Mk 84 2,000-lb (907-kg) GP free-fall bomb							
Mk 83 1,000-lb (454-kg) GP free-fall bomb							
Mk 82 500-lb (227-kg) GP free-fall or retarded bomb							
General Electric Gepod 30-mm cannon pod							

171

Seen in flight with triplets of Mk 82 Snakeye 500-lb (227-kg) high-drag bombs is an AV-8B of VMA-331, the US Marine Corps' first Harrier II squadron, part of the 2nd Marine Aircraft Wing's Marine Aircraft Group 32 and based at the MCAS Cherry Point.

With STOVL types such as the AV-8B the payload/ range equation becomes very important, only modest loads being carried over longer ranges if short take-off capability is to be retained. These VFMA-331 Harrier IIs are lightly armed, each carrying the GAU-12/U25-mm cannon system in its two under-fuselage strakes plus Mk 82 Snakeye 500-lb (227-kg) high-drag bombs under the wings.

Just after release, the retarding tails of the Mk 82 Snakeye 500-lb (227-kg) bombs open to slow the weapons and so allow the low-level AV-8B to exit the target area before the bombs detonate.

Harrier GR.Mk 5: British version of the Harrier II with the 21,750-lb (9866-kg) Pegasus Mk 105 vectored-thrust turbofan; a moving map display; Ferranti inertial navigation system; British radar-warning receiver; additional electronic countermeasures (including Marconi/Northrop Zeus active countermeasures); BAe MIRLS (MIniature Infra-Red LineScan); an inbuilt armament of two 25-mm Aden cannon and provision for two AIM-9 Sidewinder air-to-air missiles forward of the wing-mounted outriggers.

Above *Where range is unimportant the AV-8B can deliver a heavy blow, as witness this load of 16 Mk 82 bombs, each having a nominal weight of 500 lb (227 kg) but an actual weight of 570 lb (259 kg) for a total payload of 9,120 lb (4,137 kg) carried as two on the centreline, three each on the inner and central underwing, and one each on the outer underwing hardpoints.*

Below *Compared with the Harrier GR.Mk 3, the much improved Harrier GR.MK 5 (developed jointly by McDonnell Douglas and BAe) offers greater agility and payload thanks to the refinement of virtually the whole airframe, the installation of a more powerful engine, and the use of a lighter wing of supercritical section and greater area (but fitted with slotted flaps and two additional hardpoints).*

Among the diversity of the weapons that can be delivered by the AV-8B are missiles, rockets and bombs of various types. Seen here (from front to back) are four AIM-9L Sidewinder AAMs; four LAU-10 and six LAU-68 rocket-launchers (total weight 3,604 lb/1,635 kg); six LAU-61 and four LAU-68 rocket-launchers (total weight 4,396 lb/1,994 kg); six LAU-10 and four LAU-61 rocket-launchers (5,630 lb/2,554 kg); 10 Mk 77 520-lb (236-kg) bombs; 10 Mk 20 490-lb (222-kg) bombs; 15 Mk 81 270-lb (122-kg) bombs; 16 Mk 82 570-lb (259-kg) bombs and a triple ejector rack able to carry another three such bombs six Mk 83 985-lb (447-kg) bombs; and four triple ejector racks. Not shown are the air-to-air surface missiles and guided bombs that can be carried by the AV-8B (includes the Walleye, Paveway, Maverick and Harpoon) and specialist weapons such as cluster bombs and anti-runway munitions.

Messerschmitt-Bölkow-Blohm PAH-1

Type: two-seat anti-tank helicopter.

Internal armament: provision for one Rheinmetall HBS 202 fixed under-fuselage 20-mm cannon system, or for one side-mounted Emerson Flexible Turret System with a 7.62-mm (0.3-in) General Electric GAU-2/A Minigun.

Disposable armament: up to 1000 kg (2,205 lb) of disposable stores carried on two hardpoints (one on each side of the fuselage on outriggers).

Electronics and operational equipment: normal communication and navigation equipment, plus Singer-Kearfott ASN-128 Doppler navigation and (HOT installation) APX 397 or (TOW installation) Hughes M65 roof-mounted stabilized sight.

Current variants and operators

BO 105B: in its time an advanced utility helicopter with a semi-rigid main rotor, the BO 105 first flew in February 1967 and was the world's first series-produced twin-turboshaft helicopter. The type is used by a number of air arms in the utility and liaison roles with two 400-shp (298-kW) Allison 250-C20 turboshafts. The series serves with Colombia; Indonesia; Iraq; Malaysia; Mexico; Netherlands; Nigeria; Philippines; Spain; Sweden; West Germany. Some of the Iraqi and Spanish helicopters have an under-fuselage HBS 202 cannon installation (with a 20-mm Rheinmetall MK 20 Rh 202 cannon plus 525 rounds).

BO 105CB: improved model available from 1975 with 420-shp (313-kW) Allison 250-C20B turboshafts. The Swedish anti-tank helicopters have an armament of eight

West Germany's equivalent of the French SA342M is the PAH-1 with six HOT tube-launched anti-tank missiles and the same SFIM APX 397 stabilized roof sight.

The semi-rigid rotor and considerable power of the PAH-1 allow the West German army to make full use of the type's agility for nap-of-the-earth operations to secure maximum protection from ground-based defences until the helicopter pops up to fire one of its six HOT missiles.

BGM-71 TOW missiles and the appropriate sight system, while the maritime versions operated by Colombia and Mexico have search radar, a rescue winch, flotation equipment and folding rotor blades.

BO 105CBS: version with the cabin lengthened by 25 cm (7.6-in); this is the model often used for search-and-rescue work.

BO 105LS: version for 'hot-and-high' operations with 550-shp (410-kW) Allison 250-C28C turboshafts.

BO 105M: VBH liaison and scout version for the West German army with strengthened dynamic system and airframe, high-impact landing gear, and rupture-resistance fuel tanks.

BO 105P: PAH-1 anti-tank version for the West German army with features similar to those of the BO 105M plus role equipment/armament.

MBB PAH-1

hardpoint rating

	500 kg (1,102 lb)	500 kg (1,102 lb)
Euromissile HOT anti-tank missile		
Hughes BGM-71 TOW anti-tank missile		

177

Mikoyan-Gurevich MiG-15bis 'Fagot'

Type: single-seat fighter and ground-attack aircraft.
Internal armament: one 37-mm NS-37 cannon plus 40 rounds in the starboard side of the nose, and two 23-mm NR-23 cannon plus 80 rounds per gun in the port side of the nose.
Disposable armament: up to 500 kg (1,102 lb) of disposable stores carried on two hardpoints (one under each wing).
Electronics and operational equipment: normal communication and navigation equipment, plus a gyro sight.

Current variants and operators
MiG-15bis 'Fagot': definitive version of the MiG-15 fighter that first flew in prototype form during May 1948. The type is obsolete by all but third-world standards, and the type is operated mainly as an advanced trainer and light attack aircraft by Albania; Algeria; Angola; Bulgaria; China; Cuba; Czechoslovakia; East Germany; Guinea; Hungary; Iraq; Mali; Mongolia; North Korea; Poland; Romania; Somali Republic; South Yemen; Syria; Tanzania; USSR and Vietnam.
MiG-15UTI 'Midget': two-seat advanced and conversion trainer derivative.

The MiG-15 single-seater still serves with a number of third-world air arms in the front-line role, but this MiG-15UTI two-seat conversion trainer type is today more common.

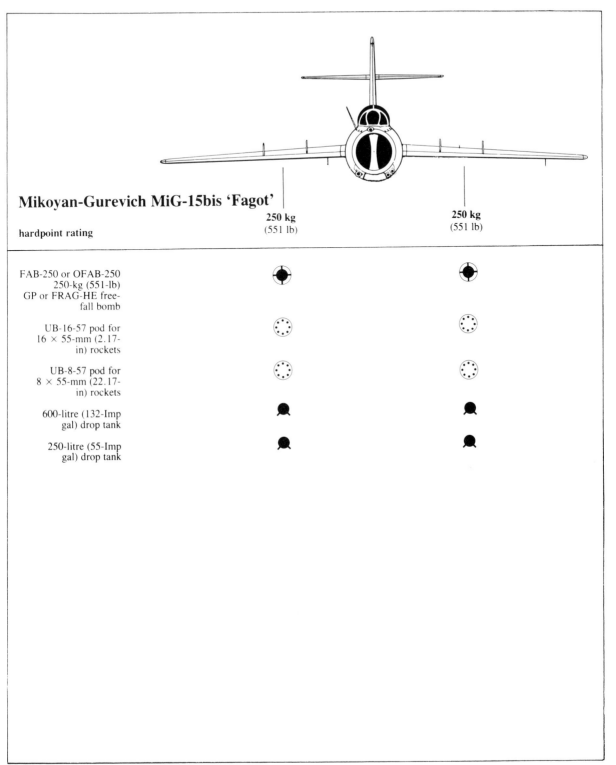

Mikoyan-Gurevich MiG-15bis 'Fagot'

hardpoint rating

	250 kg (551 lb)	250 kg (551 lb)
FAB-250 or OFAB-250 250-kg (551-lb) GP or FRAG-HE free-fall bomb	⊕	⊕
UB-16-57 pod for 16 × 55-mm (2.17-in) rockets	⊙	⊙
UB-8-57 pod for 8 × 55-mm (22.17-in) rockets	⊙	⊙
600-litre (132-Imp gal) drop tank	●	●
250-litre (55-Imp gal) drop tank	●	●

Mikoyan-Gurevich MiG-17F 'Fresco-C'

Type: single-seat fighter and ground-attack aircraft.

Internal armament: one 37-mm N-37 cannon plus 40 rounds in the starboard side of the nose and two 23-mm NR-23 cannon plus 80 rounds per gun in the port side of the nose.

Disposable armament: up to 500 kg (1,102 lb) of disposable stores carried on two hardpoints (one under each wing).

Electronics and operational equipment: normal communication and navigation equipment, plus gyro sight.

Current variants and operators

MiG-17F 'Fresco-C': the MiG-17 first flew in January 1950 as a developed version of the MiG-15 with a new wing and other modifications to overcome some of the earlier aircraft's aerodynamic limitations. The definitive MiG-17F day fighter introduced the Klimov VK-1F afterburning turbojet, and though the type was built in several day and night versions most surviving aircraft are to 'Fresco-C' standard in the advanced training and light attack roles. Current operators include Afghanistan; Albania; Algeria; Angola; Bulgaria; China; Cuba; Czechoslovakia; East Germany; Hungary; Iraq; Mali; North Korea; North Yemen; Poland; Romania; Somali Republic; South Yemen; Syria; USSR; Vietnam.

Shenyang J-5: this is the Chinese-built copy of the MiG-17F, exported as the F-5 to Chinese clients such as Albania, Bangladesh, Kampuchea, Sudan, Tanzania and Vietnam.

Shenyang J-5A: Chinese-built version of the MiG-17PF with elderly radar (range portion in an inlet lip fairing and scan portion in a circular fairing on the inlet splitter plate) and beam-riding air-to-air missiles, exported as the F-5A.

Shenyang JJ-5: two-seat operational conversion trainer developed in China with the nose section of the MiG-15UTI grafted onto the J-5A, and exported with the designation FT-5 and F-5T to operators of the F-5 and to Pakistan.

Though the MiG-17 is now to be found in several museums (this 'Fresco' having full cannon armament, two drop tanks and two UB-8-57 rocket-launchers), the type is still in moderately widespread service as a ground-attack aircraft and advanced /operational trainer.

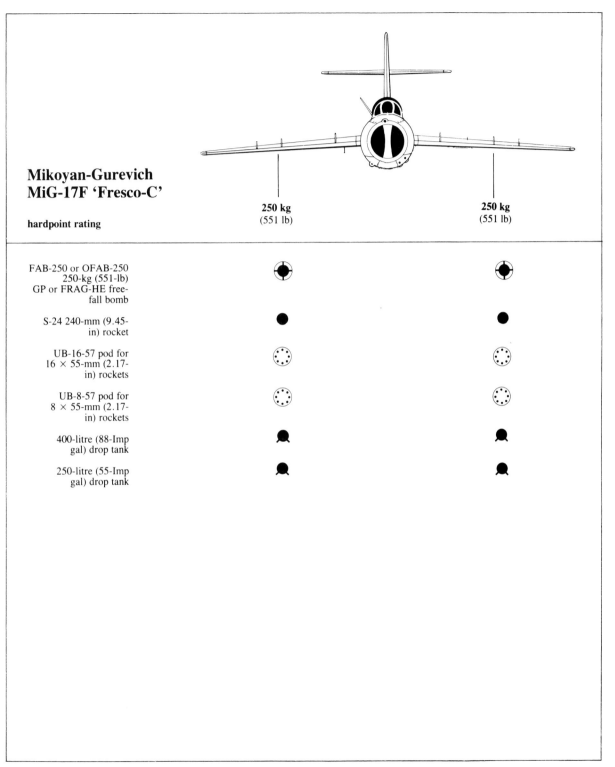

**Mikoyan-Gurevich
MiG-17F 'Fresco-C'**

hardpoint rating

250 kg
(551 lb)

250 kg
(551 lb)

FAB-250 or OFAB-250
250-kg (551-lb)
GP or FRAG-HE free-
fall bomb

S-24 240-mm (9.45-
in) rocket

UB-16-57 pod for
16 × 55-mm (2.17-
in) rockets

UB-8-57 pod for
8 × 55-mm (2.17-
in) rockets

400-litre (88-Imp
gal) drop tank

250-litre (55-Imp
gal) drop tank

Mikoyan-Gurevich MiG-19S 'Farmer-C'

Type: single-seat fighter, light attack and reconnaissance aircraft.

Internal armament: three 30-mm NR-30 cannon plus 80 rounds per gun, located as one on the starboard side of the nose and one in each wing root.

Disposable armament: up to 500 kg (1,102 lb) of disposable stores carried on two hardpoints (one under each wing inboard of the dedicated drop tank hardpoints each able to carry a single 800-litre/176-Imp gal tank).

Electronics and operational equipment: normal communication and navigation equipment, plus reflector sight.

Current variants and operators

MiG-19S 'Farmer-C': certainly Europe's and possibly the world's first supersonic fighter, the MiG-19 probably first flew in prototype form during October 1952 as a radical development of the MiG-17 basic concept with a long-span wing (of low thickness/chord ratio and 55-degree sweep), comparable tailplane set low on the highly-swept fin and two Tumansky-designed afterburning turbojets. Early models suffered from longitudinal control problems and were (from 1955) replaced by the MiG-19S with slab tailplane: this basic type led to the radar- and missile-equipped MiG-19SF 'Farmer-D' which is no longer in service, leaving the fast-climbing and supremely agile MiG-19S as the primary Soviet-built version in service with Afghanistan, Albania, Angola, Bulgaria, Cuba, Iraq, North Korea, USSR and Vietnam.

Shenyang J-6: unlicensed Chinese copy of the MiG-19S, exported with the designation F-6 to Albania, Bangladesh, Egypt, Iran, Pakistan (whose aircraft have outboard launchers for PL-2B air-to-air missiles), Tanzania and Vietnam.

Shenyang J-6A: Chinese version of the MiG-19PF 'Farmer-D' limited all-weather fighter with small radar and gun/rocket armament.

Shenyang J-6B: Chinese version of the MiG-19PF 'Farmer-D' based on the MiG-19PF

Two Shenyang J-6 aircraft (Chinese copies of the Soviet MiG-19) of the Pakistan Air Force on the runway at Peshwar.

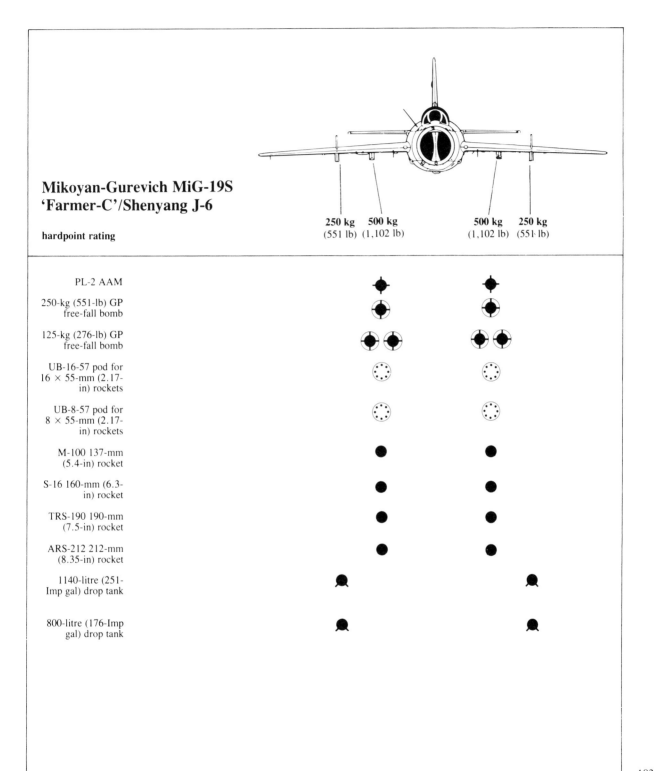

Mikoyan-Gurevich MiG-19S 'Farmer-C'/Shenyang J-6

hardpoint rating

	250 kg (551 lb)	500 kg (1,102 lb)	500 kg (1,102 lb)	250 kg (551 lb)
PL-2 AAM	●			●
250-kg (551-lb) GP free-fall bomb	●			●
125-kg (276-lb) GP free-fall bomb	● ●			● ●
UB-16-57 pod for 16 × 55-mm (2.17-in) rockets	●			●
UB-8-57 pod for 8 × 55-mm (2.17-in) rockets	●			●
M-100 137-mm (5.4-in) rocket		●	●	
S-16 160-mm (6.3-in) rocket		●	●	
TRS-190 190-mm (7.5-in) rocket		●	●	
ARS-212 212-mm (8.35-in) rocket		●	●	
1140-litre (251-Imp gal) drop tank	●			●
800-litre (176-Imp gal) drop tank	●			●

without cannon armament and fitted for four K-5M (AA-1 'Alkali') beam-riding air-to-air missiles under the wings.

Shenyang J-6C: Chinese development of the J-6 with excellent standards of manufacture and the braking parachute relocated from the original ventral location to a bullet fairing at the bottom of the rudder.

Shenyang J-6Xin: version of the J-6A with a Chinese-developed interception radar in a pointed centrebody of the inlet splitter plate.

Shenyang JJ-6: combat-capable two-seat operational conversion trainer armed with the nose cannon only.

Shenyang JZ-6: reconnaissance fighter similar to the MiG-19R with cameras instead of the nose-mounted 30-mm cannon installation.

Mikoyan-Gurevich MiG-21bisF 'Fishbed-N'

Type: single-seat dual-role fighter and ground-attack aircraft.

Internal armament: one 23-mm GSh-23L twin-barrel cannon plus 200 rounds in a GP-9 belly pack.

Disposable armament: up to 2500 kg (5,511 lb) of disposable stores carried on five hardpoints (one under the fuselage for a reconnaissance pod or drop tank, and two under each wing).

Electronics and operational equipment: normal communication and navigation equipment, plus 'Jay Bird' search and tracking radar; gyro sight; head-down display; twin-gyro navigation system; Doppler navigation; Sirena 3 radar-warning receiver; 'Odd Rods' IFF; ARL-5 data-link equipment; plus provision for a reconnaissance pod (various types are in service with the Soviet forces, the most common housing one forward and three oblique cameras, one infra-red linescanner and a chaff dispenser) and a number of electronic countermeasures systems including (on Arab aircraft) the Elettronica ALQ-234 equipment.

Current variants and operators

MiG-21F 'Fishbed-C': the MiG-21 was conceived as a clear-weather interceptor with high performance but only limited range and armament and first flew as the E-6 prototype early in 1957. The MiG-21F is powered by the 5100-kg (11,243-lb) Tumansky R-11 afterburning turbojet plus 2340 litres (515-Imp gal) and is decidedly short on range even with the limited armament of two AA-2 'Atoll' air-to-air missiles

The MiG-21F was in itself a clear-weather interceptor of drastically limited range and firepower (one NR-30 30-mm cannon and usually two AA-2 'Atoll' AAMs), but paved the way for much improved dual- and multi-role models.

The MiG-21bis 'Fishbed-L' introduced a re-engineered airframe and updated avionics in preparation for the final MiG-21bisF 'Fishbed-N' model with a new powerplant. Visible under the fuselage are the barrels of the two GSh-23L 23-mm cannon in a GP-9 belly pack, but the only stores carried on the one under-fuselage and four underwing hardpoints are a pair of 490-litre (108-gal) supersonic drop tanks.

(or two UB-16-57 rocket pods) and one 30-mm cannon. The MiG-21 series had been produced in vast numbers and the type serves (in its various marks) with Afghanistan; Algeria; Angola; Bangladesh; Bulgaria; Cuba; Czechoslovakia; East Germany; Egypt; Ethiopia; Finland; Hungary; India; Iraq; Laos; Madagascar; Mongolia; Mozambique; Nigeria; North Korea; North Yemen; Poland; Romania; Somali Republic; South Yemen; Sudan; Syria; USSR; Vietnam; Yugoslavia and Zambia.

MiG21PF 'Fishbed-D': improved variant of 1960 with a larger inlet whose centrebody accommodates the antenna for the R1L 'Spin Scan-A' radar to provide the aircraft with limited all-weather capability. The type has the 5950-kg (13,117-lb) R-11F turbojet and 2850 litres (627 Imp gal) of fuel. Later in the production run flap-blowing was added in the MiG-21PFS variant, reducing landing speed by 40 km/h (25 mph), and the export model was the MiG-21FL with the 6200-kg (13,668-lb) R-11-300 turbojet and more capable R2L 'Spin Scan-B' radar.

MiG-21 'Fishbed-E': variant of the MiG-21PF with broader-chord verticaltail, relocated braking parachute and armament improved by provision for a GP-9 gun pack with a 23-mm GSh-23L twin-barrel cannon in place of the centreline drop tank.

MiG-21PFM 'Fishbed-F': derivative of the MiG-21PFS with the broader tail introduced by the 'Fishbed-E', R2L radar, the R-11-300 turbojet and a revised canopy, the earlier single-piece front-hinged type being abandoned in favour of a conventional enclosure with fixed windscreen and side-hinged canopy.

MiG-21R 'Fishbed-H': tactical reconnaissance derivative of the MiG-21PFMA with three cameras in a bay just aft of the nosewheel and able to carry podded equipment such as a side-looking airborne radar and various types of electronic intelligence gatherers.

MiG-21PFMA 'Fishbed-J': this second-generation variant in 1965 introduced to the MiG-21 series a limited but nonetheless genuine dual-role capability with a revised and considerably larger dorsal hump for avionics; the R-11-300 turbojet (though with fuel reduced to 2600 litres/572 Imp gal); more capable 'Jay Bird' radar; a zero/zero ejector seat; two more underwing hardpoints for additional disposable armament and, on late-production aircraft, an internal GSh-23L cannon installation.

MiG-21MF 'Fishbed-J': 1970 variant of the MiG-21PFMA with the 6600-kg

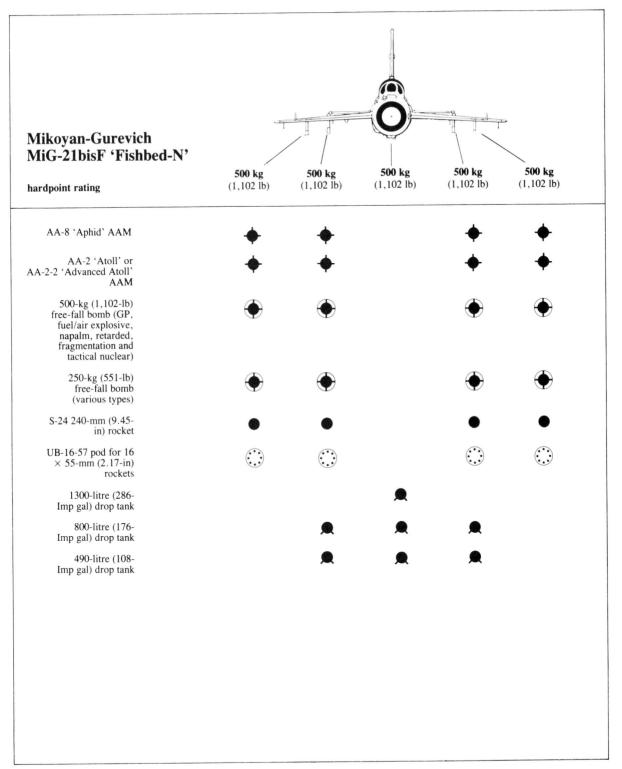

Mikoyan-Gurevich
MiG-21bisF 'Fishbed-N'

hardpoint rating

	500 kg (1,102 lb)	500 kg (1,102 lb)	500 kg (1,102 lb)	500 kg (1,102 lb)	500 kg (1,102 lb)
AA-8 'Aphid' AAM	⊕	⊕		⊕	⊕
AA-2 'Atoll' or AA-2-2 'Advanced Atoll' AAM	⊕	⊕		⊕	⊕
500-kg (1,102-lb) free-fall bomb (GP, fuel/air explosive, napalm, retarded, fragmentation and tactical nuclear)	⊕	⊕		⊕	⊕
250-kg (551-lb) free-fall bomb (various types)	⊕	⊕		⊕	⊕
S-24 240-mm (9.45-in) rocket	●	●		●	●
UB-16-57 pod for 16 × 55-mm (2.17-in) rockets	⊙	⊙		⊙	⊙
1300-litre (286-Imp gal) drop tank			●		
800-litre (176-Imp gal) drop tank		●	●	●	
490-litre (108-Imp gal) drop tank		●	●	●	

(14,550-lb) R-13-300 afterburning turbojet and a number of detail improvements. The type was exported as the MiG-21M with the internal gun installation.

MiG-21RF 'Fishbed-H': tactical reconnaissance version of the MiG-21MF with the same role equipment as the MiG-21R.

MiG-21 'Fishbed-K': originally thought to be designated MiG-21SMT, this is an improved MiG-21MF with a higher bulge to the dorsal hump offering additional volume as well as improved aerodynamics. The type can also carry electronic counter-measures/intelligence equipment in detachable pods at the wingtips.

MiG21bis 'Fishbed-L': interim third-generation development introduced in about 1971, combining the powerplant of the MiG-21MF with tankage for 2900 litres (638 Imp gal) of fuel, a yet-larger dorsal hump, a restressed and re-engineered airframe (offering greater strength with reduced maintenance requirements) and updated avionics to provide significantly enhanced operational capabilities.

MiG-21bisF 'Fishbed-N': definitive third-generation development of the MiG-21 series introduced in 1975 with the 7500-kg (16,535-lb) R-25 afterburning turbojet and yet further improved avionics, especially for the delivery of air-to-surface weapons. This variant can be fitted with the AA-2-2 'Advanced Atoll' and AA-8 'Aphid' air-to-air missiles as well as the earlier AA-2 'Atoll' type.

MiG-21U 'Mongol-A': combat-capable operational conversion and proficiency trainer based on the MiG-21F with features of the MiG-21PF.

MiG-21US 'Mongol-B': development of the MiG-21U with broad-chord vertical tail, blown flaps and a retractable periscope for the instructor.

MiG-21UM 'Mongol-B': two-seat version of the MiG-21MF with R-13 turbojet.

Mikoyan-Gurevich MiG-23MF 'Flogger-G'

Type: single-seat variable-geometry air combat fighter with secondary attack capability.

Internal armament: one 23-mm GSh-23L twin-barrel cannon plus 400 rounds in a GP-9 belly pack.

Disposable armament: up to 3000+ kg (6,614+ lb) of disposable stores carried on five hardpoints (one under the fuselage for a drop tank, one under each inlet and one under each fixed inner-wing panel, the wing hardpoints being fitted for twin or triple ejector racks or tandem twin racks).

Electronics and operational equipment: normal communication and navigation equipment, plus 'High Lark' pulse-Doppler radar (with look-down search and track, ground mapping, and terrain avoidance capabilities); laser ranger; electro-optical tracker; Sirena 3 radar-warning receiver; 'Odd Rods' IFF; electronic countermeasures and Doppler navigation.

Current variants and operators

MiG-23M 'Flogger-B': introduced in 1972, this was the initial production model of the MiG-23 series, which first flew in 1966 as the variable-geometry successor to the MiG-21. The pre-production MiG-21S/SM 'Flogger-A' variants had used the 10000-kg (22,046-lb) Lyulka AL-7F-1 afterburning turbojet, but the production series introduced the smaller and lighter 10200-kg (22,487-lb) Tumansky R-27 afterburning turbojet, requiring the forward movement of wings and the shortening of the tail section. The series has matured into a capable combat type of singular importance to the USSR's tactical and air-defence forces and is also operated by Algeria; Angola; Bulgaria; Cuba; Czechoslovakia; East Germany; Egypt; Hungary; India; Iraq; Libya; North Korea; Poland; Syria and Vietnam.

MiG-23MF 'Flogger-B': improved version of the MiG-23M from 1975 with the 12500-kg (27,557-lb) Tumansky R-29B afterburning turbojet and more comprehensive avionics including 'High Lark' radar and a laser ranger; 'High Lark' has a search range of 85 km (53 miles) and a locked-on tracking range of 54 km (34 miles).

Now available in large numbers, and nearly a technological match for Western contemporaries, the MiG-23 series offers the USSR great versatility in offence and defence. This is a MiG-23MF 'Flogger-B' notable for its considerable ECM capability and under-nose IR seeker, plus AA-7 long-range and AA-8 short-range AAMs.

MiG-23U 'Flogger-C': two-seat operational conversion and proficiency trainer based on the MiG-23M and using the R-27 turbojet. The second cockpit is installed behind and slightly above the standard cockpit.

MiG-23 'Flogger-E': export derivative of the MiG-23M with lower standards of equipment, most notably the 'Jay Bird' rather than 'High Lark' radar, with search range of 30 km (18.6 miles) and tracking range of 20 km (12.4 miles), though without any look-down capability. As the variant also lacks Doppler navigation and the infra-red tracker, its capabilities (with missiles limited to the elderly AA-2 'Atoll' type) are distinctly limited.

MiG-23BM 'Flogger-F': fighter-bomber derivative of the MiG-23MF series designed primarily for Warsaw Pact countries and for export to Soviet clients. The type combines the airframe and powerplant of the MiG-23 with the forward fuselage (with laser ranger in place of the MiG-23's nose radar) and cockpit of the MiG-27: the type thus has variable inlet/nozzle geometries and an internal GSh-23L cannon.

MiG-23MF 'Flogger-G': revised version of the 'Flogger-B' from 1978 with the R-29B turbojet, a smaller dorsal fin, revised nosewheel unit, a new undernose sensor pod and a lighter version of the 'High Lark' radar.

MiG-23BN 'Flogger-H': variant of the 'Flogger-F' with wing root extensions and a small avionics fairing on each side of the lower fuselage (just forward of the nosewheel) for missile-guidance equipment, but with the two glove bullet fairings deleted.

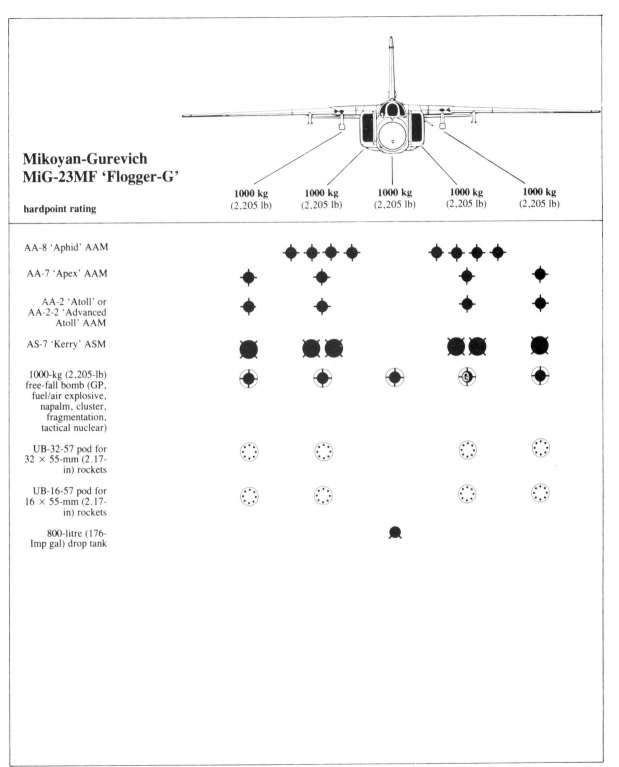

Mikoyan-Gurevich MiG-23MF 'Flogger-G'

hardpoint rating	1000 kg (2,205 lb)	1000 kg (2,205 lb)	1000 kg (2,205 lb)	1000 kg (2,205 lb)	1000 kg (2,205 lb)
AA-8 'Aphid' AAM		●●●●		●●●●	
AA-7 'Apex' AAM	●	●		●	●
AA-2 'Atoll' or AA-2-2 'Advanced Atoll' AAM	●	●		●	●
AS-7 'Kerry' ASM	●	●●		●●	●
1000-kg (2,205-lb) free-fall bomb (GP, fuel/air explosive, napalm, cluster, fragmentation, tactical nuclear)	●	●	●	●	●
UB-32-57 pod for 32 × 55-mm (2.17-in) rockets	●	●		●	●
UB-16-57 pod for 16 × 55-mm (2.17-in) rockets	●	●		●	●
800-litre (176-Imp gal) drop tank			●		

Mikoyan-Gurevich MiG-25 'Foxbat-A'

Type: single-seat high-altitude interceptor.

Internal armament: none.

Disposable armament: up to 3000 kg (6,614 lb) of disposable stores carried on four hardpoints (two under each wing).

Electronics and operational equipment: normal communication and navigation equipment, plus 'Fox Fire' search, tracking and target-illumination radar; Sirena 3 radar-warning receiver; infra-red warning receiver; central computer; Doppler navigation; data-link and active/passive electronic countermeasures.

Current variants and operators

MiG-25 'Foxbat-A': this exceptional but nonetheless limited interceptor was schemed in the late 1950s as the Soviet riposte to the North American B-70 Valkyrie Mach 3 strategic bomber, and despite the cancellation of the US high-altitude bomber the MiG-25 continued in development, first flying in 1964 or early 1965 and entering service in about 1966 with two 12250-kg (27,007-lb) Tumansky R-31 afterburning turbojets as a pure interceptor capable of very high speeds at high altitude, but possessing minimum manoeuvrability. The powerful radar has a search range of 120 km (75 miles) and a single-target tracking range of 70 km (43 miles), but lacks look-down capability.

MiG-25R 'Foxbat-B': dedicated reconnaissance model that began to enter service in 1971 with a revised nose accommodating five cameras, reduced span on a wing of straight rather than compound sweep and possessing also a side-looking airborne radar.

Converted from the MiG-25 'Foxbat-A', the 'Foxbat-E' has revised avionics and weapons to provide the series with a limited look-down/shoot-down capability against low-level intruders and cruise missiles.

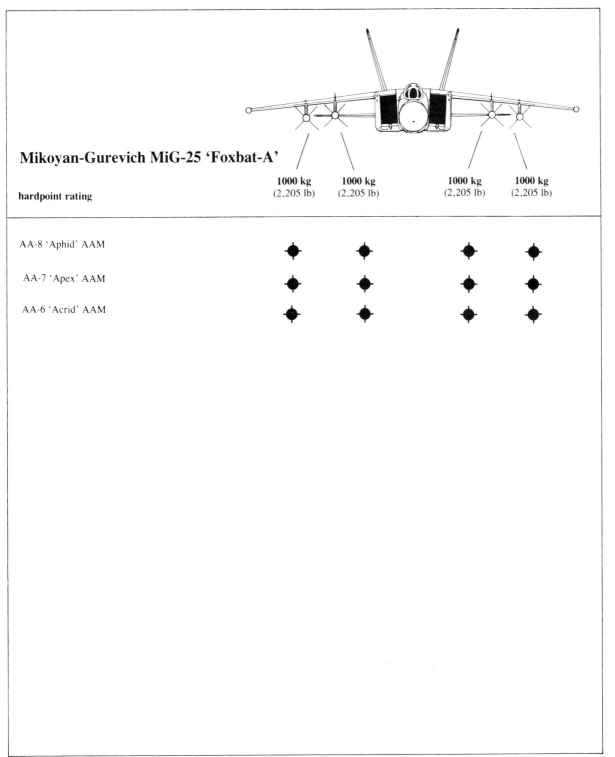

Mikoyan-Gurevich MiG-25 'Foxbat-A'

hardpoint rating

	1000 kg (2,205 lb)	1000 kg (2,205 lb)		1000 kg (2,205 lb)	1000 kg (2,205 lb)
AA-8 'Aphid' AAM	●	●		●	●
AA-7 'Apex' AAM	●	●		●	●
AA-6 'Acrid' AAM	●	●		●	●

Carrying four AA-6 'Acrid' AAMs (two of the IR-homing variety on the inner hard-points and two of the semi-active radar homing variety on the outer hardpoints), the pilot of this MiG-25M 'Foxbat-E' has every chance to score a 'kill' under most operational conditions.

MiG-25U 'Foxbat-C': two-seat operational conversion and proficiency trainer based on the 'Foxbat-A' with a new nose in which the radar and other avionics are replaced by a cockpit for the trainee pilot.

MiG-25R 'Foxbat-D': electronic reconnaissance derivative of the 'Foxbat-B' without cameras but featuring a larger number of dielectric panels and a large side-looking airborne radar apparently capable of surface search to the right of the aircraft at a range of 200 km (124 miles).

MiG-25M 'Foxbat-E': much improved development of the basic 'Foxbat-A' with improved performance (deriving largely from the use of two 14000-kg/30,865-lb Tumansky R-31F afterburning turbojets) and improved capabilities bestowed by the incorporation of a new pulse-Doppler radar for genuine look-down/shoot-down capability.

Mikoyan-Gurevich MiG-27 'Flogger-D'

Type: single-seat variable-geometry ground-attack aircraft.

Internal armament: one 23-mm six-barrel rotary cannon plus about 700 rounds in the lower fuselage.

Disposable armament: up to 4000 kg (8,818 lb) of disposable stores carried on five hardpoints (one under the fuselage used for a drop tank, one under each inlet and one under each fixed inner-wing panel) and two rear-fuselage multiple ejector racks. Jettisonable non-swivelling hardpoints are provided under the outer-wing panels for the carriage of ferry tanks.

Electronics and operational equipment: normal communication and navigation equipment, plus head-up display; laser ranger and marked-target seeker; missile-guidance system; terrain-avoidance radar; Doppler navigation; 'Odd Rods' IFF; Sirena 3 radar-warning receiver and electronic countermeasures (both internal and pod-mounted external types).

Current variants and operators

MiG-27 'Flogger-D': this is the dedicated attack variant of the basic MiG-23 air combat fighter, with the 11500-kg (25,353-lb) Tumansky R-29-300 afterburning turbojet together with fixed inlet/nozzle geometries optimized for the low-altitude role, and a revised (acutely sloped and tapered) nose offering the higher-seated pilot better forward and downward fields of vision as no search radar is carried. The weapons and role equipment are geared for the ground-attack mission and armour is fitted internally and externally to the forward fuselage. The type is used by Cuba, East Germany, Poland, Syria and the USSR.

MiG-27M 'Flogger-J': used by the USSR and India, this is an improved 'Flogger-D' with detail aerodynamic modifications, a multi-sensor nose and provision for 23-mm GSh-23L cannon pods with the twin barrels angled down at 14 degrees for ground-attack purposes.

The Mikoyan MiG-27 tactical fighter known to NATO as 'Flogger-D'.

To the Soviets the MiG-27 is a vital part of the USSR's tactical air power. This posed shot nevertheless gives an unusual ground perspective on this potent machine (Tass).

Mikoyan-Gurevich
MiG-27 'Flogger-D'

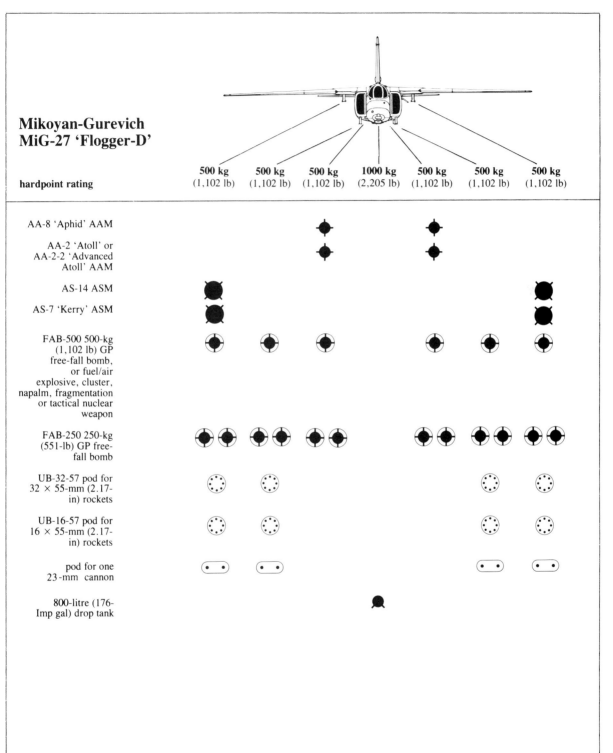

hardpoint rating	500 kg (1,102 lb)	500 kg (1,102 lb)	500 kg (1,102 lb)	1000 kg (2,205 lb)	500 kg (1,102 lb)	500 kg (1,102 lb)	500 kg (1,102 lb)
AA-8 'Aphid' AAM			●		●		
AA-2 'Atoll' or AA-2-2 'Advanced Atoll' AAM			●		●		
AS-14 ASM	●						●
AS-7 'Kerry' ASM	●						●
FAB-500 500-kg (1,102 lb) GP free-fall bomb, or fuel/air explosive, cluster, napalm, fragmentation or tactical nuclear weapon	●	●	●		●	●	●
FAB-250 250-kg (551-lb) GP free-fall bomb	● ●	● ●	● ●		● ●	● ●	● ●
UB-32-57 pod for 32 × 55-mm (2.17-in) rockets	●	●				●	●
UB-16-57 pod for 16 × 55-mm (2.17-in) rockets	●	●				●	●
pod for one 23-mm cannon	●	●				●	●
800-litre (176-Imp gal) drop tank				●			

Mikoyan-Gurevich MiG-29 'Fulcrum'

Type: single-seat air combat fighter.

Internal armament: one 30-mm twin-barrel cannon plus rounds in the port wing leading-edge root extension.

Disposable armament: up to 4000 kg (8,818 lb) of disposable stores carried on six hardpoints (one under each inlet duct and two under each wing).

Electronics and operational equipment: normal communication and navigation equipment, plus pulse-Doppler search and track radar; infra-red sensor; head-up display; central computer; data-link; Doppler navigation; Sirena 3 radar-warning receiver; 'Odd Rods' IFF and electronic countermeasures.

The MiG-29 'Fulcrum' mirrors the design of current US fighter types in its twin vertical tail surfaces and blended fuselage/wing configuration, and offers the Soviet air arm a potent combination of performance, electronic capability and advanced weapons. This artist's impression was made before the type was first seen in the West, and shows the type with AA-10 AAMs.

Current variant and operators

MiG-29 'Fulcrum': developed during the early 1970s for a first flight not later than 1977, the MiG-29 is a potent warplane (using composite materials in an airframe of relaxed stability with 'fly-by-wire' controls), optimized for the air combat role but almost certainly possessing an attack capability. The type began to enter service in 1984 and is in most respects comparable to the General Dynamics F-16 Fighting Falcon though in appearance it resembles a scaled-down McDonnell Douglas F-15 Eagle. Indeed, performance may be markedly superior as the MiG-29 possesses considerably greater power in the form of two 8300-kg (18,298-lb) Tumansky R-33D afterburning turbofans. The radar is believed to have a range of 40 km (25 miles) and a genuine look-down/shoot-down capability. The type is operated by India, Syria and the USSR.

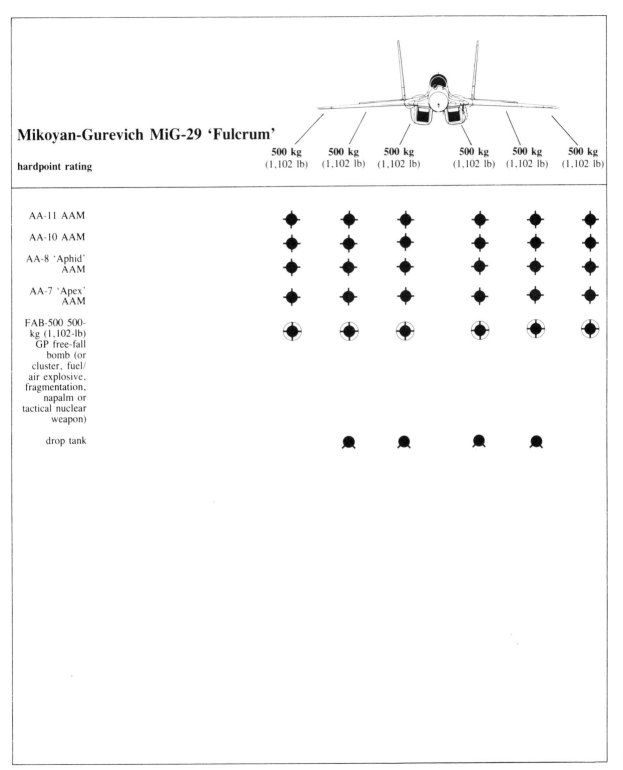

Mikoyan-Gurevich MiG-29 'Fulcrum'

hardpoint rating

	500 kg (1,102 lb)	500 kg (1,102 lb)	500 kg (1,102 lb)	500 kg (1,102 lb)	500 kg (1,102 lb)	500 kg (1,102 lb)
AA-11 AAM	●	●	●	●	●	●
AA-10 AAM	●	●	●	●	●	●
AA-8 'Aphid' AAM	●	●	●	●	●	●
AA-7 'Apex' AAM	●	●	●	●	●	●
FAB-500 500-kg (1,102-lb) GP free-fall bomb (or cluster, fuel/air explosive, fragmentation, napalm or tactical nuclear weapon)	◉	◉	◉	◉	◉	◉
drop tank		●	●		●	●

Mikoyan-Gurevich MiG-31 'Foxhound'

Type: two-seat long-range interceptor.

Internal armament: one 23-mm GSh-23L twin-barrel cannon plus 200 rounds in a GP-9 belly pack or (according to some reports) one 30-mm rotary cannon.

Disposable armament: up to 3000 kg (6,607 lb) of disposable stores carried on eight hardpoints (two tandem pairs under the fuselage and two under each wing).

Electronics and operational equipment: normal communication and navigation equipment, plus pulse-Doppler search-and-track radar; infra-red sensor; head-up display; head-down displays; central computer; data-link; Sirena 3 radar-warning receiver; 'Odd Rods' IFF; internal electronic and infra-red countermeasures.

Current variant and operator

MiG-31 'Foxhound': based conceptually on the MiG-25 but stretched to accommodate a second crew member and additional fuel, the MiG-31 is a formidable medium-altitude interceptor with exceptional range and a potent combination of pulse-Doppler radar and AA-9 missiles for a very real look-down/shoot-down capability. The AA-9 has its own active terminal guidance and the MiG-31 thus possesses a multiple engagement capability against targets such as cruise missiles. The type is used only by the USSR and began to enter service in 1983.

The MiG-31 'Foxhound' is one of the most important Soviet aircraft to have entered service in recent years, its combination of AA-9 long-range/snap-down AAM with capable long-range radar of the pulse-Doppler look-down variety making it a severe threat to US penetration aircraft and cruise missiles.

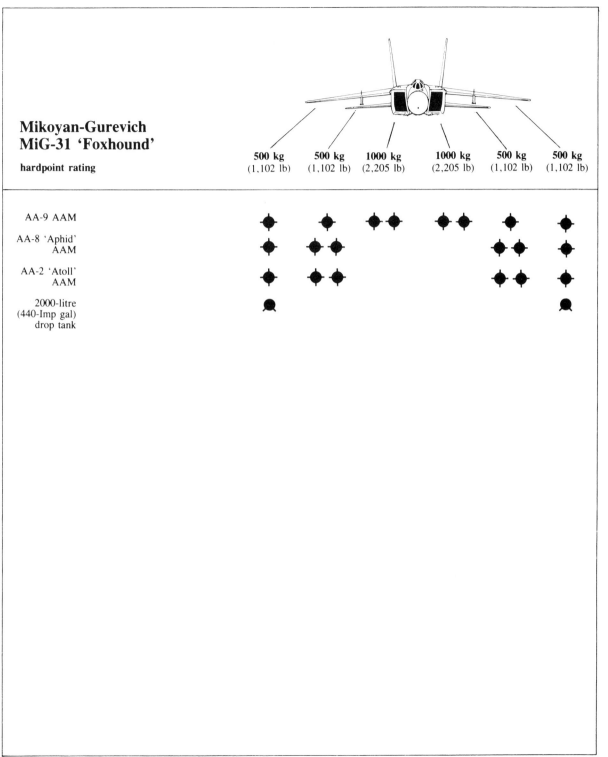

Mikoyan-Gurevich
MiG-31 'Foxhound'

hardpoint rating

	500 kg (1,102 lb)	500 kg (1,102 lb)	1000 kg (2,205 lb)	1000 kg (2,205 lb)	500 kg (1,102 lb)	500 kg (1,102 lb)
AA-9 AAM	●	●	● ●	● ●	●	●
AA-8 'Aphid' AAM	●	● ●			● ●	●
AA-2 'Atoll' AAM	●	● ●			● ●	●
2000-litre (440-Imp gal) drop tank	●					●

Mil Mi-8 'Hip-E'

Type: three-crew multi-role attack helicopter.

Internal armament: one 12.7-mm (0.5-in) DShK heavy machine-gun plus rounds in a flexible nose mounting.

Disposable armament: up to 1500 kg (3,307 lb) of disposable stores carried on ten hardpoints (three below and two above each lateral stores outrigger).

Electronics and operational equipment: normal communication and navigation equipment, plus optical sights.

Current variants and operators

Mi-8 'Hip-C': based conceptually on the successful Mi-4 series but featuring a turboshaft powerplant for better performance at reduced weight, the Mi-8 first flew as the NATO-designated 'Hip-A' in early 1961 with a single 2013-kW (2,700-shp) Soloviev D-25 turboshaft. The type was then developed as the 'Hip-B' with a five rather than four-blade main rotor and two 1267-kW (1,700-shp) Isotov TV2-117A turboshafts. The helicopter entered military service as the 'Hip-C' with accommodation for 24 troops or 4000 kg (8,818 lb) of freight and can carry an armament of four UB-32-57 pods each with 32 55-mm (2.17-in) rockets or four AT-2 'Swatter' anti-tank missiles. The 'Hip' series is used by Afghanistan; Algeria; Angola; Bangladesh; Bulgaria; Cuba; Czechoslovakia; East Germany; Egypt; Ethiopia; Finland; Guinea-Bissau; Hungary; India; Laos; Libya; Madagascar; Mali; Mongolia; Mozambique; Nicaragua; North Korea; North Yemen; Peru; Poland; Romania; Somali Republic; Sudan; Syria; USSR; Vietnam; Yugoslavia; Zambia and at least six other countries.

The great load-carrying capability of the Mi-8 series is attested by the fact that the 'Hip-E' illustrated can carry its full complement of embarked troops yet still lift an external armament load of six UB-32-57 rocket pods or other stores under the outrigger pylons together with four AT-2 'Swatter' anti-tank missiles above them and a 12.7-mm (0.5-in) machine-gun in the nose.

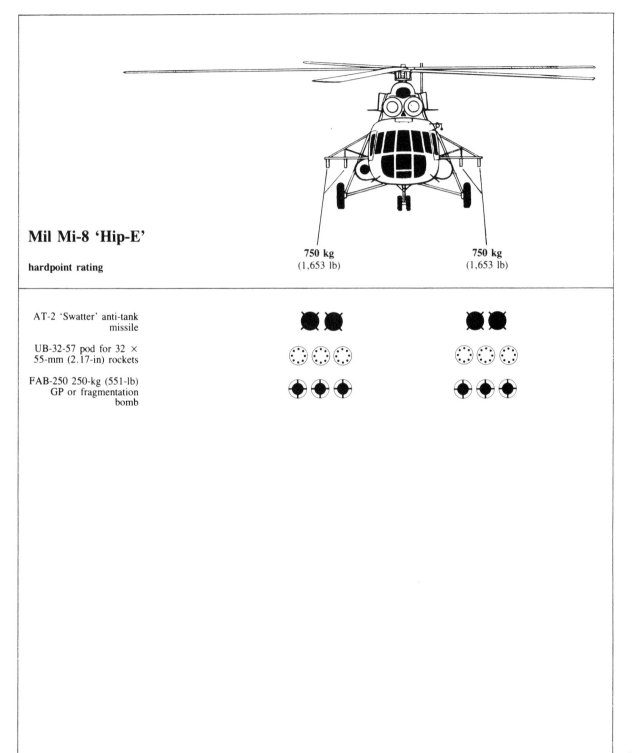

Mil Mi-8 'Hip-E'

hardpoint rating

750 kg
(1,653 lb)

750 kg
(1,653 lb)

AT-2 'Swatter' anti-tank
missile

UB-32-57 pod for 32 ×
55-mm (2.17-in) rockets

FAB-250 250-kg (551-lb)
GP or fragmentation
bomb

Mi-8 'Hip-D': battlefield communications relay derivative of the 'Hip-C'.

Mi-8 'Hip-E': assault version of the 'Hip-C' with nose-mounted machine-gun and the ability to carry six UB-32-57 pods below the stores outriggers and four AT-2 'Swatter' missiles above them.

Mi-8 'Hip-F': export derivative of the 'Hip-E' with six AT-3 'Sagger' missiles instead of the four 'Swatters'.

Mi-8 'Hip-G': battlefield communications relay derivative of the 'Hip-C'.

Mi-8 'Hip-J': battlefield electronic countermeasures derivative of the 'Hip-C'.

Mi-8 'Hip-K': battlefield electronic countermeasures (communications jamming) derivative of the 'Hip-C' featuring a revised equipment fit compared with the 'Hip-J'.

Mi-14 'Haze-A': this is a dedicated anti-submarine derivative of the Mi-8 with a boat hull; stabilizing sponsons; retractable landing gear; search radar; magnetic anomaly detection; chutes for the launch of sonobuoys and/or flares, Doppler navigation; two 1641-kW (2,200-shp) TV3-117MT turboshafts and an armament that includes torpedoes and/or depth bombs. The Mi-14 series is used by Bulgaria, Cuba, East Germany, Libya and the USSR.

Mi-14 'Haze-B: dedicated mine countermeasures version of the 'Haze-A'.

Mi-17 'Hip-H': this is the uprated version of the Mi-8 for 'hot-and-high' operations and differs from the earlier model in having the tail rotor relocated to the port side of the fin and power provided by two TV3-117MT turboshafts driving the strengthened dynamic system of the Mi-14.

Mil Mi-24 'Hind-D'

Type: two/three-seat assault and gunship helicopter.
Internal armament: one 12.7-mm (0.5-in) four-barrel rotary machine-gun plus ? rounds in a remotely-controlled under-nose turret.
Disposable armament: up to 1500 kg (3,307 lb) of disposable stores carried on eight hardpoints (two below and two above each stub wing).
Electronics and operational equipment: normal communication and navigation equipment, plus 'Odd Rods' IFF; low-light-level TV; forward-looking infra-red; terrain-avoidance radar; laser ranger and marked-target seeker; optical sights; missile guidance system(s) and internal electronic and infra-red countermeasures.

Current variants and operators
Mi-24 'Hind-A': this was in fact the second production version of the 'Hind' assault transport series, with cabin accommodation for eight infantrymen or an anti-tank squad with launcher and missiles. Compared with the initial model this has the tail rotor relocated to the port side of the fin, extra armour, larger anhedralled stub wings with six hardpoints (four for rocket pods, or single 160-mm/6.3-in S-16 or 220-mm/8.66-in S-21 rockets under the wings and two double rails at the tips for four AT-2 'Swatter' anti-tank missiles) and a 12.7-mm (0.5-in) DShK heavy machine-gun in the nose: the total disposable load is 1275 kg (2,811 lb).
Mi-24 'Hind-B': initial 1971 limited-production model of the prototype that first flew in the late 1960s after derivation from the Mi-8/17 series as a battlefield assault transport

The powerful weapons system of the Mi-24 'Hind-D' gunship includes a number of sensors, a four-barrel 12.7-mm (0.5-in) machine-gun in an under-nose turret, underwing accommodation for four UB-32-57 (illustrated) or UB-16-57 rocket-launcher pods, and rails for four AT-2 'Swatter' anti-tank missiles.

offering greater survivability through the use of smaller dimensions; greater performance; better protection and purpose-designed armament. This variant has straight wings and only four hardpoints (two under the wings and two at the tips) in later examples.

Mi-24 'Hind-C': 1975 variant of the 'Hind-A' without the nose gun and wingtip missile rails, and intended primarily for assault transport and supply.

Mi-24 'Hind-D': much developed two/three-seat gunship version with revised titanium armour nose with vertically-staggered seating for the gunner (forward) and pilot (aft), extensive titanium construction in the rotor head and main rotor blades, and upgraded sensor and air-data suites for accurate weapon delivery. This is a formidable battlefield weapon with advanced weapons and sensors, but is hampered by its very size and comparative lack of manoeuvrability.

Mi-24 'Hind-E': improved version of the 'Hind-D' with AT-6 'Spiral' laser-homing anti-tank missiles in place of the command-to-line-of-sight (plus IR homing) AT-2 'Swatter', and an enlarged sensor pod on the port underside of the nose.

Mi-24 'Hind-?': derivative of the 'Hind-E' with a fixed 23-mm twin-barrel cannon pack on the starboard side of the nose in place of the under-nose machine-gun turret.

Mi-25 'Hind': designation of the export derivative of the Mi-24 'Hind-D' with lower equipment standards.

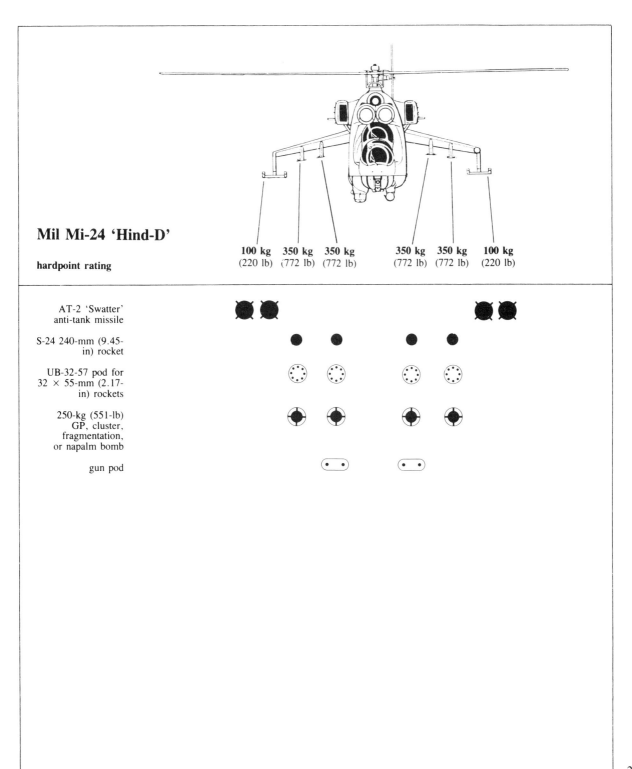

Mil Mi-24 'Hind-D'

hardpoint rating

	100 kg (220 lb)	350 kg (772 lb)	350 kg (772 lb)	350 kg (772 lb)	350 kg (772 lb)	100 kg (220 lb)
AT-2 'Swatter' anti-tank missile	● ●				● ●	
S-24 240-mm (9.45-in) rocket		●	●	●	●	
UB-32-57 pod for 32 × 55-mm (2.17-in) rockets		◉	◉	◉	◉	
250-kg (551-lb) GP, cluster, fragmentation, or napalm bomb		◉	◉	◉	◉	
gun pod		▢		▢		

Mil Mi-28 'Havoc'

Type: two-seat anti-tank and battlefield helicopter.
Internal armament: one 23- or 30-mm cannon plus ? rounds in a remotely-controlled under-nose turret.
Disposable armament: up to 1400 kg (3,086 lb) of disposable stores carried on four hardpoints (two under each stub wing).
Electronics and operational equipment: normal communication and navigation equipment, plus (probably) millimetre-wavelength radar; laser ranger and marked-target seeker; forward-looking infra-red; other electro-optical sensors and electronic and infra-red countermeasures.

Current variant and operators

Mi-28 'Havoc': this powerful battlefield helicopter is entering service with the USSR in 1987 and is probably derived from the Mi-24 (at least in its dynamic system) in the light of combat experience in Afghanistan. The result is a battlefield and combat helicopter akin to the Hughes AH-64A Apache with a carefully refined fuselage, pod-mounted engines and a number of defensive improvements, both active and passive. The type is designed for the use of advanced air-to-surface and anti-helicopter weapons.

Designed to undertake a similar operational role to the Hughes AH-64A Apache, the Mil Mi-28 Havoc is a potent battlefield helicopter.

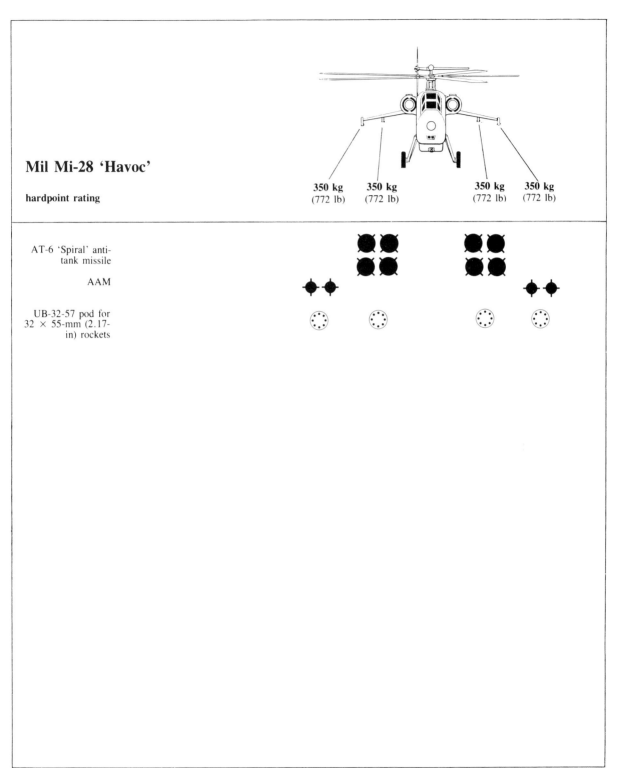

Mil Mi-28 'Havoc'

hardpoint rating

350 kg
(772 lb)

350 kg
(772 lb)

350 kg
(772 lb)

350 kg
(772 lb)

AT-6 'Spiral' anti-
tank missile

AAM

UB-32-57 pod for
32 × 55-mm (2.17-
in) rockets

Japan

Mitsubishi F-1

Type: single-seat close-support and attack fighter.

Internal armament: one 20-mm General Electric M61A1 Vulcan six-barrel rotary cannon plus 750 rounds in the port side of the lower forward fuselage.

Disposable armament: up to 2780 kg (6,129 lb) of disposable stores carried on five hardpoints (one under the fuselage and two under each wing) and on two wingtip missile rails.

Electronics and operational equipment: normal communication and navigation equipment, plus Mitsubishi Electric J/AWG-12 fire-control system (the whole integrated system including Mitsubishi multi-mode radar with air-to-air, air-to-surface, ground mapping and terrain-avoidance capabilities; a Mitsubishi bombing computer and a Mitsubishi/Thomson-CSF head-up display); central computer; Mitsubishi/Ferranti 6TNJ-F inertial navigation system; Tokyo Keiki APR-4 radar-warning receiver; ASM-1 missile-control system and (in the near future) Tokyo Keiki ALQ-6 jamming system.

Current variants and operator

F-1: this Japanese-developed light attack fighter was evolved from the T-2 supersonic trainer, itself remarkably similar to the SEPECAT Jaguar and powered like that aircraft by two Rolls-Royce/Turboméca Adour afterburning turbofans. The first F-1s were modified T-2s (the rear cockpit being plated over to provide volume for specialized mission avionics) and flew in June 1975.

T-2: supersonic trainer first flown in July 1971.

T-2A: supersonic flying and weapons trainer with secondary light attack capability provided by the fitment of five hardpoints for the same basic weapon load as the F-1 though without most of the advanced avionics.

Bearing considerable similarities to the SEPECAT Jaguar, the F-1 is Japan's sole indigenously-designed combat aircraft and was developed from the T-2 advanced trainer (illustrated here): the rear cockpit was replaced by additional avionics which are, however, inferior to those of most Western aircraft.

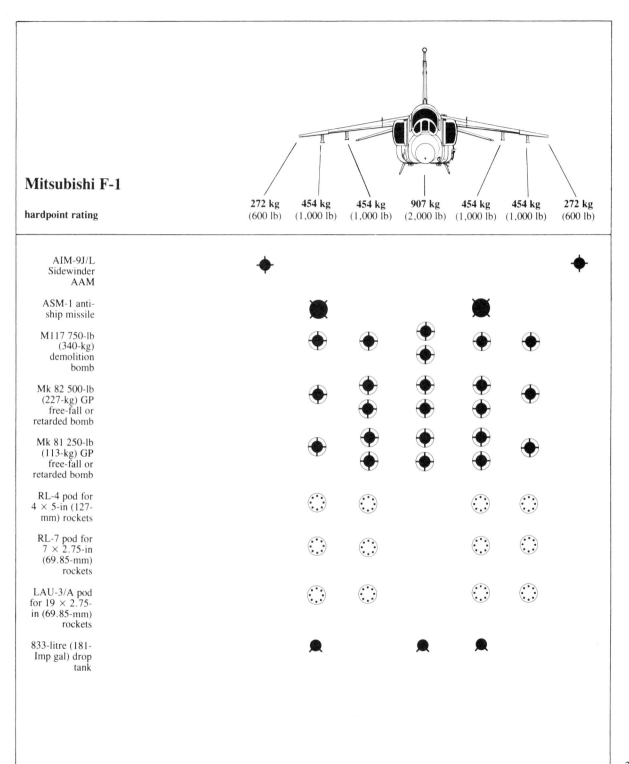

Mitsubishi F-1

hardpoint rating

	272 kg (600 lb)	454 kg (1,000 lb)	454 kg (1,000 lb)	907 kg (2,000 lb)	454 kg (1,000 lb)	454 kg (1,000 lb)	272 kg (600 lb)

AIM-9J/L Sidewinder AAM

ASM-1 anti-ship missile

M117 750-lb (340-kg) demolition bomb

Mk 82 500-lb (227-kg) GP free-fall or retarded bomb

Mk 81 250-lb (113-kg) GP free-fall or retarded bomb

RL-4 pod for 4 × 5-in (127-mm) rockets

RL-7 pod for 7 × 2.75-in (69.85-mm) rockets

LAU-3/A pod for 19 × 2.75-in (69.85-mm) rockets

833-litre (181-Imp gal) drop tank

211

Nanchang Q-5 'Fantan-A'

Type: single-seat attack aircraft.

Internal armament: two 23-mm cannon plus 100 rounds per gun in the wing roots.

Disposable armament: up to 2000 kg (4,409 lb) of disposable stores carried in the under-fuselage weapons bay (rarely, as this is generally used for additional fuel) and on eight hardpoints (two tandem pairs under the fuselage and two under each wing).

Electronics and operational equipment: normal communication and navigation equipment, plus (possibly as a retrofit) Western radar-warning receiver and electronic countermeasures.

Current variant and operators

Q-5: this is a radical Chinese development of the Mikoyan-Gurevich MiG-19, itself in production and under continued development in China as the Shenyang J-6 series. In the Q-5 the Chinese have produced a limited but nonetheless cost-effective clear-weather attack aircraft with the fuselage lengthened and widened to allow the incorporation of a weapons bay for four 250-kg (551-lb) bombs or one tactical nuclear weapon of 5/20-kiloton yield. The nose inlet has been replaced by lateral inlets (possibly to allow the use of a nose radar—in the event not yet adopted) and several other modifications have been made to produce an attack-optimized design used by China and (as the A-5 export derivative) Pakistan.

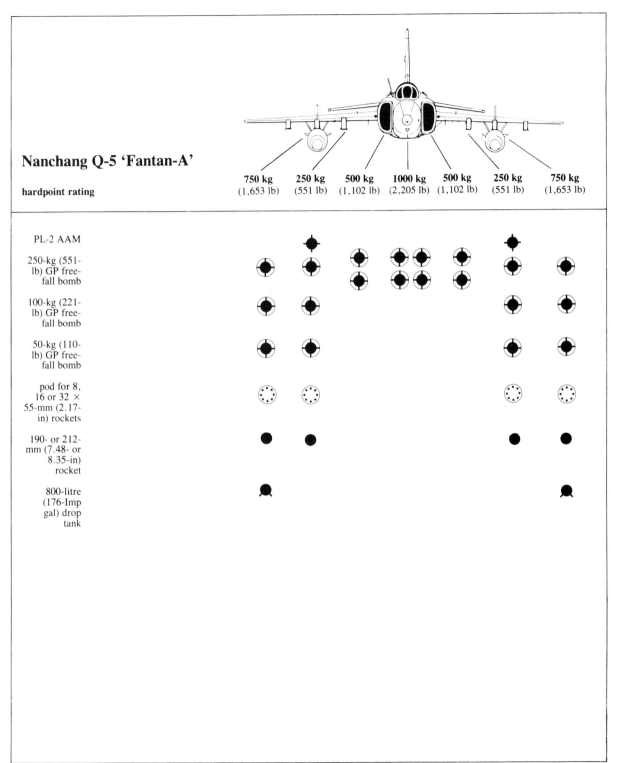

Nanchang Q-5 'Fantan-A'

hardpoint rating

	750 kg (1,653 lb)	250 kg (551 lb)	500 kg (1,102 lb)	1000 kg (2,205 lb)	500 kg (1,102 lb)	250 kg (551 lb)	750 kg (1,653 lb)
PL-2 AAM		●				●	
250-kg (551-lb) GP free-fall bomb	●	●	●●	●●	●●	●	●
100-kg (221-lb) GP free-fall bomb	●	●				●	●
50-kg (110-lb) GP free-fall bomb	●	●				●	●
pod for 8, 16 or 32 × 55-mm (2.17-in) rockets	⊙	⊙				⊙	⊙
190- or 212-mm (7.48- or 8.35-in) rocket	●	●				●	●
800-litre (176-Imp gal) drop tank	✪						✪

Northrop F-5E Tiger II

Type: single-seat light tactical and attack fighter.

Internal armament: two 20-mm Pontiac M39A2 cannon plus 280 rounds per gun in the underside of the nose.

Disposable armamant: up to 7,400 lb (3357 kg) of disposable stores carried on five hardpoints (one under the fuselage and two under each wing) and two wingtip missile rails.

Electronics and operational equipment: normal communication and navigation equipment, plus Emerson APQ-153 or APQ-159(V) multi-mode radar with search air-to-air missile and gun and (in the APQ-159) electro-optical air-to-surface missile modes; General Electric ASG-29 optical sight; air-data system and options such as a Litton inertial navigation system; Itek ALR-46 programmable digital radar-warning receiver; Northrop ALQ-171 conformal electronic countermeasures Tracor ALE-40 chaff/flare dispenser.

Current variants and operators

F-5A Freedom Fighter: first flown in July 1959 as the private-venture Northrop N-156, the F-5A was produced with US government backing as a supersonic tactical fighter with limited offensive capabilities and thus suitable for export to US allies requiring a modern fighter of limited cost, operating and maintenance requirements. The type is powered by two 4,080-lb (1850-kg) General Electric J85-GE-13 afterburning turbojets, and proved highly successful despite its lack of radar and a load of 6,200 lb

The F-5 Freedom Fighter was an interesting and highly worthwhile exercise in reducing purchase and operating costs by offering a capable fighter matched to the requirements of the USA's less technologically advanced (and generally less threatened) allies. The result was a trim aircraft of good performance and adequate payload, but without inordinately expensive electronics.

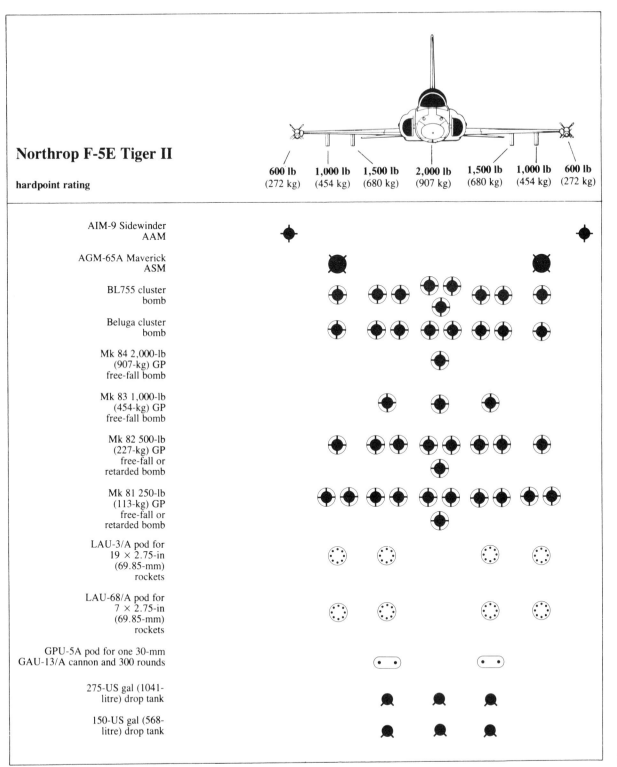

Northrop F-5E Tiger II

hardpoint rating

	600 lb (272 kg)	1,000 lb (454 kg)	1,500 lb (680 kg)	2,000 lb (907 kg)	1,500 lb (680 kg)	1,000 lb (454 kg)	600 lb (272 kg)

AIM-9 Sidewinder AAM

AGM-65A Maverick ASM

BL755 cluster bomb

Beluga cluster bomb

Mk 84 2,000-lb (907-kg) GP free-fall bomb

Mk 83 1,000-lb (454-kg) GP free-fall bomb

Mk 82 500-lb (227-kg) GP free-fall or retarded bomb

Mk 81 250-lb (113-kg) GP free-fall or retarded bomb

LAU-3/A pod for 19 × 2.75-in (69.85-mm) rockets

LAU-68/A pod for 7 × 2.75-in (69.85-mm) rockets

GPU-5A pod for one 30-mm GAU-13/A cannon and 300 rounds

275-US gal (1041-litre) drop tank

150-US gal (568-litre) drop tank

(2812 kg) including the two M39 cannon and two AIM-9 Sidewinder air-to-air missiles on the wingtips. The F-5 series is currently operated by Canada; Ethiopia; Greece; Jordan; Morocco; Netherlands; Norway; Philippines; South Korea; Spain; Taiwan; Thailand; Turkey; USA and Venezuela.

CF-5A: designation of the improved version built in Canada by Canadair with manoeuvring flaps and other detail modifications such as more powerful Canadian-built engines.

NF-5A: Canadair-built version for the Netherlands.

RF-5A Freedom Fighter: tactical reconnaissance version of the F-5A with four KS-92 cameras in a modified nose. The Norwegian variant is the RF-5G which is being upgraded with electronic countermeasures.

SF-5A: CASA-built version for Spain.

F-5B Freedom Fighter: tandem two-seat operational conversion trainer model without nose armament.

NF-5B: Canadair-built version of the F-5B for the Netherlands.

SF-5B: CASA-built version of the F-5B for Spain.

CF-5D: Canadair-built version of the F-5B for Canada.

F-5E Tiger II: much improved derivative of the F-5A with radar, greater weapons capability and improved performance thanks to the use of two 5,000-lb (2268-kg) J85-GE-21A afterburning turbojets. This type first flew in March 1969 and the series has since been sold to Bahrain; Brazil; Chile; Ethiopia; Indonesia; Iran; Jordan; Kenya; Malaysia; Mexico; Morocco; North Yemen; Saudi Arabia; Singapore; South Korea; Sudan; Switzerland; Taiwan; Thailand; Tunisia and USA.

RF-5E Tigereye: tactical reconnaissance version of the F-5E with a lengthened nose to provide accommodation for any of three pallet-mounted reconnaissance packages (cameras and infra-red linescanners).

F-5F Tiger II: two-seat operational conversion trainer with limited attack capability. This variant has a lengthened fuselage, Emerson APQ-137 radar, Northrop AVQ-27 laser target-designation equipment, and only one M39A2 cannon.

T-38A Talon: supersonic trainer version of the N-156 design for the USAF and also operated by West Germany.

Panavia Tornado IDS

Italy/UK/West Germany

Type: two-seat variable-geometry multi-role combat aircraft optimized for the interdiction and strike roles.

Internal armament: two 27-mm IKWA-Mauser cannon plus 360 rounds per gun in the underside of the nose.

Disposable armament: up to 8165 kg (18,000 lb) of disposable stores carried on nine hardpoints (one centreline and four lateral under the fuselage, the latter being two tandem pairs each able to accept twin or triple ejector racks, and two swivelling under each wing).

Electronics and operational equipment: normal communication and navigation equipment, plus Texas Instruments nose radar (one GMR unit for ground mapping, high-accuracy navigation update and air-to-air/air-to-surface target identification and one TFR unit for terrain-following at supersonic speeds down to 200 ft/61 m); Smiths/Teldix/OMI head-up and head-down displays; Ferranti FIN1010 digital inertial navigation; Plessey 72 Doppler navigation; Litef Spirit 3 digital central computer; Microtecnica air-data system; Ferranti laser ranger and marked-target seeker; Westinghouse ASQ-153(V) 'Pave Spike' laser pod (British aircraft); Marconi/Selenia stores-management system; data-link pod; MBB reconnaissance pod; BAe Linescan

Even when carrying a useful load of defensive weapons and electronic warfare pods, the Tornado IDS can tote a buddy refuelling pod to make possible the tactical situation revealed here as a Tornado of the Marine-flieger's MFG1 passes fuel to a similar aircraft carrying a pair of Kormoran anti-ship missiles. Each aircraft carries a BOZ-100 ECM pod under the port wing and a Cerberus jammer under the starboard wing.

Quartet of Tornado GR.Mk 1s of No. 31 Squadron, RAF Germany, based at Bruggen, in the deep strike role.

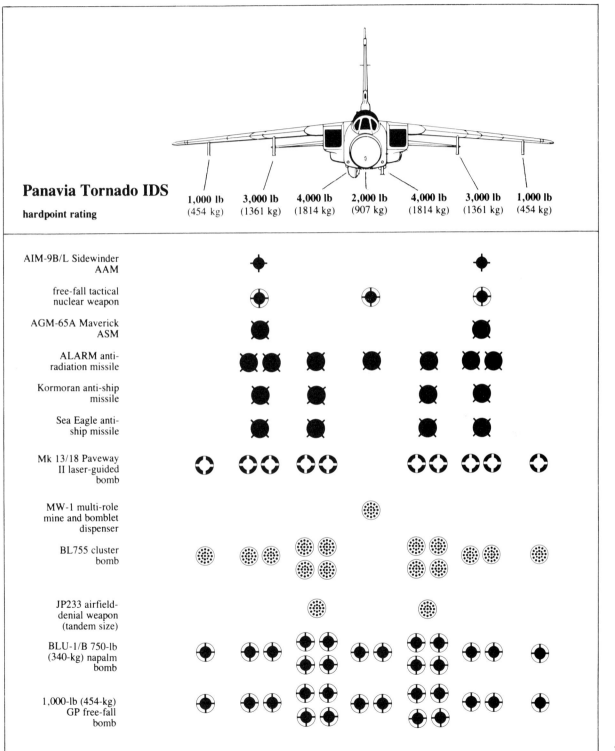

Panavia Tornado IDS

hardpoint rating

	1,000 lb (454 kg)	3,000 lb (1361 kg)	4,000 lb (1814 kg)	2,000 lb (907 kg)	4,000 lb (1814 kg)	3,000 lb (1361 kg)	1,000 lb (454 kg)
AIM-9B/L Sidewinder AAM	●					●	
free-fall tactical nuclear weapon	●			●		●	
AGM-65A Maverick ASM	●					●	
ALARM anti-radiation missile	●●	●	●		●	●●	
Kormoran anti-ship missile	●	●			●	●	
Sea Eagle anti-ship missile	●	●			●	●	
Mk 13/18 Paveway II laser-guided bomb	●	●●	●●		●●	●●	●
MW-1 multi-role mine and bomblet dispenser				●			
BL755 cluster bomb	●	●●	●●●●		●●●●	●●	●
JP233 airfield-denial weapon (tandem size)			●		●		
BLU-1/B 750-lb (340-kg) napalm bomb	●	●●	●●●●	●●	●●●●	●●	●
1,000-lb (454-kg) GP free-fall bomb	●	●●	●●●●	●●	●●●●	●●	●

219

Carrying a large complement of drop tanks for long-range ferry purposes, a Tornado IDS of the Luftwaffe's JaBoG 31 fighter-bomber wing traverses 'hostile' terrain during a demonstration tour of the USA.

Clearly visible in this side view of the third Tornado ADV prototype are the revised leading edges of the wing gloves, the longer forward fuselage and the semi-recessed carriage of the four medium-range AAMs.

4000 (British aircraft); Marconi radar-warning receiver; Marconi ARI.23246/1 Sky Shadow electronic countermeasures pod (British Aircraft) or Elettronica/AEG-Telefunken EL/73 deception jammer pod (Italian and West German aircraft) and other podded electronic countermeasures systems such as the Elettronica ELT/553.

Current variants and operators

Tornado IDS: flown by or on order for Italy, Oman, Saudi Arabia, UK (Tornado GR. Mk 1) and West Germany, this powerful warplane was designed from the mid-1960s as a multi-national STOL combat aircraft suitable for blind first-pass attacks on targets deep in the enemy's rear and first flew in August 1974. The type features 'fly-by-wire' controls, extensive high-lift devices allied to variable-geometry wings and thrust reversers for a combination of range and STOL field performance and an extremely comprehensive avionics fit for navigation, attack and defence. The type has acquired a superb reputation for extreme accuracy of attack at long range and very low level. In the strike role the Tornado IDS can carry several tactical nuclear weapons, though the type would generally carry only two plus a comprehensive assortment of electronic countermeasures pods.

Tornado ADV: developed as a long-range interceptor version of the basic Tornado IDS (with which it has some 80% commonality of airframe, powerplant and systems) for the UK (and since ordered by Saudi Arabia), the Tornado ADV first flew in October 1979 and is a potent area-defence weapon. The airframe is lengthened to permit the semi-

Above *Carrying 1,000-lb (454-kg) bombs on each of their two tandem lateral hardpoints, two 1500-litre (330-Imp gal) drop tanks and two ARI.23246 Sky Shadow jammer pods, two Tornado GR.Mk 1s from No. 9 Squadron at RAF Honington depart on an exercise.*

Left *Designed specifically for the Tornado IDS aircraft of the Luftwaffe, the MW-1 is a bulky but highly impressive submunitions dispenser. The weapon comprises four 28-tube sections, each tube being designed to eject sideways a number of specialist submunitions such as the Stabo runway-cratering, MIFF acoustic-sensor active/passive and KB-44 hollow-charge anti-tank types.*

recessed carriage of four BAe Sky Flash (to be replaced later by improved Sky Flash and/or AIM-120 AMRAAM) air-to-air missiles matched to the new nose radar. The lengthening of the fuselage has the additional advantages of improving fineness ratio (and thus supersonic acceleration) and providing volume for extra avionics and some 200 Imp gal (919 litres) more fuel. The gun armament is reduced to the starboard 27-mm cannon, and provision is made under the wings for four swivelling hardpoints: the inner pair are each plumbed for the carriage of a 1,500-litre (330-Imp gal) drop tank each plus one or two AIM-9L Sidewinder short-range air-to-air missiles (to be supplanted eventually by the AIM-132). The outer pair is generally omitted except for the carriage of podded countermeasures such as the Marconi ARI.23246/1 jammer system, though it is planned that the introduction of the multi-national AIM-132 ASRAAM will witness the adoption of a triple launcher for this weapon on each outer hardpoint. The main sensor is the Foxhunter pulse-Doppler search-and-tracking radar (developed as the AI-24 by Marconi and Ferranti) with advanced electronic counter-measures and the track-while-scan ability to handle look-up/look-down multiple targets (between 12 and 20) at ranges of more than 120 miles (193 km). The Tornado ADV also has an advanced radar-warning receiver plus provision for a Singer data-link system and an electro-optical visual augmentation system for the long-range identification of possible targets. In RAF service the type is designated Tornado F.Mk 2 with Turbo-Union RB.199 Mk 103 afterburning turbofans, and Tornado F.Mk 3 with automatic scheduling of wing sweep, RB.199 Mk 104 turbofans with longer jetpipes for greater thrust, a digital engine/inlet/nozzle control system, and eventual provision for 2250-litre (495-Imp gal) drop tanks.

Right *The rear cockpit of a Tornado IDS highlights the role of the modern 'back-seater': surmounted by two old-fashioned analog instruments (altitude and combined speed indicator) is the central combined radar and projected map display flanked by two CRTs on which the operator can call up a wide diversity of data, the most common being plan, fix and nav/attack formats.*

Below *When carrying the MW-1 dispenser, the Tornado is an ideal anti-airfield and anti-armour weapon, the costly dispenser being discarded when empty to reduce drag and so enhance the Tornado's chances of escape.*

Tornado IDS aircraft of the West German Marineflieger show off the type's retractable inflight-refuelling probe, four swivelling underwing hardpoints (the inner pair being used here for the carriage of drop tanks) and, under the fuselage, two tandem hardpoints. The primary weapon of Marineflieger aircraft is the Kormoran anti-ship missile, of which four can be carried.

Tornado ECR: designation of the electronic warfare version under development for Italy and West Germany, with revised avionics (emitter locator system, data-link, digital databus, jammer pods and low/medium-altitude reconnaissance pod) together with AGM-88A HARM anti-radiation missiles.

PZL Mielec TS-11 Iskra-bis DF

Type: one/two-seat close-support and reconnaissance trainer.

Internal armament: one 23-mm NR-23 cannon plus rounds in the starboard side of the nose.

Disposable armament: up to 400 kg (882 lb) of disposable stores carried on four hardpoints (two under each wing).

Electronics and operational equipment: normal communication and navigation equipment, plus an optical sight.

Current variants and operators

TS-11 Iskra-bis A: first flown in February 1960, this trim trainer is flown only by Poland and is powered by a 1000-kg (2,205-lb) SO-3 turbojet.

TS-11 Iskra-bis B: improved version of the Iskra-bis A with weapon training capability resulting from the addition of four underwing hardpoints.

TS-11 Iskra-bis C: single-seat reconnaissance derivative with the volume of the rear cockpit used for additional fuel and for three cameras under the floor.

TS-11 Iskra-bis D: developed version of the Iskra-bis B with the 1100-kg (2,425-lb) SO-3W turbojet and provision for a greater variety of underwing stores. This model was bought by India.

TS-11 Iskra-bis DF: combat and reconnaissance trainer derived from the Iskra-bis D with three cameras (one in the underside of each inlet and one under the floor of the rear cockpit).

Used within the Warsaw Pact only by Poland, the TS-11 Iskra is elderly in concept and of real value only in the training role, in which it is hampered by its lack of staggered seating.

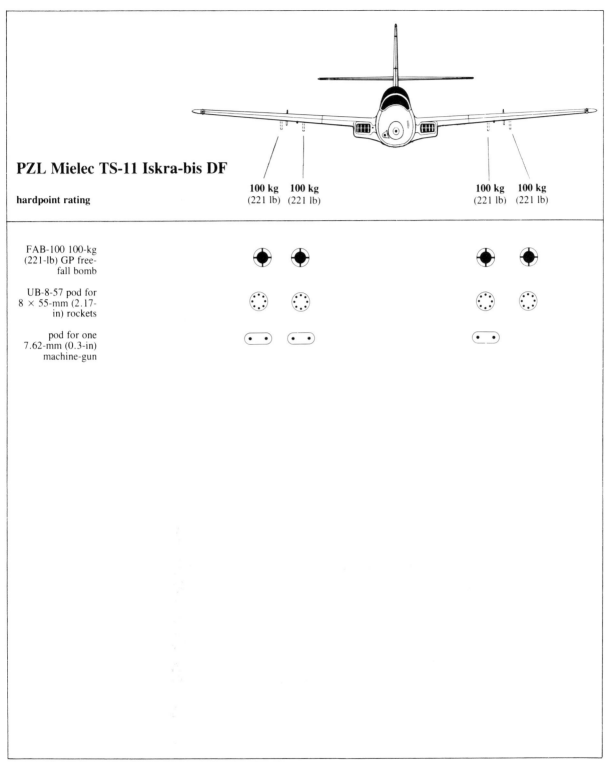

PZL Mielec TS-11 Iskra-bis DF

hardpoint rating

100 kg
(221 lb)

100 kg
(221 lb)

100 kg
(221 lb)

100 kg
(221 lb)

FAB-100 100-kg
(221-lb) GP free-
fall bomb

UB-8-57 pod for
8 × 55-mm (2.17-
in) rockets

pod for one
7.62-mm (0.3-in)
machine-gun

Rockwell B-1B

Type: four-seat variable-geometry strategic penetration bomber.

Internal armament: none.

Disposable armament: up to 92,000 lb (41731 kg) of disposable stores carried in three lower-fuselage weapons bays (a 31.25-ft/9.53-m tandem unit forward of the wing carry-through structure and a 15-ft/4.57-m unit aft of this structure) and eight hardpoints (four grouped under each side of the fuselage).

Electronics and operational equipment: normal communication and navigation equipment, plus a Westinghouse ALQ-153 pulse-Doppler tail-warning system and enormously comprehensive offensive and defensive avionics suites. The Offensive Avionics System is co-ordinated by Boeing on the basis of the same company's OAS for the Boeing B-52 bomber and comprises Singer-Kearfott inertial navigation; Teledyne Ryan APN-218 Doppler navigation; Westinghouse multi-mode offensive radar (derived from APG-66 radar of the General Dynamics F-16 and possessing a low-altitude terrain-following capability); Northrop NAS-26 astro-inertial system; IBM avionics control units; central computers; and Sperry offensive display sets. The Defensive Avionics System is co-ordinated by Eaton-AIL and based on the ALQ-161 system designed for the B-1A, and comprises Sanders display units; Raytheon phased-array antennae and Northrop jammers co-ordinated by a number of readily-reprogrammable digital computers for the near-instantaneous detection, location, analysis and jamming of hostile emitters.

Current variant and operator

B-1B: intended as successor to the B-52 in the low-level penetration role, the B-1B is designed for use only by the US Air Force as the airborne component of the USA's strategic nuclear triad; the B-1 was originally schemed as a Mach 2+ aircraft with an unrivalled combination of advanced aerodynamics, powerplant and avionics. The first B-1A flew in December 1974 and displayed excellent qualities, but the whole programme was cancelled by President Carter during 1977. President Reagan reinstated the type in October 1981, the new B-1B being intended as a cruise missile and bomb carrier and revised for lower speeds (with fixed-geometry inlets) over longer ranges with greater loads. The B-1B first flew in September 1984 and began to enter service in 1986, soon proving itself fully able to meet all requirements including a radar signature less than one-hundredth that of the B-52 by careful design of potentially reflective surfaces and by the use of radar-absorbent materials in the airframe.

The B-1 was first designed for high-altitude Mach 2 penetration, and after flying as the B-1A prototype series was cancelled but later reinstated as a low-altitude Mach 1+ penetration bomber and cruise missile platform. This illustration of a B-1A shows the type's variable-geometry wings in the fully-forward position, and the wide separation of the two engine pairs, allowing the incorporation of three substantial weapons bays in the lower fuselage. If these bays are used for fuel on very long-range missions, weapons can be accommodated in three lateral rows under the fuselage.

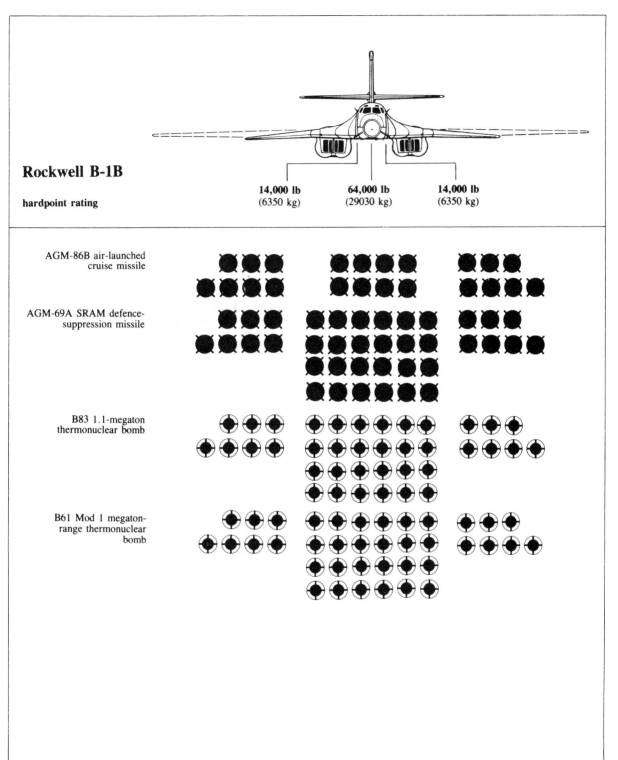

Rockwell B-1B

hardpoint rating

14,000 lb (6350 kg)	64,000 lb (29030 kg)	14,000 lb (6350 kg)

AGM-86B air-launched cruise missile

AGM-69A SRAM defence-suppression missile

B83 1.1-megaton thermonuclear bomb

B61 Mod 1 megaton-range thermonuclear bomb

Rockwell OV-10A Bronco

Type: two-seat multi-role counter-insurgency and forward air control aircraft.

Internal armament: four 7.62-mm (0.3-in) M60C machine-guns plus 500 rounds per gun, located as a pair in each fuselage sponson.

Disposable armament: up to 4,000 lb (1814 kg) of disposable stores carried on five hardpoints (one under the fuselage and two under each sponson) and on two underwing missile rails.

Electronics and operational equipment: normal communication and navigation equipment, plus an optical sight and Doppler navigation.

Current variants and operators

OV-10A Bronco: first flown in August 1967, the Bronco was the result of joint US Marine Corps and US Air Force interest in a Light Armed Reconnaissance Aircraft for the 'brushfire war' counter-insurgency and forward air control roles. Apart from its considerable armament, this STOL type can carry in the rear of the central nacelle 3,200 lb (1452 kg) of freight, or five paratroops, or two litters and one attendant.

OV-10B Bronco: target-tug version for West Germany, which also operates some OV-10A(Z) Bronco aircraft with a 2,950-lb (1339-kg) General Electric J85-GE-4 turbojet pod-mounted above the centre section for better performance.

OV-10C Bronco: version of the OV-10A for Thailand.

OV-10D Bronco: US Marine Corps aircraft modified to the night observation and gunship role with 1,040-shp (776-kW) Garrett T76-G-420/421 turboshafts in place of the standard 715-shp (533-kW) T76-G-416/417s; a Texas Instruments AAS-37 forward-looking infra-red and laser pod for observation and the guidance of advanced weapons; an E-Systems/Loral APR-39 radar-warning receiver; a Tracor ALE-39 chaff/flare dispenser and a 20-mm M97 three-barrel cannon in a remotely-controlled under-fuselage mounting.

OV-10E Bronco: version of the OV-10A for Venezuela.

OV-10F Bronco: version of the OV-10A for Indonesia.

A promotional photograph taken early in the Bronco's career shows OV-10A aircraft in the markings of the USAF, USN and USMC, though in fact the US Navy never adopted the type. Visible at the bottom of each aircraft are the weapon sponsons projecting from the sides of the fuselage.

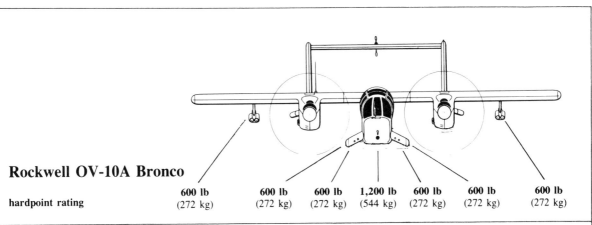

Rockwell OV-10A Bronco

hardpoint rating

	600 lb (272 kg)	600 lb (272 kg)	600 lb (272 kg)	1,200 lb (544 kg)	600 lb (272 kg)	600 lb (272 kg)	600 lb (272 kg)

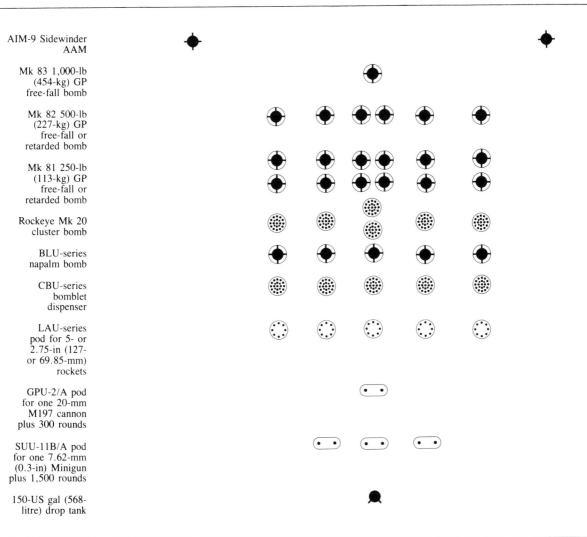

AIM-9 Sidewinder AAM

Mk 83 1,000-lb (454-kg) GP free-fall bomb

Mk 82 500-lb (227-kg) GP free-fall or retarded bomb

Mk 81 250-lb (113-kg) GP free-fall or retarded bomb

Rockeye Mk 20 cluster bomb

BLU-series napalm bomb

CBU-series bomblet dispenser

LAU-series pod for 5- or 2.75-in (127- or 69.85-mm) rockets

GPU-2/A pod for one 20-mm M197 cannon plus 300 rounds

SUU-11B/A pod for one 7.62-mm (0.3-in) Minigun plus 1,500 rounds

150-US gal (568- litre) drop tank

Sweden

Saab 105Ö

Type: two-seat trainer and light attack aircraft.

Internal armament: none.

Disposable armament: up to 2000 kg (4,409 lb) carried on six hardpoints (three under each wing).

Electronics and operational equipment: normal communication and navigation equipment, plus a Ferranti F126 ISIS sight, Saab-Scania BT9RX fire-control computer and Decca moving-map display.

Current variants and operators

Saab 105: conceived as a multi-purpose civil and military aircraft, the Saab 105 first flew in June 1963 and entered production with two 745-kg (1,642-lb) Turboméca Aubisque turbofans for the Swedish air force, which operates the type as the Sk 60A basic trainer with light attack capability, the Sk 60B attack aircraft with a maximum of 700 kg (1,643 lb) of disposable stores, and the Sk 60C attack and reconnaissance aircraft with a KB-18 camera in the nose.

Saab 105Ö: uprated version for Austria with 2,850-lb (1293-kg) General Electric J85-GE-17B turbojets and greater warload.

The Saab 105G was an uprated development of the Saab 105Ö with updated avionics and greater weapon-carrying capability, but was built only in prototype form. This underside view shows off the standard six underwing hardpoints, here loaded with free-fall 'iron' bombs.

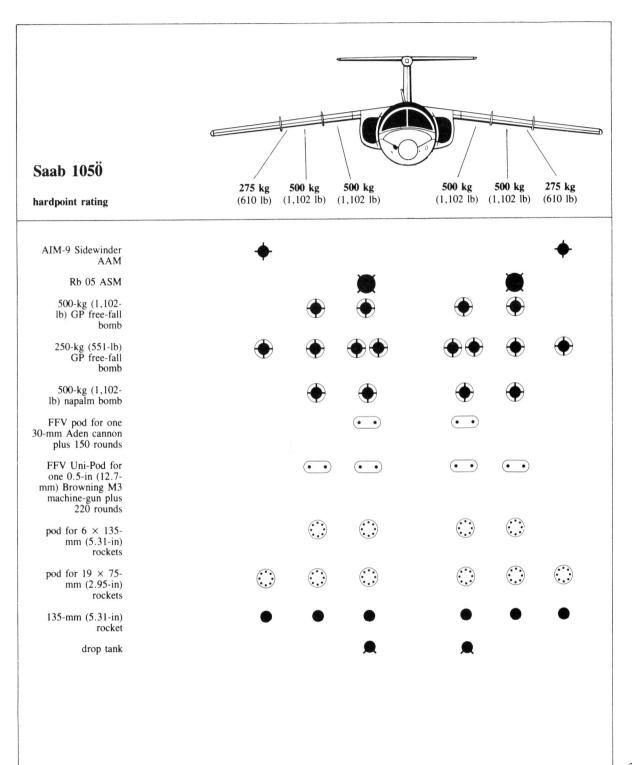

Saab 1050Ö

hardpoint rating

	275 kg (610 lb)	500 kg (1,102 lb)	500 kg (1,102 lb)	500 kg (1,102 lb)	500 kg (1,102 lb)	275 kg (610 lb)
AIM-9 Sidewinder AAM	●					●
Rb 05 ASM			●		●	
500-kg (1,102-lb) GP free-fall bomb		●	●		●	●
250-kg (551-lb) GP free-fall bomb	●	●	● ●	● ●	●	●
500-kg (1,102-lb) napalm bomb		●	●		●	●
FFV pod for one 30-mm Aden cannon plus 150 rounds			⬭		⬭	
FFV Uni-Pod for one 0.5-in (12.7-mm) Browning M3 machine-gun plus 220 rounds		⬭	⬭		⬭	⬭
pod for 6 × 135-mm (5.31-in) rockets		⊙	⊙		⊙	⊙
pod for 19 × 75-mm (2.95-in) rockets	⊙	⊙	⊙		⊙	⊙	⊙
135-mm (5.31-in) rocket	●	●	●		●	●	●
drop tank			●		●	

231

Saab J 35F Draken

Sweden

Type: single-seat all-weather fighter and attack aircraft.

Internal armament: one 30-mm Aden M/55 cannon plus 100 rounds in the starboard wing.

Disposable armament: up to 4500 kg (9,921 lb) of disposable stores carried on nine hardpoints (three under the fuselage and three under each wing).

Electronics and operational equipment: normal communication and navigation equipment, plus Ericsson UAP 13102 (PS-01/A) or UAP 13103 (PS-011/A) long-range radar (the latter used in conjunction with a Hughes S71N infra-red search-and-track system); Hughes/Saab-Scania S7B fire-control system; Saab BT9 bombing system; data-link for use with the STRIL-60 national air-defence network; integrated nav/attack system; radar-warning receiver and electronic countermeasures such as the Pod KA and Pod 70 systems.

Current variants and operators

Sk 35C Draken: tandem-seat operation conversion and proficiency trainer based on the J 35A initial-production fighter with the RM6B afterburning turbojet. For its time the Draken was a remarkably advanced aircraft. Designed from 1949 and tailored to the particular requirements of the Swedish air force, the type first flew in October 1955 and was Western Europe's first operational supersonic fighter. The Sk 35C trainer is the oldest model still in service.

J 35D Draken: improved fighter based on the J 35B collision-course interceptor but featuring the more powerful RM6C engine and advanced radar, fire-control and autopilot.

J 35F Draken: definitive Swedish interceptor model with advanced avionics for use in association with radar- and IR-homing versions of the Hughes Falcon air-to-air missiles.

The J 35S is the Finnish air force's equivalent to Sweden's J 35F, and still an effective interceptor with a primary armament of AAMs such as the Rb 24 (Sidewinder), Rb 27 (semi-active radar Falcon) and Rb 28 (IR-homing Falcon). The fairing under the nose roundel houses the IR seeker associated with the use of Rb 24 and Rb 28 AAMs.

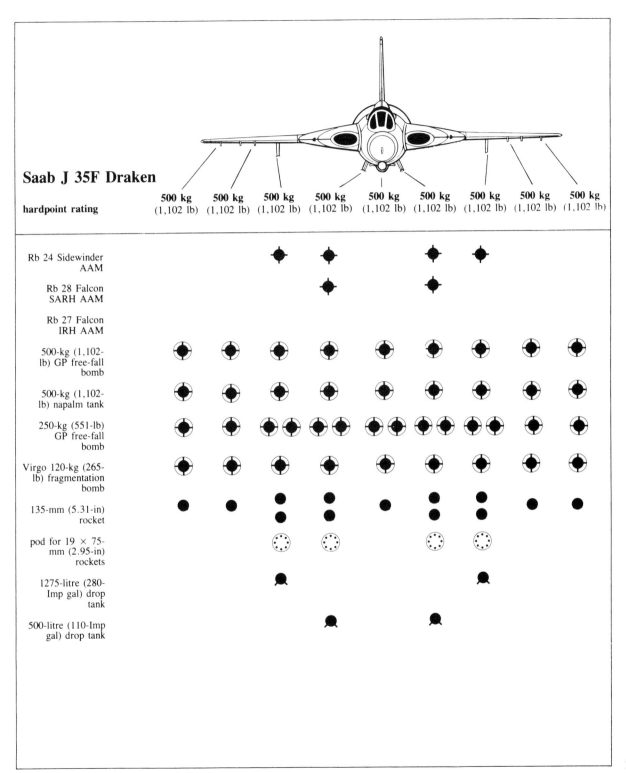

Saab J 35F Draken

hardpoint rating

	500 kg (1,102 lb)	500 kg (1,102 lb)	500 kg (1,102 lb)	500 kg (1,102 lb)	500 kg (1,102 lb)	500 kg (1,102 lb)	500 kg (1,102 lb)	500 kg (1,102 lb)	500 kg (1,102 lb)

- Rb 24 Sidewinder AAM
- Rb 28 Falcon SARH AAM
- Rb 27 Falcon IRH AAM
- 500-kg (1,102-lb) GP free-fall bomb
- 500-kg (1,102-lb) napalm tank
- 250-kg (551-lb) GP free-fall bomb
- Virgo 120-kg (265-lb) fragmentation bomb
- 135-mm (5.31-in) rocket
- pod for 19 × 75-mm (2.95-in) rockets
- 1275-litre (280-Imp gal) drop tank
- 500-litre (110-Imp gal) drop tank

Above *A side view conceals the enormous area of the Draken's double-delta wing planform, but reveals features such as the infra-red sensor under the nose, the HF/VHF blade aerial above the fuselage, the UHF/TACAN blade aerial under the fuselage, and the externally-carried armament of two Rb 27 and two Rb 28 Falcon AAMs.*

Right *A J 35 F of Flygflottilj 13 shows off the Draken's primary offensive armament of four AAMs, namely two IR-homing Rb 28 Falcons (outboard) and two semi-active radar-homing Rb 27 Falcons (inboard). Just visible in the leading edge of the starboard inlet is the port for the single Aden M/55 30-mm cannon carried by this Draken variant.*

J 35 J Draken: designation of J 35Fs reworked to more modern avionic standard and with two more hardpoints.

J 35Ö: designation of J 35Ds reworked for sale to Austria without provision for missiles.

Saab 35S: designation of the J 35F type exported to Finland as the S 35S fighter and S 35BS two-seat trainer.

Saab 35X: designation of the J 35F type exported to Denmark as the F-35 fighter (two Aden cannon and a host of avionics improvements such as a head-up display; Ferranti Type 105D laser ranger; inertial navigation system; cockpit displays; Ferranti Type 105D radar-warning receiver and electronic countermeasures mostly derived from those of the General Dynamics F-16). The RF-35 is a reconnaissance fighter with a revised nose (seven cameras) and provision for the FFV Red Baron multi-sensor night reconnaissance pod while the TF-35 is a two-seat trainer veriant.

Saab JA 37 Viggen

Sweden

Type: single-seat all-weather interceptor with secondary attack capability.

Internal armament: one 30-mm Oerlikon KCA cannon plus 150 rounds in a ventral pack offset to port but attached to the centreline hardpoint.

Disposable armament: up to 6000 kg (13,228 lb) of disposable stores carried on seven hardpoints (three under the fuselage and two under each wing).

Electronics and operational equipment: normal communication and navigation equipment, plus Ericsson UAP 1023 (PS-46/A) multi-mode pulse-Doppler radar (with search, target acquisition, target tracking, target illumination and air-to-surface ranging modes); Smiths head-up display; Svenska Radio head-down displays; Singer-Kearfott/Saab-Scania SKC-2037 digital central computer; Garrett/Saab-Scania LD-5 digital air-data computer; Singer-Kearfott KT-70L inertial navigation system; Honeywell/Saab-Scania SA07 digital automatic flight-control system; Decca 72 Doppler navigation; SATT radar-warning receiver; Svenska Radio electronic countermeasures; BOZ-100 chaff dispenser and podded electronic countermeasures such as the SATT AQ31 system.

Current variants and operator
AJ 37 Viggen: this was the first production model of the superb Viggen multi-role

The AJ 37 is the attack-optimized variant of the Viggen family, this underside view revealing an assortment of stores such as centreline drop tank flanked by two Rb 74 Maverick air-to-surface missiles, a BOZ-100 chaff dispenser under the port wing, and an AQ-series ECM jammer under the starboard wing.

An SF 37 Viggen of the Swedish air force's Flygflottilj 13 reveals on the port under-fuselage hardpoint the night illumination and camera pod (generally carried by this model in a paired installation with a Red Baron pod accommodating optical cameras and an infra-red linescanner) to complement the cameras in the nose. The dogtooth in the leading edge of each wing is the location of the two forward-facing receivers for the SATT radar-warning receiver system.

aircraft, which made its maiden flight in February 1967 and is operated only by Sweden as successor to the Saab 35 Draken series. The design pioneered many features of later aircraft, notably the canard configuration and thrust-reversible afterburning turbofan (the 11800-kg/26,014-lb Flygmotor RM8A derived from the Pratt & Whitney JT8D civil engine) for dispersed STOL operations off lengths of road. Designed as an integrated part of Sweden's STRIL-60 air-defence network, the type can carry a wide assortment of weapons in its 6000-kg (13,228-lb) disposable load, and is generally the only type to carry the Rb 04E anti-ship, Rb 05A air-to-surface and RBS 15F anti-ship missiles. As with all models before the JA 37, the type has earlier Ericsson radar; a Marconi-Elliott head-up display; a Philips Elektroniksindustrier air-data computer, and other differences including provision for Rb 24 Sidewinder and Rb 28 Falcon air-to-air missiles and for the carriage of an FFV pod with one 30-mm Aden cannon plus 150/200 rounds on the centreline hardpoint.

SF 37 Viggen: dedicated overland reconnaissance version of the AJ 37 with the nose radar replaced by six cameras (four low-altitude and two high-altitude); an infra-red linescanner; an infra-red sensor; a data recorder and electro-magnetic registration equipment (all controlled by the central computer); plus provision for ventral tanks and one active and one passive electronic countermeasures pod on the inner underwing hardpoints.

SH 37 Viggen: dedicated maritime reconnaissance version of the AJ 37 retaining the nose radar but adding a data recorder; active/passive electronic countermeasures pods and two

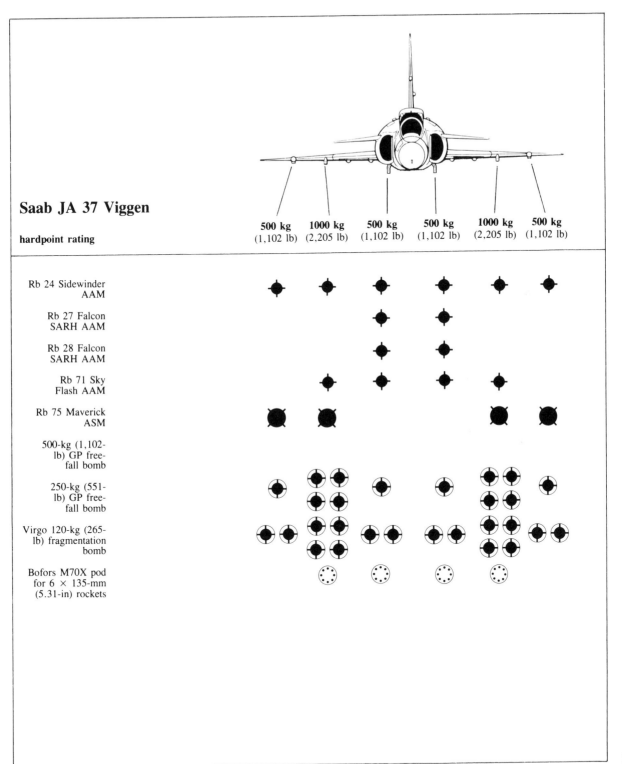

Saab JA 37 Viggen

hardpoint rating

	500 kg (1,102 lb)	1000 kg (2,205 lb)	500 kg (1,102 lb)	500 kg (1,102 lb)	1000 kg (2,205 lb)	500 kg (1,102 lb)
Rb 24 Sidewinder AAM	●	●	●	●	●	●
Rb 27 Falcon SARH AAM			●	●		
Rb 28 Falcon SARH AAM			●	●		
Rb 71 Sky Flash AAM		●	●	●	●	
Rb 75 Maverick ASM	●	●			●	●
500-kg (1,102-lb) GP free-fall bomb						
250-kg (551-lb) GP free-fall bomb	●	●● / ●●	●	●	●● / ●●	●
Virgo 120-kg (265-lb) fragmentation bomb	●●	●● / ●●	●●	●●	●● / ●●	●●
Bofors M70X pod for 6 × 135-mm (5.31-in) rockets		●	●	●	●	

The JA 37 interceptor is by far the most advanced version of the Viggen family, features visible here being a pair of Rb 71 Sky Flash medium-range AAMs under the wings, the packaged Oerlikon KCA 30-mm cannon under the fuselage, and an electronic warfare pod on the starboard under-fuselage hardpoint.

reconnaissance pods. These last are (on the port under-fuselage hardpoint) a night reconnaissance type with infra-red linescan and low-light-level TV sensors, and (on the starboard under-fuselage hardpoint) either a long-range camera or Red Baron infra-red type.

Sk 37 Viggen: two-seat operational conversion and proficiency trainer with tandem cockpits and a taller fin.

JA 37 Viggen: interceptor version with secondary attack capability, powered by the 12750-kg (28,086-lb) RM8B. This model has a restressed airframe and sufficiently different avionics to be considered a second-generation derivative and is in every respect a world-class combat aircraft with excellent performance (aerodynamic and electronic, the pulse-Doppler radar having a look-down capability of more than 50 km/31 miles), agility and reliability.

SEPECAT Jaguar S

Type: single-seat all-weather attack aircraft.
Internal armament: two 30-mm Aden Mk 4 cannon plus 150 rounds per gun in the underside of the forward fuselage.
Disposable armament: up to 10,500 lb (4763 kg) of disposable stores carried on five hardpoints (one under the fuselage and two under each wing).
Electronics and operational equipment: normal communication and navigation equipment, plus Marconi NAVWASS (being replaced by Ferranti FIN1064) digital inertial navigation and weapon-aiming system; Smiths head-up display; Ferranti laser ranger and marked-target seeker; Marconi ARI.18223 radar-warning receiver; Philips/Matra Phimat chaff dispenser, and provision for systems such as a reconnaissance pod (including BAe Linescan 401) and the Westinghouse ALQ-101 electronic countermeasures pod.

Current variants and operators

Jaguar A: this is the French tactical attack and strike version of the Jaguar, a type conceived for the attack and advanced training roles in the 1960s before flying for the first time in September 1968. The Jaguar A has two 3315-kg (7,305-lb) Rolls-Royce/Turboméca Adour Mk 102 afterburning turbofans, two 30-mm DEFA cannons and a simpler avionics suite (Sagem inertial navigation system; Doppler navigation; Thomson-CSF laser ranger; Thomson-CSF 121 fire-control unit; Thomson-CSF 21 weapon-aiming system and EMD fire-control system for the Martel ASM), provision for electronic countermeasures pods and the Thomson-CSF/Martin Marietta ATLIS 2 laser designator pod for use with the AS.30L ASM. Forty-five Jaguar A aircraft are tasked

A Jaguar GR.Mk 1 of No. 2 Squadron, RAF Germany, maintains a discreet distance from possible danger during a long-distance deployment from Laarbruch. Though lacking radar, the Jaguar has impressive nav/attack accuracy at low level, and can carry a formidable assortment of tactical weapons.

Three Jaguar GR.Mk 1s from No. 14 Squadron, RAF Germany, show off a diversity of external stores while on exercise from Bruggen. The nearest aircraft carries two Sidewinders, four BL755 cluster bombs, a centreline drop tank and two Tracor chaff dispensers; the middle aircraft has a pair of Mk 13/18 Paveway laser-guided bombs, a centreline drop tank and two ECM pods outboard (a Phimat chaff/flare dispenser under the starboard wing and an ALQ-101 jammer pod under the port wing); while the furthest aircraft totes four 1,000-lb (454-kg) bombs (two on the centreline plus another two on the outer underwing hardpoints) and two drop tanks.

with tactical nuclear strike using the 15-kiloton AN 52 free-fall store carried on the centreline hardpoint.

Jaguar B: in service with the RAF as the Jaguar T.Mk 2, this is the British two-seat operational conversion and proficiency trainer with a second cockpit permitted by a lengthened fuselage.

Jaguar E: French equivalent of the Jaguar B, used mainly for advanced and conversion training.

Jaguar S: in service with the RAF as the Jaguar GR.Mk 1, this is the British equivalent to the Jaguar A with considerably higher equipment standards and powered by two 8,040-lb (3647-kg) Adour Mk 104 turbofans; this type can carry a centreline reconnaissance pod.

Jaguar International: used by Ecuador, India, Nigeria and Oman, this is a much improved export derivative with 8,400-lb (3810-kg) Adour Mk 804 or 9,270-lb (4205-kg) Adour Mk 811 turbofans, two overwing hardpoints for air-to-air missiles (generally Matra R550 Magic or AIM-9 Sidewinder), and varied avionics according to customer requirements, but generally based on the Sagem inertial platform, Ferranti COMED combined map and electronic display with options such as Thomson-CSF Agave nose radar (for use with anti-ship missiles such as the AM.39 Exocet or Kormoran) and podded sensors such as a low-light-level TV or forward-looking infra-red.

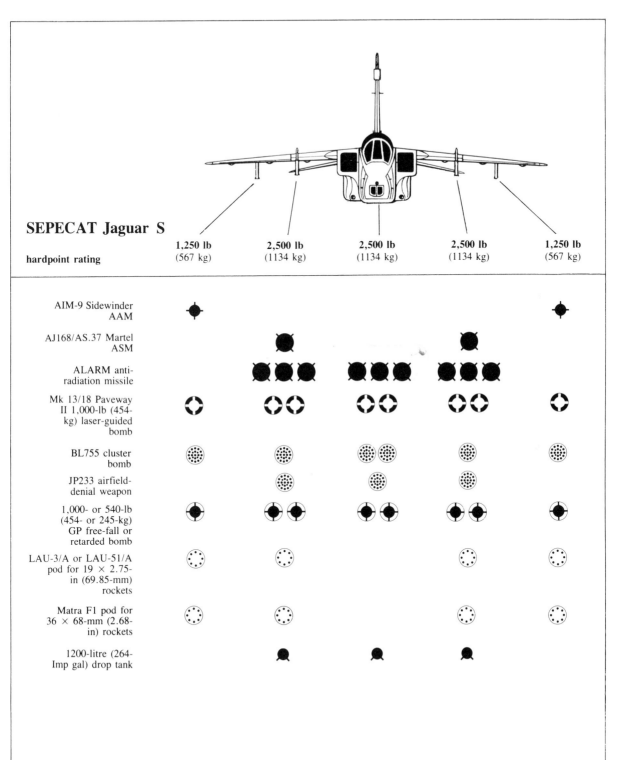

SEPECAT Jaguar S

hardpoint rating

	1,250 lb (567 kg)	2,500 lb (1134 kg)	2,500 lb (1134 kg)	2,500 lb (1134 kg)	1,250 lb (567 kg)
AIM-9 Sidewinder AAM	●				●
AJ168/AS.37 Martel ASM		●		●	
ALARM anti-radiation missile		●●●	●●●	●●●	
Mk 13/18 Paveway II 1,000-lb (454-kg) laser-guided bomb	◉	◉◉	◉◉	◉◉	◉
BL755 cluster bomb	⬤	⬤	⬤⬤	⬤	⬤
JP233 airfield-denial weapon		⬤	⬤	⬤	
1,000- or 540-lb (454- or 245-kg) GP free-fall or retarded bomb	●	●●	●●	●●	●
LAU-3/A or LAU-51/A pod for 19 × 2.75-in (69.85-mm) rockets	⊙	⊙		⊙	⊙
Matra F1 pod for 36 × 68-mm (2.68-in) rockets	⊙	⊙		⊙	⊙
1200-litre (264-Imp gal) drop tank		●	●	●	

241

Shin Meiwa PS-1

Japan

Type: 10-seat anti-submarine flying-boat.

Internal armament: none.

Disposable armament: up to 2000 kg (4,409 lb) of disposable stores carried in a fuselage weapons bay and on four hardpoints (two under the wings and two at the wingtips).

Electronics and operational equipment: normal communication and navigation equipment, plus APS-80N search radar; ASQ-101B dunking sonar; ASQ-10A magnetic anomaly detection; AQA-3 'Jezebel' passive long-range sonar detection with 20 sonobuoys; 'Julie' active acoustic ranging system with 12 charges; APN-153 Doppler navigation; AYK-2 navigation computer and N-OA-35/HSA tactical plotting group.

Current variants and operator

PS-1: this unique anti-submarine flying-boat is operated only by Japan and uses a dedicated General Electric T58 turboshaft (in addition to the four wing-mounted turboprops) to provide air for the boundary-layer control system that provides remarkable STOL performance and a patrol speed comparable with that of the boat's prey, namely nuclear-powered submarines. The type first flew in October 1967 and one of its advantages is the ability to land (even in rough seas) to use its dunking sonar.

US-1: amphibian search-and-rescue variant with a crew of nine and accommodation for 12 litters or 20 seated survivors.

US-1A: version of the US-1 with more powerful engines.

The flying boat is a rarity in modern air arms, but the PS-1 is admirably suited to Japan's anti-submarine needs with its excellent STOL performance, ability to operate from rough seas, and adequate combination of sensors and weapons.

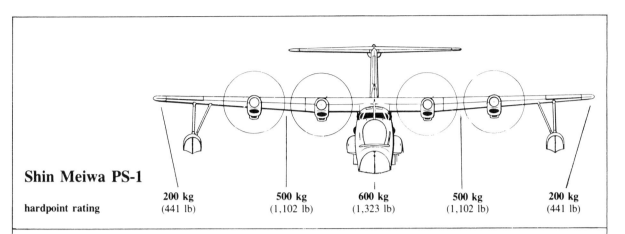

Shin Meiwa PS-1

hardpoint rating

| 200 kg
(441 lb) | 500 kg
(1,102 lb) | 600 kg
(1,323 lb) | 500 kg
(1,102 lb) | 200 kg
(441 lb) |

150-kg (331-lb)
depth bomb

Mk 46 anti-
submarine
torpedo

5-in (127-mm)
rocket

SIAI-Marchetti S.211

Type: two-seat trainer and light attack/counter-insurgency aircraft.
Internal armament: none.
Disposable armament: up to 600 kg (1,323 lb) of disposable stores carried on four hardpoints (two under each wing).
Electronics and operational equipment: normal communication and navigation equipment, plus an optical sight and provision for customer requirements such as nose radar; head-up display; Doppler navigation; radar-warning receiver; electronic counter-measures and a reconnaissance pod with four cameras and an infra-red linescanner.

Current variant and operators
S.211: designed to fill a niche at the bottom end of the jet-powered basic trainer market, the S.211 first flew in April 1981 and offers buyers low purchase and operating costs combined with moderate performance and a useful light attack (or rather counter-insurgency) capability. Current operators are Haiti and Singapore.

Bearing most unmilitary markings is this S.211 demonstrator aircraft of the manufacturer, SIAI-Marchetti.

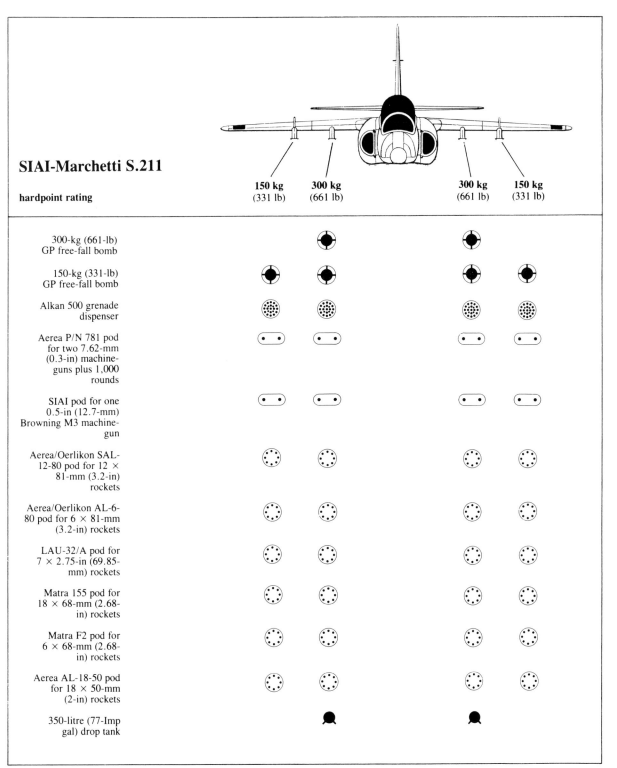

SIAI-Marchetti S.211

hardpoint rating

	150 kg (331 lb)	300 kg (661 lb)	300 kg (661 lb)	150 kg (331 lb)
300-kg (661-lb) GP free-fall bomb		●	●	
150-kg (331-lb) GP free-fall bomb	●	●	●	●
Alkan 500 grenade dispenser	●	●	●	●
Aerea P/N 781 pod for two 7.62-mm (0.3-in) machine-guns plus 1,000 rounds	●	●	●	●
SIAI pod for one 0.5-in (12.7-mm) Browning M3 machine-gun	●	●	●	●
Aerea/Oerlikon SAL-12-80 pod for 12 × 81-mm (3.2-in) rockets	●	●	●	●
Aerea/Oerlikon AL-6-80 pod for 6 × 81-mm (3.2-in) rockets	●	●	●	●
LAU-32/A pod for 7 × 2.75-in (69.85-mm) rockets	●	●	●	●
Matra 155 pod for 18 × 68-mm (2.68-in) rockets	●	●	●	●
Matra F2 pod for 6 × 68-mm (2.68-in) rockets	●	●	●	●
Aerea AL-18-50 pod for 18 × 50-mm (2-in) rockets	●	●	●	●
350-litre (77-Imp gal) drop tank		●	●	

SIAI-Marchetti SF.260W Warrior

Type: two-seat trainer and counter-insurgency aircraft.

Internal armament: none.

Disposable armament: up to 300 kg (661 lb) of disposable stores carried on four hardpoints (two under each wing).

Electronics and operational equipment: normal communication and navigation equipment, plus an optical sight and provision for a reconnaissance pod.

Current variant and operators

SF.260M: first flown as the F.250 civil prototype in July 1964, the SF.260M trainer has a 260-hp (194-kW) Avco Lycoming O-540 piston engine and began to enter service in the early 1970s with Belgium; Bolivia; Burma; Ecuador; Italy; Libya; Morocco; Philippines, Singapore; Thailand; Zaire and Zambia.

SF.260W Warrior: armed trainer and counter-insurgency version of the SF.260M sold to Brunei; Burma; the Comores; Dubai; Eire; Philippines; Somali Republic; Tunisia and Zimbabwe.

SF.260TP: version of the SF.260W with the same armament provisions but a 350-shp (261-kW) allison 250-B17C turboprop for greater performance and fuel economy. This version has been sold to Burundi, Dubai, Ghana, Haiti and Zimbabwe.

In common with other light-planes developed into useful military trainers, the SF.260 series has spawned a dedicated weapons trainer and counter-insurgency subvariant, the SF.260W Warrior, which is popular with countries operating the pure trainer.

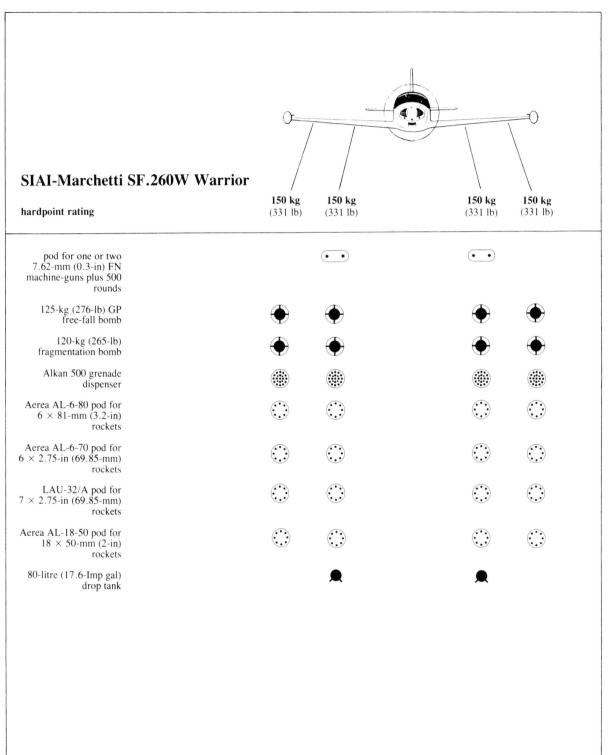

SIAI-Marchetti SF.260W Warrior

hardpoint rating	150 kg (331 lb)	150 kg (331 lb)	150 kg (331 lb)	150 kg (331 lb)
pod for one or two 7.62-mm (0.3-in) FN machine-guns plus 500 rounds	⊙		⊙	
125-kg (276-lb) GP free-fall bomb	●	●	●	●
120-kg (265-lb) fragmentation bomb	●	●	●	●
Alkan 500 grenade dispenser	◉	◉	◉	◉
Aerea AL-6-80 pod for 6 × 81-mm (3.2-in) rockets	◉	◉	◉	◉
Aerea AL-6-70 pod for 6 × 2.75-in (69.85-mm) rockets	◉	◉	◉	◉
LAU-32/A pod for 7 × 2.75-in (69.85-mm) rockets	◉	◉	◉	◉
Aerea AL-18-50 pod for 18 × 50-mm (2-in) rockets	◉	◉	◉	◉
80-litre (17.6-Imp gal) drop tank	●		●	

Sikorsky UH-60A Black Hawk

Type: 14-seat combat assault transport helicopter.
Internal armament: provision for one or two 7.62-mm (0.3-in) M60 machine-guns in the cabin doors.
Disposable armament: up to 1,600 lb (726 kg) of disposable stores carried on four hardpoints (two under each of the stub wings of the External Stores Support System).
Electronics and operational equipment: normal communication and navigation equipment, plus Dopper navigation; E-Systems/Loral APR-39 radar-warning receiver and Tracor M130 chaff/flare dispenser.

Current variants and operators
UH-60A Black Hawk: designed in the early 1970s as successor to the Bell UH-1 series as a combat assault transport able to lift a full 11-man infantry squad or a slung load of 8,000 lb (3631 kg), the Black Hawk first flew in October 1974 and has since entered widespread US Army service as a more capable if considerably more expensive companion to the long-lived UH-1. The Black Hawk was designed with provision for pintle-mounted machine-guns, but has since been developed into a more capable type with the weapons carried on the ESSS stub wings.
EH-60A Black Hawk: combat communications jamming version of the UH-60A fitted with the ESL ALQ-151 'Quick Fix II' airborne electronic warfare package.
HH-60A Night Hawk: combat search-and-rescue variant for the US Air Force with the airframe of the UH-60, the dynamic system of the SH-60; armament; armour; inflight-refuelling probe and avionics such as forward-looking infra-red; ground-mapping and terrain-avoidance/following radar; and cockpit and helmet displays.
SH-60B Seahawk: much developed version for the US Navy in the Light Airborne Multi-Purpose System Mk III role (providing destroyers and cruisers with an embarked helicopter for the utility, anti-submarine, anti-surface vessel, anti-missile and targeting information roles). The type is fully navalized, and powered by two 1,690-shp (1261-kW) General Electronic T700-GE-401 turboshafts rather than the 1,560-shp (1151-kW) T700-GE-700s of the UH-60A. The advanced avionics suite includes Texas Instruments APS-124 search radar; Texas Instruments ASQ-81 magnetic anomaly detection; chin-mounted electronic support measures pods; and a port-side pneumatic 25-round launcher array for 125 sonobuoys. The armament is two Mk 46 acoustic-homing anti-submarine torpedoes. The type has also been bought by Japan and Spain.
SH-60F Seahawk: improved version of the SH-60B with Bendix ASQ-13B dunking sonar instead of the sonobuoy system to provide anti-submarine capability for carrier battle groups.
S-70: export designation of the Black Hawk/Seahawk, produced in version similar to the UH-60A and SH-60B for sale to Australia and China, with further orders no doubt in the offing.

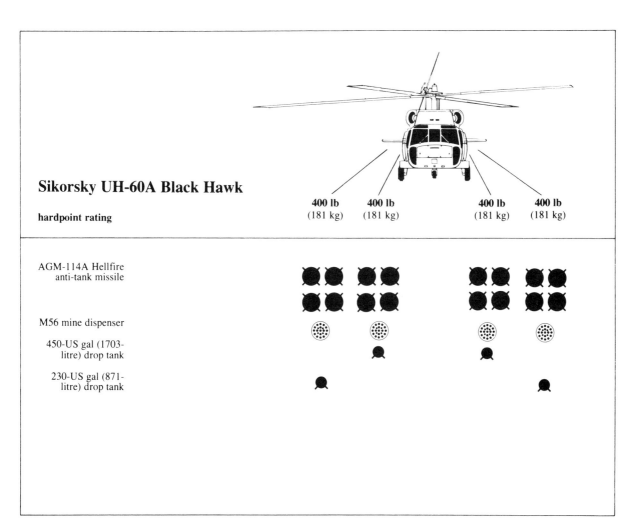

Sikorsky UH-60A Black Hawk

hardpoint rating

	400 lb (181 kg)	**400 lb** (181 kg)		**400 lb** (181 kg)	**400 lb** (181 kg)
AGM-114A Hellfire anti-tank missile	●●●●	●●●●		●●●●	●●●●
M56 mine dispenser	⊙	⊙		⊙	⊙
450-US gal (1703-litre) drop tank		●		●	
230-US gal (871-litre) drop tank	●				●

The SH-60B Seahawk is the capable ship-based Light Airborne Multi-Purpose system counterpart to the land-based UH-60A Black Hawk. Under the panel of 25 launch tubes for 125 sono-buoys is a Mk 46 lightweight anti-submarine torpedo. Other visible features are the APS-124 search radar with its radome under the fuselage and the ESM system with its antennae in box fairings under the nose.

249

Yugoslavia   Soko J-1 Jastreb

Type: single-seat light attack aircraft.

Internal armament: three 12.7-mm (0.5-in) Browning M3 machine-guns plus 135 rounds per gun in the nose.

Disposable armament: up to 800 kg (1,764 lb) of disposable stores carried on eight hardpoints (four under each wing).

Electronics and operational equipment: normal communication and navigation equipment, plus an optical sight.

Current variants and operators

G-2-A Galeb: though of Yugoslav indigenous design and production, the Galeb tandem two-seat trainer has many similarities to the Aermacchi M.B.326 series (including the Rolls-Royce/Bristol Viper non-afterburning turbojet) and first flew in May 1961. The type can be used for counter-insurgency as well as weapons training with its armament of two 12.7-mm (0.5-in) machine-guns (plus 80 rounds per gun), two 100- or 50-kg (220- or 110-lb) bombs and four 5-mm (2.17-in) or two 127-mm (5-in) rockets.

G-2-AE Galeb: export version of the G-2-A for Libya and Zambia.

J-1 Jastreb: single-seat light attack aircraft for Yugoslavia, derived from the G-2A with local strengthening and other modifications.

J-1-E Jastreb: export version of the J-1 with better avionics standards, sold to Libya and Zambia.

RJ-1 Jastreb: tactical reconnaissance version of the J-1 with cameras in the lower fuselage and in the forward portion of the tiptanks.

RJ-1-E Jastreb: export version of the RJ-1.

TJ-1 Jastreb: combat-capable two-seat conversion trainer.

This shot of the Rolls-Royce Viper-powered Soko G-2-A Galeb clearly shows the mounting of the type's only internal armament (M. Hooks).

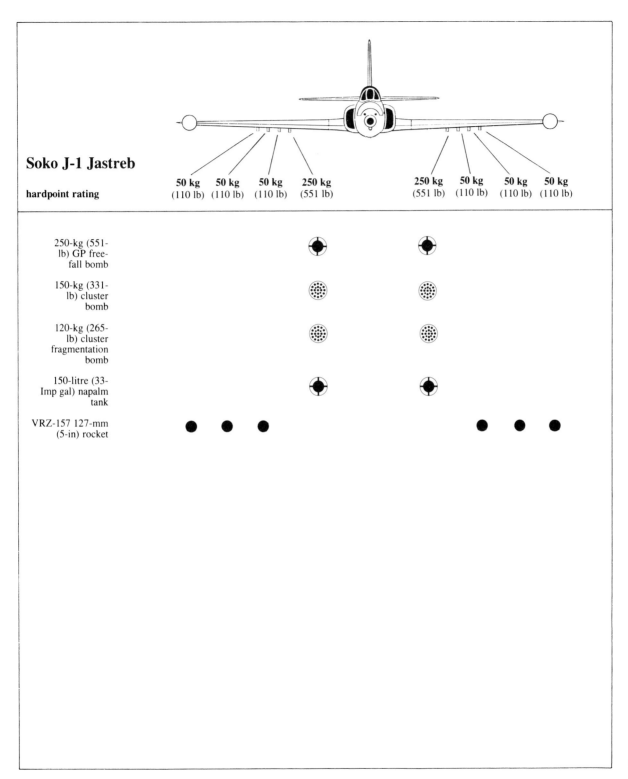

Soko J-1 Jastreb

hardpoint rating

	50 kg (110 lb)	50 kg (110 lb)	50 kg (110 lb)	250 kg (551 lb)	250 kg (551 lb)	50 kg (110 lb)	50 kg (110 lb)	50 kg (110 lb)
250-kg (551-lb) GP free-fall bomb				◉	◉			
150-kg (331-lb) cluster bomb				◉	◉			
120-kg (265-lb) cluster fragmentation bomb				◉	◉			
150-litre (33-Imp gal) napalm tank				◉	◉			
VRZ-157 127-mm (5-in) rocket	●	●	●			●	●	●

251

Soko G-4 Super Galeb

Type: two-seat trainer and light attack aircraft.

Internal armament: provision for one 23-mm GSh-23L twin-barrel cannon plus 200 rounds in a GP-9 belly pack.

Disposable armament: up to 1200 kg (2,646 lb) of disposable stores carried on four hardpoints (two under each wing).

Electronics and operational equipment: normal communication and navigation equipment, plus an optical sight and other items, and provision for a reconnaissance pod with four cameras and an infra-red linescanner.

Current variant and operator

G-4 Super Galeb: resembling the BAe Hawk in appearance and role, the Super Galeb is powered by a turbojet rather than a turbofan: the type first flew in July 1978 and is used only by Yugoslavia.

The Super Galeb is an attractive and versatile machine not very different from the BAe Hawk.

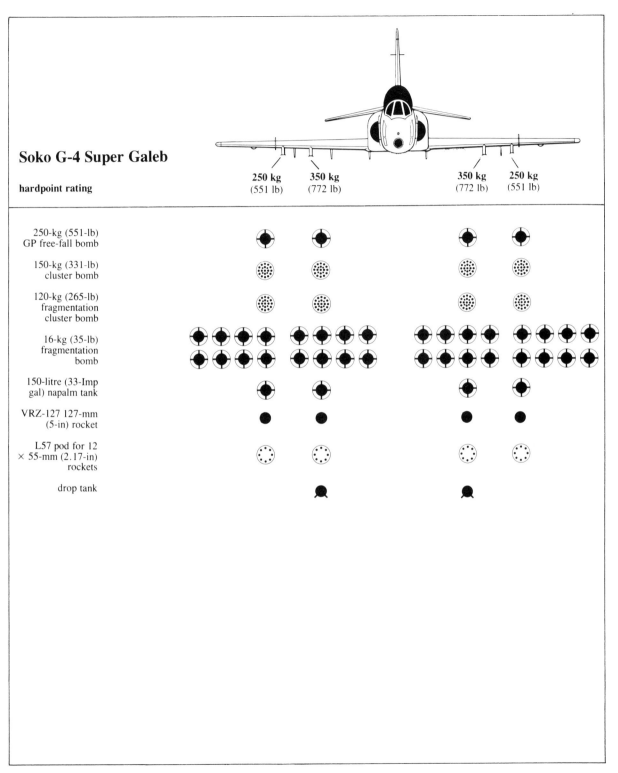

Soko G-4 Super Galeb

hardpoint rating

	250 kg (551 lb)	350 kg (772 lb)	350 kg (772 lb)	250 kg (551 lb)

250-kg (551-lb) GP free-fall bomb	●	●	●	●
150-kg (331-lb) cluster bomb	●	●	●	●
120-kg (265-lb) fragmentation cluster bomb	●	●	●	●
16-kg (35-lb) fragmentation bomb	●●●● ●●●●	●●●● ●●●●	●●●● ●●●●	●●●● ●●●●
150-litre (33-Imp gal) napalm tank	●	●	●	●
VRZ-127 127-mm (5-in) rocket	●	●	●	●
L57 pod for 12 × 55-mm (2.17-in) rockets	●	●	●	●
drop tank		●	●	

Soko Orao-B/CNIAR IAR-93B

**Yugoslavia/
Romania**

Type: single-seat close support, attack and reconnaissance aircraft.

Internal armament: two GSh-23L twin-barrel cannon, each with 200 rounds, in the underside of the forward fuselage.

Disposable armament: up to 2500 kg (5,511 lb) of disposable stores carried on five hardpoints (one under the fuselage and two under each wing).

Electronics and operational equipment: normal communication and navigation equipment, plus a head-up display and radar-warning receiver, and provision for a reconnaissance pod.

Current variants and operators

Orao-A/IAR-93A: a programme shared equally between Soviet-bloc Romania and non-aligned Yugoslavia, this aircraft is known to the former as the IAR-93 and to the latter as the Orao, the first prototype from each country flying simultaneously in October 1974. The type is available in single-seat combat and twin-seat conversion trainer variants, and this initial model is powered by two 4,000-lb (1814-kg) Rolls-Royce Viper Mk 632-41 non-afterburning turbojets. The type was produced in limited numbers for Romania and Yugoslavia.

This Jurom Orao is a single-seat Mach 1 capable fighter able to carry a variety of external stores.

Orao-B/IAR-93B: improved main-production model, again for Romania and Yugoslavia, with 5,000-lb (2268-kg) Viper Mk 633-47 afterburning turbojets.

Soko Orao-B/CNIAR IAR-93B

hardpoint rating

	500 kg (1,102 lb)	500 kg (1,102 lb)	500 kg (1,102 lb)	500 kg (1,102 lb)	500 kg (1,102 lb)
500-kg (1,102-lb) GP free-fall bomb	●	●	●	●	●
250-kg (551-lb) GP free-fall bomb	●	●	●	●	●
100-kg (220-lb) GP free-fall bomb	●● ●	●●	●●	●● ●	●●
150-kg (331-lb) cluster bomb	●●	●●	●●	●●	●●
120-kg (265-lb) fragmentation cluster bomb	●● ●	●● ●	●● ●	●● ●	●● ●
150-litre (33-Imp gal) napalm bomb	●	●	●	●	●
pod for 4 × VRZ-127 127-mm (5-in) rockets	●	●		●	●
UB-16-57 pod for 16 × 55-mm (2.17-in) rockets	●	●		●	●
L57 pod for 12 × 55-mm (2.17-in) rockets	●	●		●	●
540-litre (119-Imp gal) drop tank		●	●	●	

Sukhoi Su-7BMK 'Fitter-A'

Type: single-seat ground-attack fighter.

Internal armament: two 30-mm 2NR-30 cannon plus 70 rounds per gun in the wing roots.

Disposable armament: up to 1000 kg (2,205 lb) of disposable stores carried on six hardpoints (two under the fuselage and two under each wing). The nominal load is 2500 kg (5,511 lb), but the two under-fuselage hardpoints are invariably used for drop tanks, limiting disposable load to the figure above.

Electronics and operational equipment: normal communication and navigation equipment, plus SRD-5M 'High Fix' ranging radar; ASP-5F gyro sight; 'Odd Rods' IFF; Sirena 3 radar-warning receiver and provision for podded electronic countermeasures systems. Operators such as Egypt and India are improving the avionics with Western items such as a head-up display and superior electronic warfare equipment.

Current variants and operators

Su-7B 'Fitter-A': first flown in late 1955 as the S-1 research aircraft, the Su-7 was designed as a fighter but found its metier as an immensely capable ground-attack aircraft, although limited by very short range. Powered by the 9000-kg (19,841-lb) Lyulka AL-7F afterburning turbojet, the Su-7B was the first production model and entered service in 1959 with an armament of two NR-30 30-mm cannon and up to 1000 kg (2,205 lb) of disposable stores on two underwing hardpoints, the two under-fuselage stations being reserved for 600-litre (132-Imp gal) drop tanks. The Su-7 series is in service with Afghanistan; Algeria; Czechoslovakia; Egypt; Hungary; India; Iraq; North Korea; Poland; Romania; Syria; USSR and Vietnam.

Su-7BKL 'Fitter-A': version optimized for soft-field operations with skids outboard of the wheels on the longer-stroke main landing gear units, a larger nose wheel and twin braking parachutes. The type also introduced two additional underwing hardpoints.

The Su-7BMK 'Fitter-A' is always characterized as woefully deficient in the payload and range parameters of its capabilities, but is a comparatively tractable aircraft of immense strength and phenomenal weapon-delivery accuracy. Such an aircraft is seen here with a pair of RATO units under the rear fuselage.

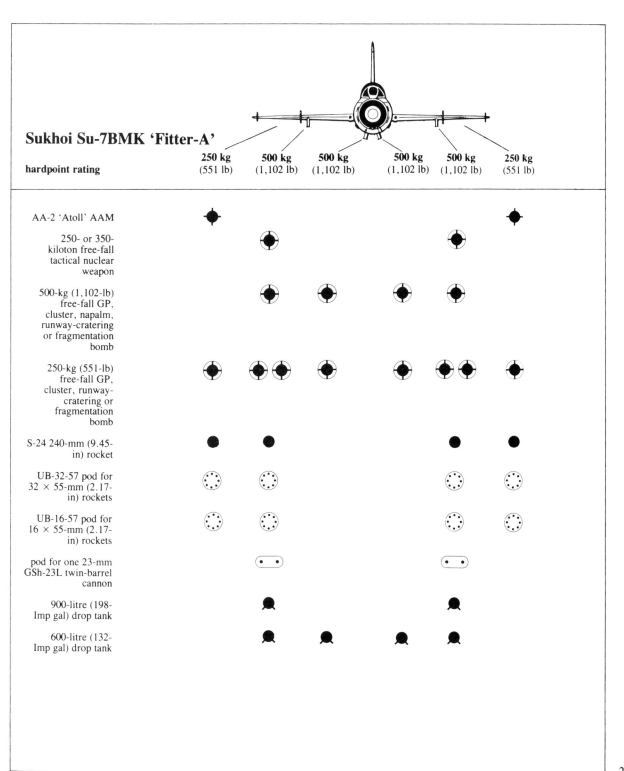

Sukhoi Su-7BMK 'Fitter-A'

hardpoint rating	250 kg (551 lb)	500 kg (1,102 lb)	500 kg (1,102 lb)	500 kg (1,102 lb)	500 kg (1,102 lb)	250 kg (551 lb)
AA-2 'Atoll' AAM	●					●
250- or 350-kiloton free-fall tactical nuclear weapon		●			●	
500-kg (1,102-lb) free-fall GP, cluster, napalm, runway-cratering or fragmentation bomb		●	●	●	●	
250-kg (551-lb) free-fall GP, cluster, runway-cratering or fragmentation bomb	●	● ●	●		● ●	●
S-24 240-mm (9.45-in) rocket	●	●			●	●
UB-32-57 pod for 32 × 55-mm (2.17-in) rockets	⊙	⊙			⊙	⊙
UB-16-57 pod for 16 × 55-mm (2.17-in) rockets	⊙	⊙			⊙	⊙
pod for one 23-mm GSh-23L twin-barrel cannon		⬭			⬭	
900-litre (198-Imp gal) drop tank		●			●	
600-litre (132-Imp gal) drop tank		●	●	●	●	

Su-7BM 'Fitter-A': improved version with higher-velocity 2NR-30 cannon, the 9600-kg (21,164-lb) Lyulka AL-7F-1 engine and a ballistic computer served by air-data sensors on a nose-mounted probe.

Su-7BMK 'Fitter-A': improved Su-7BM with Sirena 3 non-directional radar-warning receiver and two additional (but optional and rarely used) underwing hardpoints aft of the main landing gear legs for a nominal weapon load of 4000 kg (8,818 lb).

Su-7U 'Moujik': two-seat operational conversion and proficiency trainer series, produced in parallel with the main single-seat series and thus in service as the Su-7U, Su-7UKL, Su-7UM, and Su-7UKM.

Sukhoi Su-17M 'Fitter-C'

Type: single-seat variable-geometry ground-attack fighter.

Internal armament: two 30-mm 2NR-30 cannon plus 70 rounds per gun in the wing roots.

Disposable armament: up to 5000 kg (11,023 lb) of disposable stores carried on eight hardpoints (two tandem pairs under the fuselage, one under each wing glove and one under the fence at each wing pivot point).

Electronics and operational equipment: normal communication and navigation equipment, plus SRD-5M 'High Fix' ranging radar, ASP-5ND fire-control system with appropriate air-data sensors, 'Odd Rods' IFF, Sirena 3 radar-warning receiver and other electronic countermeasures systems.

Current variants and operators

Su-17M 'Fitter-C': first flown as the Su-7IG prototype in 1966, the Su-17M is a simple yet highly successful development of the Su-7BMK with pivoting outer-wing panels to overcome the Su-7's limitations in field performance and payload/range balance, and fitted with the 11200-kg (24,692-lb) Lyulka AL-21F-3 afterburning turbojet (plus additional internal fuel capacity) and more hardpoints to improve weapons-carrying capability. The Su-17 series is used exclusively by the USSR.

Su-20 'Fitter-C': version of the Su-17 supplied from 1979 to Warsaw Pact and more client countries (Algeria, Czechoslovakia, Iraq, Poland and Vietnam) and possessing less capable avionics than Soviet aircraft.

Su-20M 'Fitter-D': improved version of the Su-17, introduced in 1976 with a lengthened forward fuselage for more comprehensive avionics, which include a laser ranger and marked-target seeker in the inlet centrebody, terrain-avoidance or terrain-following radar and Doppler navigation in an under-nose fairing, an improved radar-warning receiver, an internal chaff dispenser, and a head-up display. This is the USSR's most

The Su-7 series of tactical fighters suffers insuperable payload/range problems as a consequence of its AL-7 turbojet's thirst, and an interesting response to this problem is the Su-17/20 series with variable geometry outer panels to the wings, which improve field performance and range while also permitting greater loads on four under-fuselage (two tandem pairs), two glove and two hinge fence hardpoints. This appears to be a 'Fitter-D' with terrain-avoidance radar under the nose.

important version and can be used to deliver a pair of tactical nuclear weapons for battlefield use.

Su-17U 'Fitter-E': two-seat operational conversion and proficiency trainer based on the Su-17M, but with a down-tilted forward fuselage for better fields of vision and only one 30-mm cannon, though retaining the eight hardpoints of the single-seaters.

Su-22 'Fitter-F': 1977 export derivative of the Su-17M for Angola and Peru, and having inferior avionics standards. The variant introduced extra vertical tail area through an enlargement of the dorsal fin and features a larger dorsal spine for greater internal volume (largely for fuel and avionics) and reduced supersonic drag. The type is powered by an 11500-kg (25,353-lb) Tumansky R-29B afterburning turbojet, this engine's lower weight offering improvements in payload and range.

Su-22U 'Fitter-G': two-seat operational conversion and proficiency trainer based on the Su-20U but fitted with a small ventral fin, the larger dorsal spine and the laser ranger and marked-target seeker in the inlet centrebody.

Su-20M 'Fitter-H': derivative of the Su-17M 'Fitter-C' with the aerodynamic improvements of the 'Fitter-G' (and the down-tilted forward fuselage), more modern avionics and provision for two additional underwing hardpoints.

Su-22BKL 'Fitter-J': version of the 'Fitter-H' with the R-29B turbojet and equipped to carry AA-2 'Atoll' and/or AA-2-2 'Advanced Atoll' air-to-air missiles. This type is flown by Libya, North Yemen and South Yemen.

Su-20 'Fitter-K': version of the basic Su-17 with the cooling air inlet in the base of the fin extended forward of the leading edge. This model is operated by the USSR and Poland and possibly other Warsaw Pact countries.

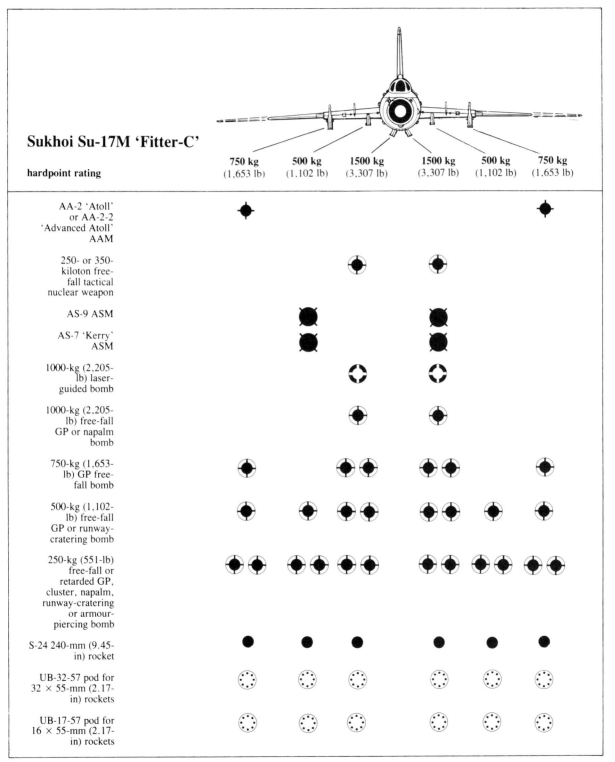

Sukhoi Su-17M 'Fitter-C'

hardpoint rating	750 kg (1,653 lb)	500 kg (1,102 lb)	1500 kg (3,307 lb)	1500 kg (3,307 lb)	500 kg (1,102 lb)	750 kg (1,653 lb)
AA-2 'Atoll' or AA-2-2 'Advanced Atoll' AAM	●					●
250- or 350-kiloton free-fall tactical nuclear weapon		●		●		
AS-9 ASM		●		●		
AS-7 'Kerry' ASM		●		●		
1000-kg (2,205-lb) laser-guided bomb			◐	◐		
1000-kg (2,205-lb) free-fall GP or napalm bomb		●		●		
750-kg (1,653-lb) GP free-fall bomb	●		● ●	● ●		●
500-kg (1,102-lb) free-fall GP or runway-cratering bomb	●	●	● ●	● ●	●	●
250-kg (551-lb) free-fall or retarded GP, cluster, napalm, runway-cratering or armour-piercing bomb	● ●	● ●	● ●	● ●	● ●	● ●
S-24 240-mm (9.45-in) rocket	●	●	●	●	●	●
UB-32-57 pod for 32 × 55-mm (2.17-in) rockets	⊛	⊛	⊛	⊛	⊛	⊛
UB-17-57 pod for 16 × 55-mm (2.17-in) rockets	⊛	⊛	⊛	⊛	⊛	⊛

261

Sukhoi Su-21 'Flagon-F'

Type: single-seat all-weather interceptor.

Internal armament: none.

Disposable armament: up to 1500 kg (3,307 lb) of disposable stores carried on six hardpoints (two under the fuselage and two under each wing).

Electronics and operational equipment: normal communication and navigation equipment, plus 'Improved Skip Spin' or 'Twin Scan' interception radar used in conjunction with a visual augmentation system for target identification at long range, 'Odd Rods' IFF, Sirena 3 radar-warning receiver, and (probably) several electronic countermeasures systems.

Current variants and operator

Su-15U 'Flagon-C': the Su-15 series first flew in prototype from during 1965, and entered service as the Su-15 'Flagon-A' dedicated interceptor of high performance but limited agility, within the Soviet ground-controlled interception system. The oldest version in service is the Su-15 'Flagon-C' two-seat conversion and proficiency trainer based on the 'Flagon-A' and using the same powerplant of two 10000-kg (22,046-lb) Lyulka AL-21F-1 afterburning turbojets.

Su-21 'Flagon-E': second-generation interceptor introduced in about 1973 and based on the Su-15 'Flagon-D' definitive first-generation fighter with wings of compound sweep, but powered by two 11200-kg (24,691-lb) PL-21F-3 afterburning turbojets and featuring much updated electronics combined with powerful radar of limited performance.

Su-21 'Flagon-F': ultimate development with an ogival rather than conical radome for aerodynamic reasons. The type is generally seen with AA-8 'Aphid' short-range air-to-air missiles partnering the decidely obsolescent AA-3 'Anab' weapons first fielded on the Su-15.

Su-21 'Flagon-G': two-seat operational conversion and proficiency trainer.

Originally thought to be the Su-15 in Soviet service, the 'Flagon-F' interceptor is now known to be designated Su-21, and is here seen with AA-3 'Anab' AAMs, the type with the rounded nose being the IR-homing variety and that with the pointed nose using semi-active radar homing matched to the continuous-wave illumination provided by the 'Improved Skip Spin' nose radar of the launch aircraft.

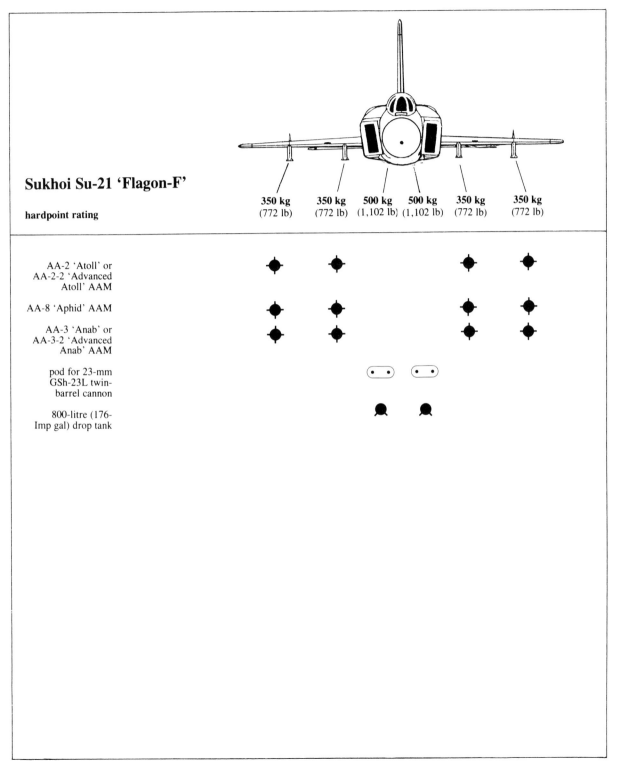

Sukhoi Su-21 'Flagon-F'

hardpoint rating

	350 kg (772 lb)	350 kg (772 lb)	500 kg (1,102 lb)	500 kg (1,102 lb)	350 kg (772 lb)	350 kg (772 lb)
AA-2 'Atoll' or AA-2-2 'Advanced Atoll' AAM	●	●			●	●
AA-8 'Aphid' AAM	●	●			●	●
AA-3 'Anab' or AA-3-2 'Advanced Anab' AAM	●	●			●	●
pod for 23-mm GSh-23L twin-barrel cannon			⊙⊙	⊙⊙		
800-litre (176-Imp gal) drop tank			♠	♠		

Sukhoi Su-24 'Fencer-C'

Type: two-seat variable-geometry all-weather attack and interdiction aircraft.

Internal armament: one 30-mm six-barrel cannon plus ? rounds in the port underfuselage fairing, and possibly one 30-mm single-barrel cannon plus rounds in the starboard fairing.

Disposable armament: up to 11000 kg (24,250 lb) of disposable stores carried on eight hardpoints (four under the fuselage as one tandem pair and two lateral units, one under each wing glove, and one under each swivelling outer-wing panel).

Electronics and operational equipment: normal communication and navigation equipment, plus an unknown type of pulse-Doppler multi-mode radar; twin terrain-following radars; head-up display; advanced fire-control system with appropriate air-data sensors and computer system; radar and infra-red warning receivers; internal electronic and infra-red active/passive countermeasures; podded electronic countermeasures systems; Doppler navigation and (probably) forward-looking infra-red; electro-optical target-acquisition system; continuous-wave illuminator and other systems associated with 'smart' weapons.

Current variants and operator

Su-24 'Fencer-A': used only by the USSR, the 'Fencer' first flew in 1970 and is the Soviet counterpart to the General Dynamics F-111. The 'Fencer-A' entered service in 1974 and is a formidable medium-range interdiction type offering a good combination of range, payload, comparatively buffet-free low-level penetration at high speeds and advanced sensor weapon-delivery systems. The type can carry two free-fall nuclear weapons in the theatre nuclear role.

Su-24 'Fencer-B': derivative with a braking parachute bullet fairing at the base of the rudder.

Su-24 'Fencer-C': introduced in 1981, this variant is based on the 'Fencer-B' but has a radar-warning receiver system with antennae on the fin and on the inlet lips, a revised air-data probe, an underfuselage aerial (possibly for mid-course missile-update purposes) and modified tailpipes, the last suggesting that the variant is possibly powered by two uprated AL-21F-3 turbojets in place of the earlier models' AL-21F-1 engines.

Su-24 'Fencer-D': variant similar to the 'Fencer-C' but with a retractable rather than fixed inflight-refuelling probe, a broader-chord lower portion to the fin, the nose section forward of the cockpit lengthened by 0.75 m (29.5 in) possibly indicating a new radar type, glove pylons integral with the large overwing fences, and an undernose blister window/fairing.

Su-24 'Fencer-E': electronic warfare variant designed to supplant the Yak-28 'Brewer-E' in the escort and stand-off roles.

Su-24 'Fencer-F': reconnaissance variant with internal side-looking airborne radar, infra-red linescanner and cameras.

The Su-24 'Fencer' is one of the USSR's most important combat aircraft, this variable-geometry inter-diction aircraft possessing excellent avionics and being able to deliver substantial nuclear or conventional war-loads over most of Western Europe without refuelling. Visible in this rear view are the two swivelling underwing hardpoints (complemented by four beneath the fuselage and two glove fixed hard-points), the rearward-facing infra-red warning receiver just above the rudder, and the rearward-facing antenna of the radar-warning receiver system in a small bullet just below the rudder and above the fairing for the braking parachute.

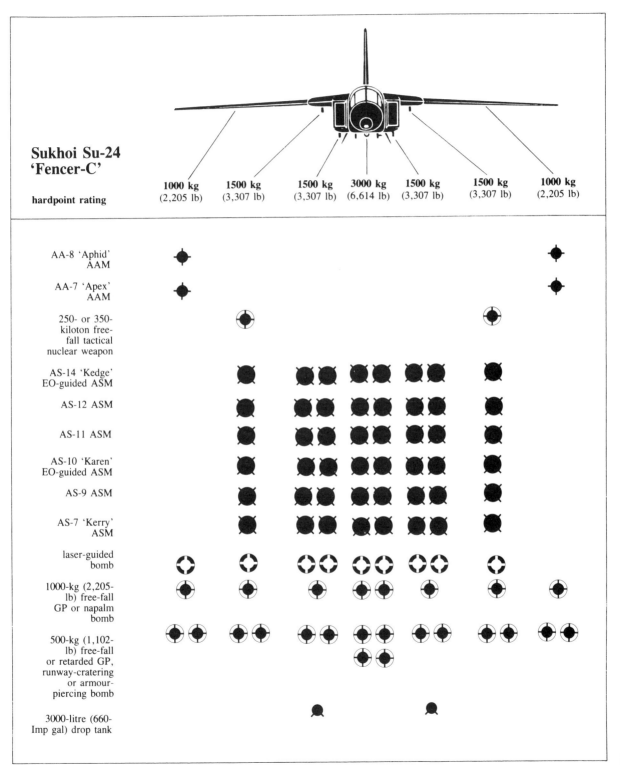

Sukhoi Su-24 'Fencer-C'

hardpoint rating

	1000 kg (2,205 lb)	1500 kg (3,307 lb)	1500 kg (3,307 lb)	3000 kg (6,614 lb)	1500 kg (3,307 lb)	1500 kg (3,307 lb)	1000 kg (2,205 lb)
AA-8 'Aphid' AAM	●						●
AA-7 'Apex' AAM	●						●
250- or 350-kiloton free-fall tactical nuclear weapon		●				●	
AS-14 'Kedge' EO-guided ASM		●	● ●	● ●	● ●	●	
AS-12 ASM		●	● ●	● ●	● ●	●	
AS-11 ASM		●	● ●	● ●	● ●	●	
AS-10 'Karen' EO-guided ASM		●	● ●	● ●	● ●	●	
AS-9 ASM		●	● ●	● ●	● ●	●	
AS-7 'Kerry' ASM		●	● ●	● ●	● ●	●	
laser-guided bomb	●	●	● ●	● ●	● ●	●	
1000-kg (2,205-lb) free-fall GP or napalm bomb	●	●	●	● ●	●	●	●
500-kg (1,102-lb) free-fall or retarded GP, runway-cratering or armour-piercing bomb	● ●	● ●	● ●	● ● ● ●	● ●	● ●	● ●
3000-litre (660-Imp gal) drop tank			●		●		

265

Sukhoi Su-25 'Frogfoot-B'

Type: single-seat close support aircraft.

Internal armament: one 30-mm multi-barrel rotary cannon plus ? rounds in the underside of the nose.

Disposable armament: up to 4000 kg (8,818 lb) of disposable stores carried on 10 hardpoints (five under each wing).

Electronics and operational equipment: normal communication and navigation equipment; radar and infra-red warning systems and (probably) terrain-avoidance radar; forward-looking infra-red; laser ranger and marked-target seeker and other target acquisition/designation systems, plus podded electronic countermeasures.

Current variants and operators

Su-25 'Frogfoot-A': the USSR was slow to develop an aircraft fulfilling the same basic role as the US Air Force's Fairchild Republic A-10A, but in the late 1970s first flew a close-support machine resembling the Northrop A-9, the losing competitor in the USAF'S AX competition won by the A-10. This offers less agility and loiter time than the A-10, but in turn provides greater performance over the battlefield. The initial 'Frogfoot-A' was used in limited numbers in Afghanistan to prove the basic concept, and was probably armed with a 23-mm cannon in additional to its load of disposable stores.

Su-25 'Frogfoot-B': definitive aircraft with enhanced countermeasures, detail modifications and a 30-mm internal cannon. The type is in service with Czechoslovakia and East Germany as well as the USSR.

The Su-25 'Frogfoot' is another new Soviet type, clearly influenced by the US development of a battlefield support type but resembling the loser in the US Air Force's A-X competition, the Northrop A-9, rather than the winner, the A-10A. The Soviet aircraft possesses higher performance than its US opposite number, but still provides considerable scope for offensive firepower with ten underwing hardpoints.

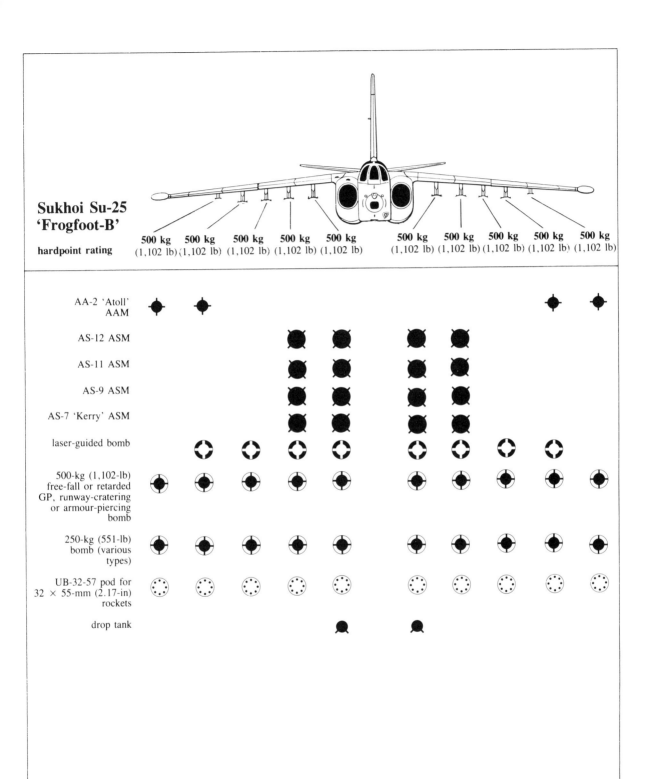

Sukhoi Su-25 'Frogfoot-B'

hardpoint rating

500 kg (1,102 lb)	500 kg (1,102 lb)	500 kg (1,102 lb)	500 kg (1,102 lb)	500 kg (1,102 lb)	500 kg (1,102 lb)	500 kg (1,102 lb)	500 kg (1,102 lb)	500 kg (1,102 lb)	500 kg (1,102 lb)

AA-2 'Atoll' AAM

AS-12 ASM

AS-11 ASM

AS-9 ASM

AS-7 'Kerry' ASM

laser-guided bomb

500-kg (1,102-lb) free-fall or retarded GP, runway-cratering or armour-piercing bomb

250-kg (551-lb) bomb (various types)

UB-32-57 pod for 32 × 55-mm (2.17-in) rockets

drop tank

Sukhoi Su-27 'Flanker'

Type: single-seat multi-role interceptor and air-superiority figher.

Internal armament: probably one 30-mm six barrel cannon plus ? rounds in the lower fuselage.

Disposable armament: up to 6000 kg (13,228 lb) of disposable stores carried on eight hardpoints (two under the fuselage and three under each wing).

Electronics and operational equipment: normal communication and navigation equipment, plus pulse-Doppler radar (with search and search-while-track modes and good look-down capability) used in conjunction with a visual augmentation system and advanced fire-control system; infra-red search and tracking system; head-up display; central computer; air-data system; radar-warning receiver and advanced electronic countermeasures, plus provision for a reconnaissance pod.

Current variant and operators

Su-27 'Flanker': an immensely powerful and successful fighter with good capabilities against targets flying well below it, the 'Flanker' was designed in response to the US Air Force's McDonnell Douglas F-15, and began to enter service in 1985 with the USSR, aircraft later also being supplied to Syria. The 'Flanker' offers conclusive proof that the Soviet air force has entered a new level of capability, the radar being credited with a search range of 240 km (150 miles) and a tracking range of 185 km (115 miles) which, with look-down/shoot-down missiles matched to the radar's capabilities offers a potent threat to low-level intruders.

An artist's impression of the Su-27 'Flanker' armed with AA-10 and AA-8 'Aphid' air-to-air missiles, offering a potent response to low-level intruders.

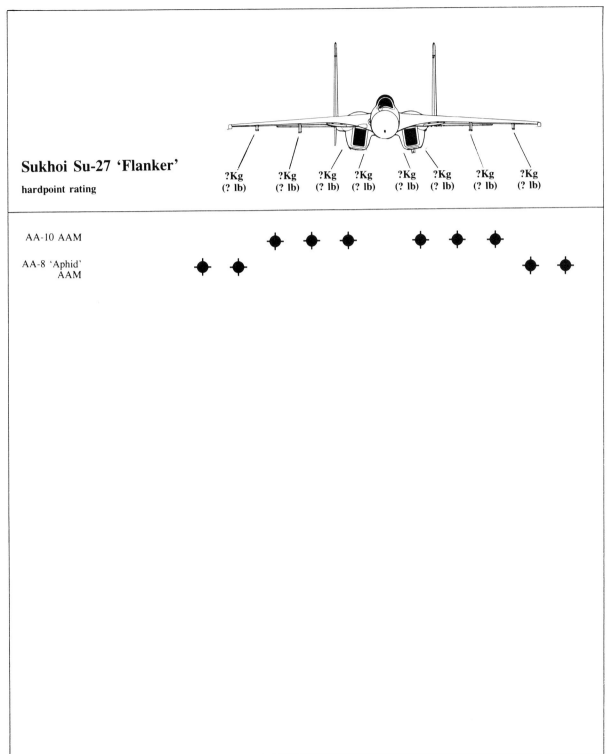

Sukhoi Su-27 'Flanker'
hardpoint rating

?Kg (? lb) ?Kg (? lb) ?Kg (? lb) ?Kg (? lb) ?Kg (? lb) ?Kg (? lb) ?Kg (? lb) ?Kg (? lb)

AA-10 AAM

AA-8 'Aphid'
AAM

Tupolev Tu-16 'Badger-G'

Type: six-seat missile-carrier.

Internal armament: seven 23-mm cannon plus rounds, located as a single fixed gun in the starboard side of the nose, two guns in a manned rear turret and two guns each in remotely-controlled ventral and dorsal barbettes.

Disposable armament: up to 10000 kg (22,046 lb) of disposable stores carried on two hardpoints (one under each wing).

Electronics and operational equipment: normal communication and navigation equipment, plus 'Short Horn' navigation and bombing radar, 'Bee Hind' tail-warning and gunlaying radar, A-322Z Doppler navigation, and chaff/flare dispensers.

Current variants and operators

Tu-16 'Badger-A': introduced as a strategic bomber to parallel the US Air Force's Boeing B-47, the Tu-16 first flew as a prototype in 1952 and began to enter service in 1954. Despite their age many of these fine aircraft remain in valuable service, though the 'Badger-A' has generally been converted from a bomber (with Argon navigation/attack radar and some 9000 kg/19,841 lb of stores, including one or two 5-, 20- or 50-megaton free-fall thermonuclear weapons, carried in a 6.5-m/21.33-ft lower-fuselage weapons bay) into an inflight-refuelling tanker with additional fuel tanks in the weapons bay and a single hose unit trailed from the starboard wingtip. The 'Badger-A' is also flown by Iraq and Libya.

Tu-16 'Badger-B': anti-shipping model with two underwing hardpoints for a pair of AS-1 'Kennel' missiles, Komet III target-acquisition radar, A-322Z Doppler navigation and other avionics modifications. The 'Kennel' is now out of service and the aircraft are used in the conventional role.

Tu-16 'Badger-C': anti-shipping model introduced in 1961 with the weapons bay revised to allow accommodation of one megaton-yield AS-2 'Kipper' missile. This variant has a modified nose (without fixed gun or bomb-aimer's position) incorporating 'Puff Ball' target-acquisition radar and the A-329Z missile-guidance system; the type is now armed with one or two 350-kiloton AS-6 'Kingfish' missiles carried under the wings as the 'Badger-C [Modified]'.

Tu-16 'Badger-D': maritime multi-sensor reconnaissance and electronic intelligence model based on the 'Badger-C' but lacking the missile-guidance system and any offensive capability. The type has a longitudinal row of three blister fairings under the fuselage.

Tu-16 'Badger-E': designation of 'Badger-A' aircraft rebuilt for optical reconnaissance with pallet-mounted systems in the erstwhile weapons bay.

Tu-16 'Badger-F': derivative of the 'Badger-E' with pylon-mounted electronic intelligence pods under the wings.

Tu-16 'Badger-G': major type in the anti-ship and stand-off strike roles, produced by converting 'Badger-B' aircraft with an armament of two AS-5 'Kelt' missiles (now replaced by one or two AS-6 'Kingfish' missiles in the 'Badger-C [Modified]' subvariant) supported by 'Short Horn' navigation and attack radar plus other avionics changes. The type is also used by Egypt in a form with less capable avionics.

Tu-16 'Badger-H': electronic warfare model based on the 'Badger-A' with the weapons bay devoted to multi-waveband receiving, analysis and jamming equipment, supported by a large chaff cutter/dispenser in the rear fuselage.

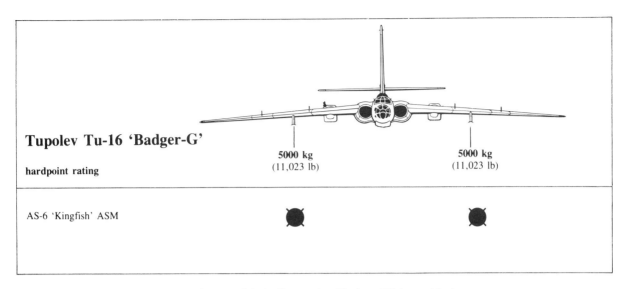

Tupolev Tu-16 'Badger-G'

hardpoint rating

	5000 kg (11,023 lb)	5000 kg (11,023 lb)
AS-6 'Kingfish' ASM	●	●

Tu-16 'Badger-J': electronic warfare model similar to the 'Badger-H' but with the dispensers replaced by more receiving, analysis and jamming equipment. This variant is distinguishable by its large ventral canoe fairing.

Tu-16 'Badger-K': electronic intelligence model for long-range missions with additional fuel and a greater number of aerials.

Tu-16 'Badger-L': variant with thimble nose radome and a new chin radar characterized by a rotary strip antenna in a flat dish radome.

Xian H-6: unlicensed Chinese copy of the Tu-16 'Badger-A' used in the strategic role with one or two free-fall thermonuclear weapons.

Xian H-6D: Chinese equivalent of 'Badger-C/G' with two underwing C-601 anti-ship missiles.

Left *The 'Badger-G (Mod)' is an advanced anti-ship version of the Tu-16 series, seen here with an AS-6 'Kingfish' missile under the starboard wing.*

Below *The Tu-16 is powered by two huge root-mounted turbojets, and the basic 'Badger-A' bomber has remained in useful service for many years, surplus airframes slowly being revised for the inflight-refuelling tanker and reconnaissance roles.*

Tupolev Tu-22 'Blinder-B'

Type: three-seat missile-carrier.

Internal armament: one 23-mm NR-23 cannon plus rounds in a remotely-controlled tail barbette.

Disposable armament: up to 6000 kg (13,228 lb) of disposable stores carried under the fuselage.

Electronics and operational equipment: normal communication and navigation equipment, plus 'Down Beat' navigation and target-acquisition radar, 'Fan Tail' rear-warning and gunlaying radar, Sirena 3 radar-warning receiver, 'Odd Rods' IFF and electronic and infra-red active/passive countermeasures.

Current variants and operators

Tu-22 'Blinder-A': first flown in 1959, the 'Blinder' was for its time an advanced aircraft, designed for long-range strategic bombing with supersonic dash capability, but in the event proved too short of range for all but the theatre role. The 'Blinder-A' has a lower-fuselage weapons bay for some 10000 kg (22,046 lb) of disposable stores (including one 5-, 20- or 50-megaton free-fall thermonuclear weapon), and its avionics fit includes 'Short Horn' navigation and boming radar. The type is operated by Iraq, Libya and the USSR.

Tu-22 'Blinder-B': missile-carrier model with provision for one 200-kiloton AS-4 'Kitchen' missile semi-recessed under the fuselage.

Tu-22 'Blinder-C': multi-sensor reconnaissance model with six or seven cameras, side-looking airborne radar. infra-red linescan, electronic intelligence and electronic countermeasures.

Tu-22 'Blinder-D': operational conversion model with an instructor's cockpit added behind and above the standard cockpit.

The Tu-22 proved a disappointment in operational service, largely as a result of its limited range, and the 'Blinder-A' version of this supersonic bomber has been released for export to countries such as Libya, one of whose conventional bombers is illustrated here. The white fairing below the engine nozzles covers the antenna for the 'Fan Tail' radar used to direct the rear armament of one 23-mm cannon, which can also be used to dispense chaff.

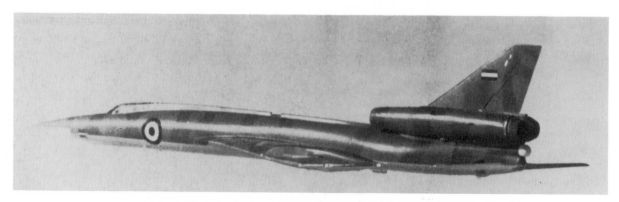

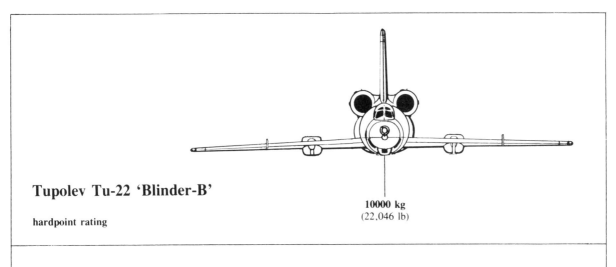

Tupolev Tu-22 'Blinder-B'

hardpoint rating

10000 kg
(22,046 lb)

AS-4 'Kitchen' ASM

Tupolev Tu-26 'Backfire-B'

Type: four-seat variable-geometry operational/strategic bomber.

Internal armament: two 23-mm NR-23 cannon plus rounds in a remotely-controlled tail barbette.

Disposable armament: up to 12000 kg (26,455 lb) of disposable stores carried in a presumed lower-fuselage weapons bay, on two hardpoints (one under each wing glove) and on two triple tandem racks (one under each inlet duct).

Electronics and operational equipment: normal communication and navigation equipment, plus 'Down Beat' navigation and bombing radar, 'Fan Tail' rear-warning and gunlaying radar, 'Odd Rods' IFF, Sirena 3 radar-warning receiver and a wide assortment of internal electronic countermeasures.

Current variants and operator

Tu-22M 'Backfire-A': this initial model was derived from the Tu-22 'Blinder' in an effort to overcome the Tu-22's poor range and indifferent supersonic performance, the process being analogous to that which saw the evolution of the variable-geometry Sukhoi Su-17 series from the fixed-geometry Su-7. The Tu-22M first flew in the late 1960s before entering limited Soviet service in about 1974.

Tu-26 'Backfire-B': the 'Backfire-A' still had limitations in supersonic performance and range, resulting in the much-improved Tu-26 with extensive redesign, a new rear fuselage and altered landing gear (retracting inwards rather than rearwards into large trailing-edge pods, which generated great drag on the 'Backfire-A').

Tu-26 'Backfire-C': revised 'Backfire-B' with wedge inlets, and possibly engines other than the Kuznetsov NK-144 derivative used in the 'Backfire-A' and 'Backfire-B'.

The Tu-26 'Backfire' is a truly formidable weapon system, providing the Soviet air forces with a bomber and missile carrier able to operate over long ranges with high dash speeds and considerable offensive loads. This is a 'Backfire-B' with its wings half-swept, and visible at the tail are the two 23-mm defensive cannon and their 'Fan Tail' fire-control radar.

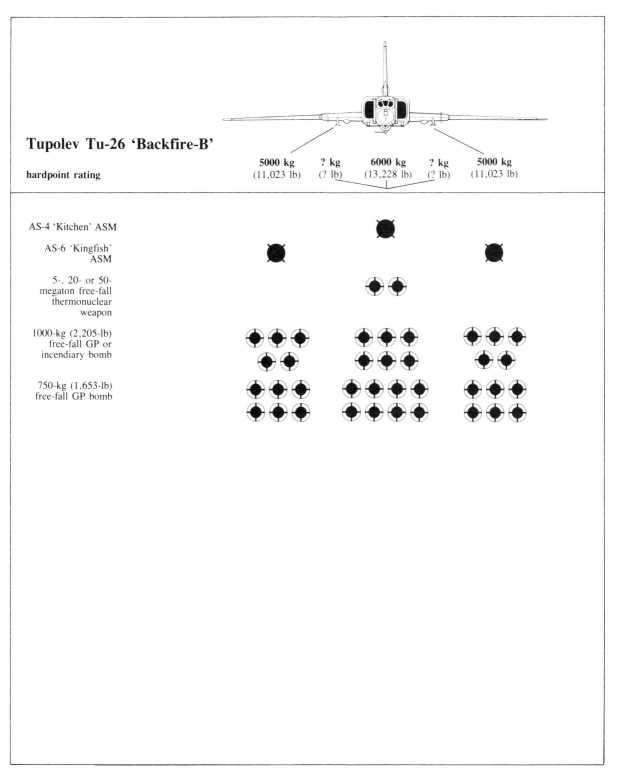

Tupolev Tu-26 'Backfire-B'

hardpoint rating

	5000 kg (11,023 lb)	? kg (? lb)	6000 kg (13,228 lb)	? kg (? lb)	5000 kg (11,023 lb)
AS-4 'Kitchen' ASM			●		
AS-6 'Kingfish' ASM	●				●
5-, 20- or 50-megaton free-fall thermonuclear weapon			● ●		
1000-kg (2,205-lb) free-fall GP or incendiary bomb	● ● ● ● ●		● ● ● ● ● ●		● ● ● ● ●
750-kg (1,653-lb) free-fall GP bomb	● ● ● ● ● ●		● ● ● ● ● ● ● ●		● ● ● ● ● ●

Tupolev Tu-28P 'Fiddler-B'

Type: two-seat long-range interceptor.
Internal armament: none.
Disposable armament: up to 2000 kg (4,409 lb) of disposable stores carried on four hardpoints (two under each wing).
Electronics and operational equipment: normal communication and navigation equipment, plus 'Big Nose' search, tracking and target-illumination radar, and Doppler navigation.

Current variant and operator
Tu-28P 'Fiddler-B': built in only one form for the USSR alone, the Tu-28P is a massive long-range/high-endurance interceptor designed to guard the USSR's vulnerable approaches, which are vast in extent but poorly provided with air bases. The type first flew in the late 1950s and has been seen with only one type of armament (though this AA-5 'Ash' air-to-air missile is available in radar- and IR-homing versions). The powerful radar can detect targets at ranges of nearly 200 km (124 miles) and lock on to fighter-type targets at 80 km (50 miles).

Produced as the world's largest interceptor and designed for long-range patrol of the USSR's lonely northern reaches, the Tu-28P is fitted with 'Big Nose' radar and can carry up to four massive AA-5 'Ash' AAMs, in this instance two of the IR-homing variety with a conical seeker nose rather than the bulged type of the semi-active radar variant.

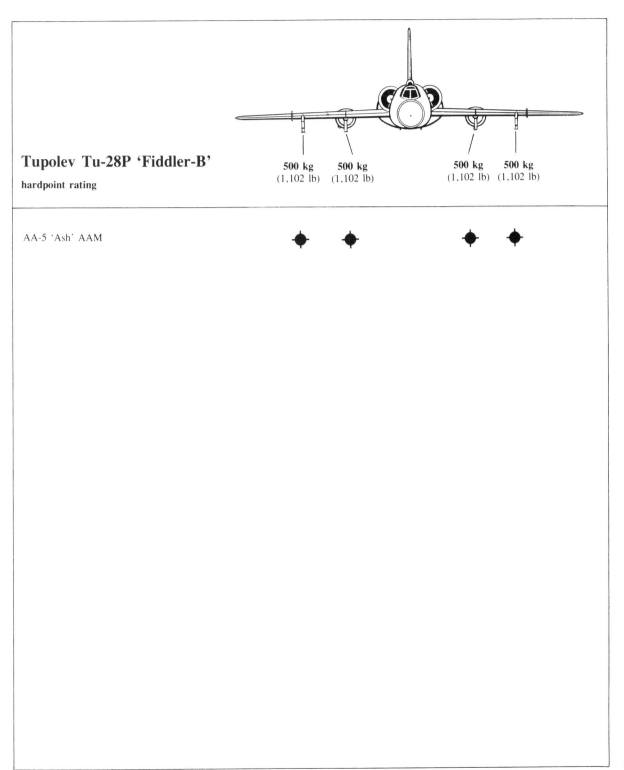

Tupolev Tu-28P 'Fiddler-B'

hardpoint rating

500 kg
(1,102 lb)

500 kg
(1,102 lb)

500 kg
(1,102 lb)

500 kg
(1,102 lb)

AA-5 `Ash` AAM

Tupolev Tu-95 'Bear-A'

Type: 10-seat strategic heavy bomber.

Internal armament: six 23-mm NR-23 cannon plus rounds, located as two each in a manned tail turret and two remotely-controlled barbettes (one dorsal and one ventral).

Disposable armament: up to 20000 kg (44,092 lb) of disposable stores carried in two lower-fuselage weapons bays.

Electronics and operational equipment: normal communication and navigation equipment, plus 'Short Horn' navigation and bombing radar, 'Bee Hind' tail-warning and gunlaying radar, A-322Z Doppler navigation and various electronic countermeasures.

Current variants and operator

Tu-95 'Bear-A': like the same design bureau's Tu-16 'Badger', the Tu-95 'Bear' has proved extraordinarily long-lived, the type having first flown in the late summer of 1954 and using, in the full production version from 1958, four 11033-ekW (14,795-eshp) Kuznetsov NK-12M turboprop engines driving vast counter-rotating propellers for great range and high subsonic performance. Each of the weapons bays was sized to accommodate one 5-, 20- or 50-megaton free-fall thermonuclear weapon, an alternative being 20000 kg (44,092 lb) of conventional ordnance.

Tu-95 'Bear-B': 1960 missile-carrier derivative with the large 1-megaton AS-3 'Kangaroo' stand-off missile recessed into a weapons bay. Target information is provided by 'Crown Drum' radar, and an A-336Z missile-guidance system is fitted. The type is now generally seen with the smaller but more modern 200-kiloton AS-4 'Kitchen', and some are used for strategic reconnaissance with a blister fairing on the starboard side of the rear fuselage.

Tu-95 'Bear-C': 1964 maritime reconnaissance model based on the 'Bear-B' but carrying no weapons so that large quantities of optical and electronic reconnaissance can be accommodated. This variant also has an inflight-refuelling probe.

Tu-95 'Bear-D': 1967 derivative of the 'Bear-A' for multi-sensor maritime reconnaissance with 'Mushroom' chin radar; 'Big Bulge' ventral radar; antennae at the tips of the tailplane; 'Box Tail' rear-warning and gunlaying radar and A-346Z digital data-link for the transmission of target data to missile-armed warships. From 1978 some 'Bear-D' aircraft have been modified with additional electronics in a long fairing instead of the tail turret.

Below right The 'Bear-E' is based on the Tu-95 'Bear-A' bomber, but revised for multi-sensor reconnaissance with the rear weapons bay occupied by additional fuel and a conformal optical/IR reconnaissance pallet.

Below The 'Bear-B' was developed from the Tu-95 'Bear-A' bomber as the launch platform for the mighty AS-3 'Kangaroo' cruise missile, whose retirement permitted surplus aircraft to be transformed into reconnaissance aircraft identifiable by the blister on the starboard side of the rear fuselage.

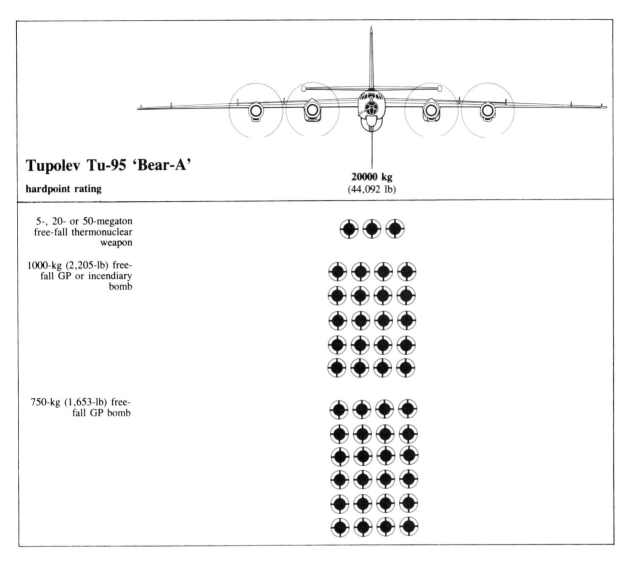

Tupolev Tu-95 'Bear-A'

hardpoint rating

20000 kg
(44,092 lb)

5-, 20- or 50-megaton free-fall thermonuclear weapon

1000-kg (2,205-lb) free-fall GP or incendiary bomb

750-kg (1,653-lb) free-fall GP bomb

Tu-95 'Bear-E': designation of 'Bear-A' aircraft rebuilt for the maritime reconnaissance role with the rear weapons bay occupied by additional tankage and supporting a conformal sensor package of six or seven cameras plus side-looking airborrne radar and infra-red linescan.

Tu-142 'Bear-F': introduced in the early 1970s, with the revised designation indicating new-build rather than rebuilt aircraft, this is a highly capable oceanic anti-submarine variant with a revised structure; different avionics (ventral and chin radars of undesignated type, magnetic anomaly detection, sonobuoys and other items); greater fuel capacity; a tactical compartment; a rest area and role-dedicated armament of types as yet unknown.

Tu-95 'Bear-G': designation of 'Bear-B' and (possibly) 'Bear-C' aircraft converted to missile-carriers with a semi-recessed installation for the AS-4 'Kitchen'.

Tu-142 'Bear-H': another new-build model with the fuselage revised to allow the carriage of four to six 250-kiloton AS-15 air-launched cruise missiles.

Tupolev Tu-? 'Blackjack'

Type: multi-seat variable-geometry strategic heavy bomber.
Internal armament: none.
Disposable armament: up to 16500 kg (36,376 lb) of disposable stores carried in a lower-fuselage weapons bay.
Electronics and operational equipment: normal communication and navigation equipment, plus navigation and bombing radar, terrain-following radar and extremely comprehensive electronic and infra-red countermeasures.

Current variant and operator
Tu-? 'Blackjack-A': designed as the Soviet parallel to the US Air Force's Rockwell B-1B, but a larger aircraft with higher performance, the 'Blackjack-A' is due to start replacing the Tu-95 series in the bomber role from 1987 or 1988. Very little of a definite nature is known of the type.

Details of the 'Blackjack' supersonic heavy bomber are singularly vague, the type's weights, dimensions and performance being largely conjectural. This US official impression shows the type's basic configuration, but shows nothing of armament capability.

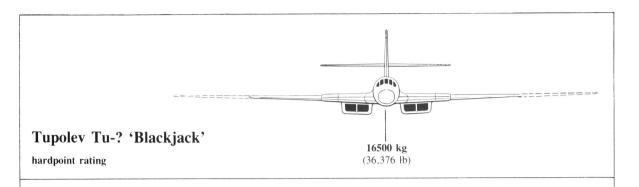

Tupolev Tu-? 'Blackjack'

hardpoint rating

16500 kg
(36,376 lb)

5-, 20- or 50-megaton
free-fall thermonuclear
weapon

AS-15 air-launched cruise
missile

1000-kg (2,205-lb) free-
fall GP or incendiary
bomb

750-kg (1,653-lb) free-
fall GP bomb

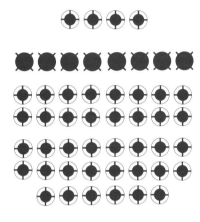

Vought A-7E Corsair II

The offensive capability of US Navy A-7E light attack aircraft has been considerably enhanced by the addition of Texas Instruments AAR-42 FLIR in a pod under the starboard wing. Though this occupies a hardpoint otherwise usable for weapons, the system provides the pilot with far better target-recognition capability as it feeds information through the new Marconi raster HUD. These aricraft are from one of USS Constellation's two light attack squadrons.

Type: single-seat carrier-borne strike and attack aircraft.

Internal armament: one General Electric M61A1 Vulcan six-barrel rotary cannon plus 1,032 rounds in the port side of the lower forward fuselage.

Disposable armament: up to 15,000 lb (6804 kg) of disposable stores carried on eight hardpoints (two on the fuselage sides and three under each wing).

Electronics and operational equipment: normal communication and navigation equipment, plus Texas Instruments APQ-126(V) multi-mode navigation and attack radar (with ground mapping; air-to-surface ranging; air-to-air ranging; terrain avoidance; terrain following; cross-scan terrain avoidance/following; cross-scan terrain following/ground mapping; beacon; TV and radar warning modes), AVQ-7(V) head-up display (being replaced by a Marconi raster head-up display in aircraft fitted with the Texas Instruments AAR-42 forward-looking infra-red pod under the starboard wing); ASN-90 carrier inertial navigation system; ASN-190 Doppler navigation; ASN-91 central computer for navigation and fire-control; air-data computer; ASU-99 projected map display; Itek ALR-45 radar-warning receiver;

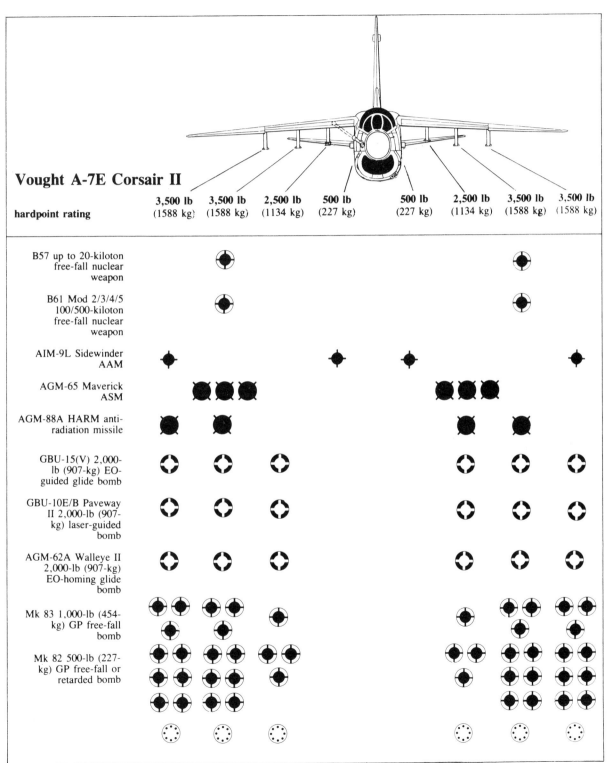

Vought A-7E Corsair II

hardpoint rating	3,500 lb (1588 kg)	3,500 lb (1588 kg)	2,500 lb (1134 kg)	500 lb (227 kg)		500 lb (227 kg)	2,500 lb (1134 kg)	3,500 lb (1588 kg)	3,500 lb (1588 kg)
B57 up to 20-kiloton free-fall nuclear weapon		⊙						⊙	
B61 Mod 2/3/4/5 100/500-kiloton free-fall nuclear weapon		⊙						⊙	
AIM-9L Sidewinder AAM	⊙			⊙		⊙			⊙
AGM-65 Maverick ASM		● ● ●					● ● ●		
AGM-88A HARM anti-radiation missile	●	●					●	●	
GBU-15(V) 2,000-lb (907-kg) EO-guided glide bomb	◉	◉	◉				◉	◉	◉
GBU-10E/B Paveway II 2,000-lb (907-kg) laser-guided bomb	◉	◉	◉				◉	◉	◉
AGM-62A Walleye II 2,000-lb (907-kg) EO-homing glide bomb	◉	◉	◉				◉	◉	◉
Mk 83 1,000-lb (454-kg) GP free-fall bomb	⊕⊕ ⊕	⊕⊕ ⊕	⊕			⊕	⊕⊕ ⊕	⊕⊕ ⊕	⊕⊕ ⊕
Mk 82 500-lb (227-kg) GP free-fall or retarded bomb	⊕⊕ ⊕⊕ ⊕⊕	⊕⊕ ⊕⊕ ⊕⊕	⊕⊕ ⊕			⊕	⊕⊕ ⊕⊕ ⊕⊕	⊕⊕ ⊕⊕ ⊕⊕	⊕⊕ ⊕⊕ ⊕⊕
	⊙	⊙	⊙				⊙	⊙	⊙

Magnavox ALR-50 SAM-launch warning system; Sanders ALQ-126 active electronic countermeasures; Loral APR-43 tactical radar warning receiver and Tracor ALE-39 chaff/flare dispenser plus various podded systems such as Westinghouse ALQ-119 electronic countermeasures; Xerox ALQ-123 infra-red countermeasures; Sanders ALQ-126 deception electronic countermeasures; Eaton-AIL ALQ-130 tactical communications jammer; Westinghouse ALQ-131 electronic countermeasures and Northrop ALQ-162 radar jammer.

Current variants and operators
TA-7C Corsair II: the subsonic Corsair was developed on the aerodynamic basis of the Vought F-8 Crusader supersonic fighter as successor to the Douglas A-4 Skyhawk, and has matured into a highly capable strike and attack platform for carrier-borne and land-based operations. The type first flew in September 1965 and the oldest model still in service with the US Navy is the TA-7C two-seat conversion trainer produced by conversion of A-7B and A-7C single-seaters powered by the 13,400-lb (6078-kg) Pratt & Whitney TF30-P-408 non-afterburning turbofan.

A-7D: tactical fighter for the US Air Force with the 14,250-lb (6465-kg) Allison TF41-A-1 turbofan and the much-improved ASN-91 nav/attack system. The type also carries the Martin Marietta AAS-35 'Pave Penny' laser tracking pod.

A-7E Corsair II: US Navy equivalent of the A-7D with the 15,000-lb (6804-kg) TF41-A-2.

A-7H Corsair II: version of the A-7E for Greece.

TA-7H Corsair II: two-seat version of the A-7H for Greece.

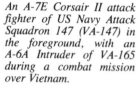

An A-7E Corsair II attack fighter of US Navy Attack Squadron 147 (VA-147) in the foreground, with an A-6A Intruder of VA-165 during a combat mission over Vietnam.

A-7K: two-seat operational conversion and proficiency trainer equivalent of the A-7D for the US Air National Guard, but powered by the TF41-A-1.

A-7P Corsair II: hybrid type for Portugal produced by converting surplus A-7As with the TF30-P-408 turbofan and the avionics of the A-7E.

A Vought A-7D Corsair II of the USAF on a practice mission in 1974.

Vought F-8E(FN) Crusader

USA

Type: single-seat carrier-borne fighter-bomber.
Internal armament: four 20-mm Pontiac M39 cannon plus 144 rounds per gun, two in each side of the forward fuselage.
Disposable armament: up to 5,000 lb (2268 kg) of disposable stores carried on four hardpoints (one on each side of the fuselage and one under each wing).
Electronics and operational equipment: normal communication and navigation equipment, plus Magnavox APQ-94 radar and other items.

Current variants and operators
F-8E(FN) Crusader: the F-8 was the US Navy's first supersonic fighter, and first flew in prototype form during September 1955. The F-8E(FN) is a developed version of the F-8E with blown trailing-edge flaps and two-stage leading-edge flaps suiting the type to France's two comparatively small aircraft-carriers.
F-8H Crusader: flown by the Philippines, the F-8H is a modernized F-8D with upgraded avionics, strengthened airframe, blown flaps and the 18,000-lb (8165-kg) Pratt & Whitney J57-P-20 afterburning turbojet. The type can carry four AIM-9 Sidewinder air-to-air missiles.

One of only two countries still operating the Crusader, the Philippines is about to dispose of its surviving F-8H land-based models in favour of F-5E Tiger II fighters. Visible here are two of the variant's four 20-mm cannon.

Vought F-8E(FN) Crusader

hardpoint rating

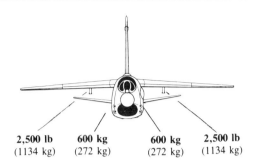

2,500 lb (1134 kg) 600 kg (272 kg) 600 kg (272 kg) 2,500 lb (1134 kg)

Matra R550 Magic or
AIM-9 sidewinder AAM

Matra R530
AAM

Mk 84 2,000-lb (907-
kg) GP free-fall bomb

Mk 83 1,000-lb (454-
kg) GP free-fall bomb

Mk 82 500-lb (227-
kg) GP free-fall bomb

Mk 81 250-lb (113-kg)
GP free-fall bomb

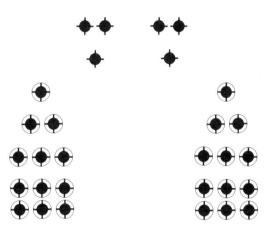

287

Westland Lynx AH.Mk 1

The Lynx HAS.Mk2 is designed for operations from platforms as small as frigates (in this instance HMS Phoebe) and its compact layout conceals its very considerable aerodynamic and electronic capabilities. This example has two (out of a possible four) Sea Skua lightweight anti-ship missiles, Ferranti Seaspray radar in the nose radome, and 'Orange Crop' ESM in a boxed fairing above the radome.

Type: 2/12-seat battlefield helicopter.

Internal armament: provision for an Emerson Flexible Turret System (previously designated MiniTAT) with one 7.62-mm (0.3-in) Minigun plus 3,000 rounds in the ventral position, or one door-mounted flexible 20-mm cannon, or two fixed 20-mm cannon, or one or two door-mounted trainable 7.62-mm (0.3-in) machine-guns (Minigun or GPMG type).

Disposable armament: up to 600 lb (272 kg) of disposable stores carried on two hardpoints (one on each side of the fuselage).

Electronics and operational equipment: normal communication and navigation equipment, plus (British helicopters) Hughes M65 stabilized roof sight and Tracor ALE-39 chaff/flare dispenser.

Current variants and operators

Lynx AH.Mk 1: the Lynx was designed as a dual-purpose army/navy helicopter offering great performance, agility and load-carrying capability in a small airframe through the use of an advanced rotor and two 900-shp (671-kW) Rolls-Royce Gem 2 turboshaft engines. The type first flew in March 1971 and has since been built in

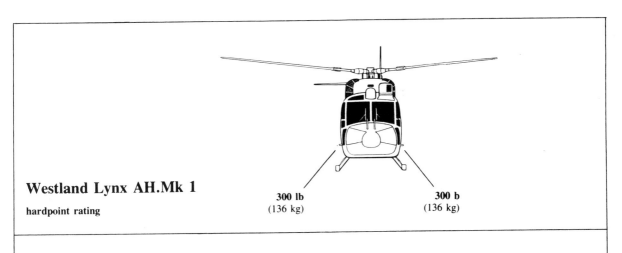

Westland Lynx AH.Mk 1

hardpoint rating

300 lb
(136 kg)

300 b
(136 kg)

BGM-71 TOW anti-
tank missile

Euromissile HOT
anti-tank missile

useful numbers. The Lynx AH.Mk 1 can carry 10 infantrymen or a Milan anti-tank missile crew with launcher and missiles, though autonomous anti-tank operations are possible with the combination of M65 sight, TOW missiles and a two-man crew.

Lynx HAS.Mk 2: baseline naval version designed for operations from small surface vessels, with modifications such as castoring tricycle landing gear instead of twin skids, a folding tail and a wholly revised avionics/armament combination. The avionics include Ferranti Seaspray lightweight search and tracking radar, Bendix ASQ-18 dunking sonar and Texas Instruments ASQ-81 magnetic anomaly detection, while the weapons include four BAe Sea Skua anti-ship missiles, or four AS.12 air-to-surface missiles (requiring the use of an AF 530 or APX 334 stabilized sight), or two torpedoes (Stingray or Mk 46), or two Mk 11 depth charges.

Lynx Mk 2: French naval version with Omera-Segid ORB 31W radar and Alcatel DUAV 4 dunking sonar.

Lynx HAS.Mk 3: uprated version of the Lynx HAS.Mk 2 with 1,120-shp (835-kW) Gem Mk 41-1 turboshafts.

Lynx Mk 4: French equivalent of the Lynx HAS.Mk 3.

Lynx AH.Mk 7: improved Lynx AH.Mk 1 with Gem 4 turboshafts, upgraded transmission and a composite-structure tail rotor.

Lynx Mk 21: version of the Lynx HAS.Mk 2 for Brazil.

Lynx Mk 23: version of the Lynx HAS.Mk 2 for Argentina.

Lynx Mk 25: search-and-rescue helicopter for the Netherlands with Gem 2 engines and local designation UH-14A.

Lynx Mk 27: anti-submarine helicopter for the Netherlands with Gem 41-1 engines, Alcatel dunking sonar and local designation SH-14B.

Lynx Mk 80: anti-submarine version of the Lynx HAS.Mk 2 for Denmark with Gem 41-1 engines.

Lynx Mk 81: anti-submarine version for the Netherlands with magnetic anomaly detection, Gem 41-1 engines and local designation SH-14C.

Lynx Mk 86: search-and-rescue version for Norway with Gem 41-1 engines.

Lynx Mk 87: improved Lynx Mk 23 for Argentina with Gem 41-2 engines.

Lynx Mk 88: anti-submarine version for West Germany with Bendix ASQ-18 dunking sonar and Gem 41-2 engines.

Lynx Mk 89: dual-role anti-submarine/search-and-rescue version for Nigeria with RCA Primus 500 radar and Gem 43-1 engines.

Lynx 3: current development model featuring a composite-structure main rotor with blades of advanced aerodynamic form, 1,115-shp (831-kW) Gem 60 engines and a stronger airframe. The type is offered in army and navy forms, the former having an armament of eight AGM-114A Hellfire anti-tank missiles and four FIM-92 Stinger missiles (the last being designed as ground-launched portable SAMs but here used as air-launched weapons to provide a capability against helicopters). The type is fitted with a MIL 1553B digital databus to allow the integration of the latest sensors and weapons.

Westland Sea King HAS.Mk 5   UK/USA

Type: four-seat anti-submarine helicopter.

Internal armament: none.

Disposable armament: up to 2,500 lb (1134 kg) of disposable stores carried on two hardpoints (one on each side of the fuselage).

Electronics and operational equipment: normal communication and navigation equipment, plus MEL ARI.5991 Sea Searcher surveillance radar; Plessey 195 dunking sonar; Ultra Electronic mini-sonobuoys; Marconi LAPADS acoustic processing and display system; Decca 71 Doppler navigation, and Tactical Air Navigation System.

Current variants and operators

Sikorsky SH-3D Sea King: this is the oldest version of the S-61 series left in US Navy service, the original HSS-2 having flown in March 1959 in response to a US Navy requirement for a twin-turbine helicopter able to undertake both hunter and killer aspects of the anti-submarine role (previously requiring separate hunter and killer helicopters working in pairs). The type entered service as the HSS-2A in September 1961 with 1,250-shp (933-kW) General Electric T58-GE-8B turboshafts, and in late 1962 was redesignated SH-3A. The SH-3D is an improved version with 1,400-shp (1044-kW) T58-GE-10 turboshafts, Bendix ASQ-13 dunking sonar and provision for 840 lb (381 kg) of torpedoes or depth bombs. The type is generally used as an adjunct of the parent ship's sensors and weapons rather than as an independent operator.

Sikorsky SH-3H Sea King: ultimate development for the US Navy as a multi-role type with improved anti-submarine avionics (ASQ-13B dunking sonar, active and passive sonobuoys, and magnetic anomaly detection) plus provision for detection of incoming anti-ship missiles with LN-66HP radar and electronic support measures equipment.

Sikorsky HH-3E Jolly Green Giant: combat search-and-rescue derivative for the US Air Force, based on the out-of-service CH-3E transport with 1,500-shp (1119-kW) T58-GE-5 turboshafts, extra fuel tankage, provision for inflight-refuelling, armour, specialist navaids, a high-capacity winch and an armament of two 7.62-mm (0.3-in) Miniguns.

Sikorsky HH-3F Pelican: unarmed and unarmoured derivative of the HH-3E for the US Coast Guard.

Sikorsky CH-124 Sea King: SH-3A equivalent for Canada.

Sikorsky S-61A: amphibious transport for Denmark with accommodation for 26 troops.

Sikorsky S-61A-4 Nuri: improved S-61A for Malaysia with accommodation for 31 troops.

Sikorsky S-61D-4: export version of the SH-3D for Argentina.

Mitsubishi HSS-2: Japanese-built equivalent of the SH-3 series with Ishikawajima-Harima T58-IHI-10 turboshafts.

Westland Sea King HAS.Mk 2: Westland started the licence-manufacture of a much improved Sea King in 1969, the initial Sea King HAS.Mk 1 helicopters being upgraded in the mid-1970s to Sea King HAS.Mk 2 standard with 1,500-shp (1119-kW) Rolls-Royce Gnome H.1400 turboshafts, improved dynamic system, Type 195 dunking sonar and AW 391 search radar in a small dorsal radome.

Westland Sea King AEW.Mk 2: designation of Sea Kings converted for the airborne early warning role with Thorn EMI ARI.5980 Searchwater radar in a swivelling radome on the starboard side of the fuselage.

Westland Sea King HAR.Mk 3: search-and-rescue version for the RAF with cabin accommodation for 19 survivors in addition to the crew.

Westland Sea King HC.Mk 4: designation of the Commando variant used by the Royal Marines for ship-to-shore assault.

Westland Sea King HAS.Mk 5: definitive anti-submarine version for the Royal Navy with 1,660-shp (1238-kW) Gnome H.1400-1 turboshafts, improved radar and the LAPADS acoustic-processing system.

Westland Sea King Mk 41: search-and-rescue version for West Germany, being upgraded in the later 1980s with Ferranti Seaspray Mk 3 radar.

Westland Sea King Mk 42: anti-submarine version for India, also produced as the Sea King Mk 42A with hauldown gear and as the Sea King Mk 42B with MEL Super Searcher radar, Marconi AQS-902 acoustic processing equipment, and provision for Sea Eagle anti-ship missiles.

Westland Sea King Mk 43: search-and-rescue version for Norway, which also operates the Sea King Mk 43A uprated version.

Westland Sea King Mk 45: anti-submarine version for Pakistan, with provision for AM.39 Exocet anti-ship missiles.

Westland Sea King Mk 47: anti-submarine version for Egypt, with provision for anti-ship missiles.

Westland Sea King Mk 48: search-and-rescue/VIP transport version for Belgium.

Westland Sea King Mk 50: anti-submarine version for Australia, fitted with ASQ-13B dunking sonar and uprated powerplant.

Westland Commando Mk 1: land-based assault transport derivative with fixed landing gear, no stabilizing sponsons and provision for a wide assortment of light armament.

Westland Commando Mk 2: improved version with accommodation for 27 rather than 21 troops, and also capable of being equipped for electronic warfare roles.

Undoubtedly the most advanced British variant, this Westland-built Sea King HAS.Mk 5 of 820 Squadron (RNAS Culdrose and HMS Invincible) shows off an armament of four Marconi Stingray lightweight anti-submarine torpedoes on MACE (Minimum-Area Crutchless Equipment) carriers and part of its sensor fit in the form of the Sea Searcher radar's dorsal radome. The type now has 'Orange Crop' ESM on the nose, and in its Advanced Sea King version can carry a pair of Sea Eagle anti-ship missiles.

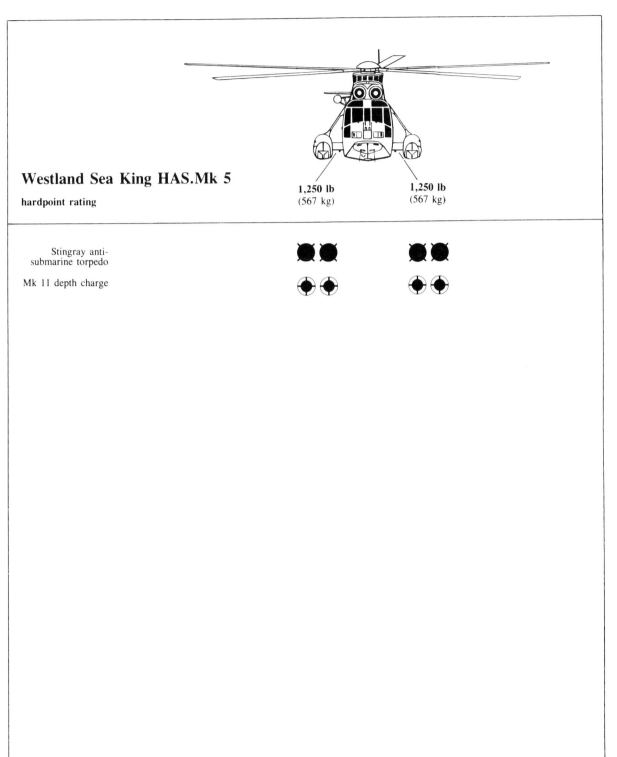

Westland Sea King HAS.Mk 5

hardpoint rating

1,250 lb
(567 kg)

1,250 lb
(567 kg)

Stingray anti-
submarine torpedo

Mk 11 depth charge

China

Xian F-7M Airguard

Type: single-seat multi-role fighter.

Internal armament: two 30-mm type 30-1 cannon plus 60 rounds per gun in the underside of the forward fuselage.

Disposable armament: up to 2000 kg (4,409 lb) of disposable stores carried on five hardpoints (one under the fuselage and two under each wing).

Electronics and operational equipment: normal communication and navigation equipment, plus Type 226 or GEC Skyranger ranging radar interfaced with the GEC Type 956 HUDWACS (Head-Up Display and Weapon-Aiming Computer System) and other items.

Current variants and operators

J-7: this is the Chinese version of the Mikoyan-Gurevich MiG-21 fighter, the type having evolved from a short-range interceptor based on the 'Fishbed-C' (with a 5100-kg/11,243-lb Wopen-7A afterburning tubojet, one 30-mm cannon and two underwing hardpoints for air-to-air missiles) to a multi-role hybrid of the 'Fishbed-E' and 'Fishbed-J' (6100-kg/13,448-lb Wopen-7B turbojet, two 30-mm cannon, four underwing hardpoints, provision for an 800-litre/176-Imp gal under-fuselage drop tank and avionics including Type 222 ranging radar tied into the SM-3A optical or AFS-3A computing sight).

F-7: export version of the later J-7 model delivered to Albania, Egypt, Iraq and Tanzania. The Egyptian aircraft are to a higher standard, having head-up displays and provision for AIM-9P Sidewinder air-to-air missiles.

F-7M Airguard: improved export model with an improved engine, much enhanced avionics and greater weapons capability.

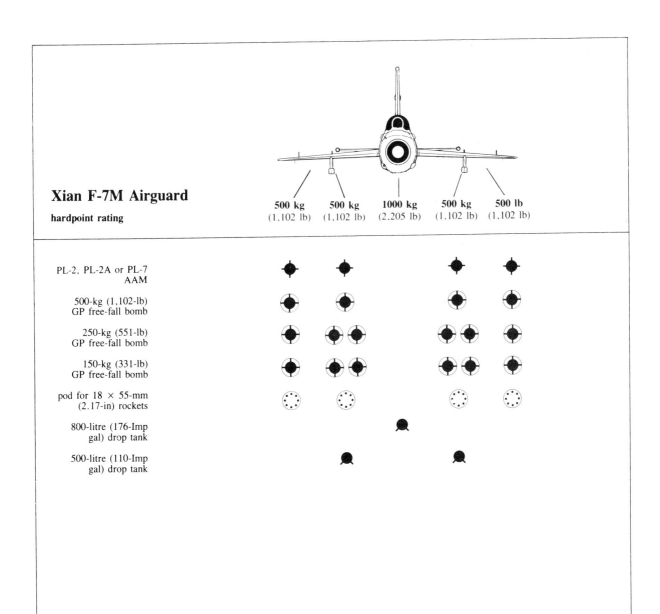

Xian F-7M Airguard

hardpoint rating

	500 kg (1,102 lb)	500 kg (1,102 lb)	1000 kg (2,205 lb)	500 kg (1,102 lb)	500 lb (1,102 lb)
PL-2, PL-2A or PL-7 AAM					
500-kg (1,102-lb) GP free-fall bomb					
250-kg (551-lb) GP free-fall bomb					
150-kg (331-lb) GP free-fall bomb					
pod for 18 × 55-mm (2.17-in) rockets					
800-litre (176-Imp gal) drop tank					
500-litre (110-Imp gal) drop tank					

Yakovlev Yak-28P 'Firebar'

Type: two-seat all-weather interceptor.
Internal armament: none.
Disposable armament: up to 800 kg (1,653 lb) of disposable stores carried on four hardpoints (two under each wing).
Electronics and operational equipment: normal communication and navigation equipment, plus 'Skip Spin' interception radar, reflector sight and (possibly) radar-warning receiver.

Current variants and operator
Yak-28R 'Brewer-D': first flown in 1959 but still in limited service with the USSR (the only operator of the Yak-28 series), the Yak-28 was developed for a variety of tactical roles with 6200-kg (13,668-lb) Tumansky R-11F afterburning turbojets for moderately high supersonic performance. The 'Brewer-D' is a multi-sensor reconnaissance aircraft introduced in the late 1960s with (probably) 'Short Horn' nose radar and any one of three pallets accommodating optical, radar or infra-red reconnaissance equipment in the erstwhile weapons bay.
Yak-28E 'Brewer-E': electronic warfare escort aircraft first seen in 1970 with a number of aerials and the weapons bay used for the jamming equipment operated by the back-seater.
Yak-28P 'Firebar': introduced in the mid-1960s, this all-weather interceptor has useful range and still in service, largely in the USSR's Far Eastern regions.
Yak-28U 'Maestro': two-seat operational conversion and proficiency trainer.

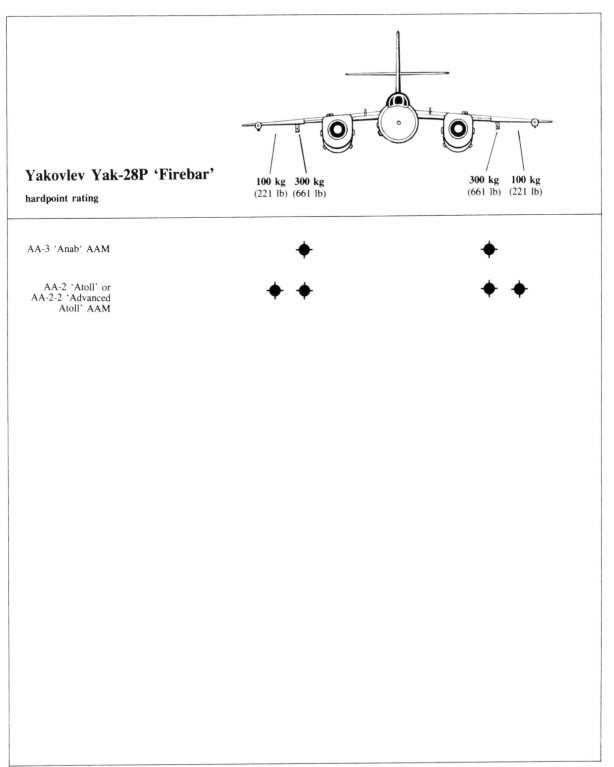

Yakovlev Yak-28P 'Firebar'

hardpoint rating

100 kg   300 kg
(221 lb) (661 lb)

300 kg   100 kg
(661 lb) (221 lb)

AA-3 'Anab' AAM

AA-2 'Atoll' or
AA-2-2 'Advanced
Atoll' AAM

Yakovlev Yak-38 'Forger-A'

Type: single-seat carrier-borne V/STOL strike fighter.
Internal armament: none.
Disposable armament: up to 3600 kg (7,937 lb) of disposable stores carried on four hardpoints (two under each wing).
Electronics and operational equipment: normal communication and navigation equipment, plus ranging radar and head-up display.

Current variants and operator
Yak-38 'Forger-A': first flown in 1971 or thereabouts, the 'Forger' has pioneered the Soviet used of fixed-wing air power at sea, and may be regarded as a development rather than full-blown operational type. Nevertheless the type has a useful if limited combat capability, though the combination of two lift jets and one vectored thrust turbofan adds complexity and weight to the detriment of performance and payload.
Yak-38 'Forger-B': two-seat operational conversion and proficiency trainer with a markedly lengthened fuselage.

Right *The Yak-38 'Forger-A' is a type about which the West has had to revise its initial adverse impressions, but the fact still remains that the reliance on two dedicated lift engines in the forward fuselage means so much dead weight to be carried in wing-borne flight, with inevitable degradation of performance and possibility of catastrophic battle damage.*

Below *Yak-38 'Forger-As' line the side of the flightdeck on a 'Kiev' class carrier, the opened hatch behind each aircraft's canopy revealing the inlets of the two dedicated lift jets. The Yak-38's four hardpoints are located on the non-folding portions of of the wings.*

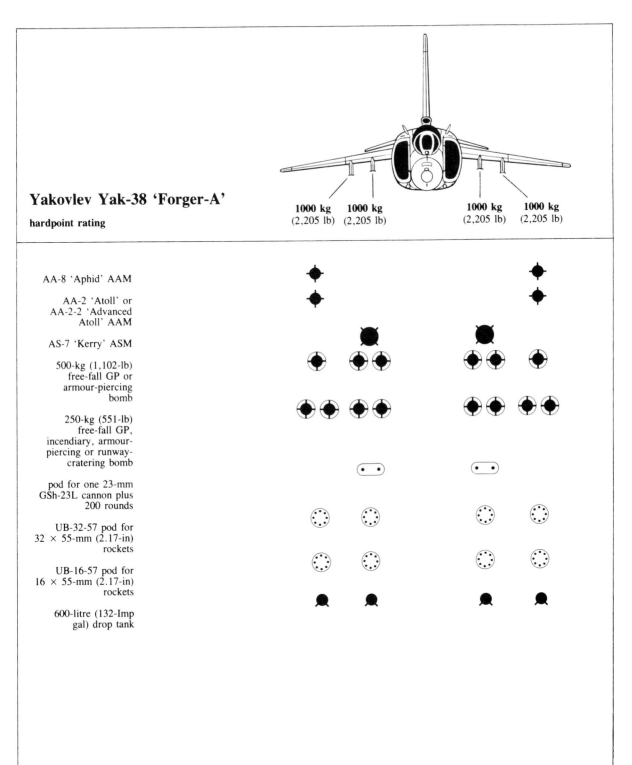

Yakovlev Yak-38 'Forger-A'

hardpoint rating

| | 1000 kg (2,205 lb) | 1000 kg (2,205 lb) | | 1000 kg (2,205 lb) | 1000 kg (2,205 lb) |

AA-8 'Aphid' AAM

AA-2 'Atoll' or AA-2-2 'Advanced Atoll' AAM

AS-7 'Kerry' ASM

500-kg (1,102-lb) free-fall GP or armour-piercing bomb

250-kg (551-lb) free-fall GP, incendiary, armour-piercing or runway-cratering bomb

pod for one 23-mm GSh-23L cannon plus 200 rounds

UB-32-57 pod for 32 × 55-mm (2.17-in) rockets

UB-16-57 pod for 16 × 55-mm (2.17-in) rockets

600-litre (132-Imp gal) drop tank

Acknowledgements

As noted in the Introduction, the subject matter of this title has been little covered in the open literature about modern combat aircraft, so the information used in the compilation of these pages has been culled mainly from aircraft manufacturers, who have been most generous with material (both textual and illustrative). I have enjoyed a fruitful correspondence with most Western aircraft manufacturers, amongst whom I should particularly like to thank (in alphabetical order) the heads and staffs of the press relations departments of the following concerns:

Boeing Military Airplane Company (Wichita, Kansas),
British Aerospace Aircraft Group (Military Aircraft Division, Kingston, Surrey, and Preston, Lancashire),
CASA (Madrid),
Cessna Aircraft Company (Wichita, Kansas),
Fairchild Republic Company (Farmingdale, New York),
General Dynamics Corporation, Fort Worth Division (Fort Worth, Texas),
Grumman Corporation (Bethpage, New York),
Israel Aircraft Industries Ltd (Ben Gurion Airport),
McDonnell Aircraft Company (St Louis, Missouri),
McDonnell Douglas Helicopter Company (Culver City, California, and Mesa, Arizona),
Panavia Aircraft GmbH (Munich),
Pilatus Britten-Norman Ltd (Bembridge, Isle of Wight),
Rockwell International Corporation, North American Aircraft Operations (Los Angeles, California),
Sikorsky Aircraft Division of United Technologies (Stratford, Connecticut),
SNI Aérospatiale, Division de Helicoptere (La Courneuve),
Westland Helicopters Ltd (Yeovil, Somerset).

Further Reading

Aircraft Armament (Interavia Data SA, various years).
Air Forces of the World (Christopher Chant, Collins-Willow, 1983).
Air International (edited William Green & Gordon Swanborough, Fine Scroll Ltd, monthly).
Aviation Fact Files (various authors, Salamander Books, various dates).
The Encyclopedia of World Air Power (edited Bill Gunston, Hamlyn-Aerospace, 1980).
Encyclopaedia of the Modern Royal Air Force (Terry Gander, Patrick Stephens Ltd, Third edition 1987).
International Defence Review (Interavia SA, monthly).
Janes All the World's Aircraft (edited J.W.R. Taylor, Janes Publishing Company, various years).
Modern Air Combat (Bill Gunston & Mike Spick, Salamander Books, 1983).
Modern Fighting Helicopters (Bill Gunston & Mike Spick, Salamander Books, 1986).
Warplane (edited Stan Morse, Orbis-Aerospace, weekly).

Index

35 (Saab Draken), *234*
37 (Saab Viggen), *235*
105 (Saab), *235*

A 129 (Agusta Mangusta), *34*
A/OA-4 (McDonnell Douglas Skyhawk II), *154*
A-5 (Nanchang 'Fantan'), *212*
A-6 (Grumman Intruder), *122*
A-7 (Vought Corsair II), *282*
A-10 (Fairchild Republic Thunderbolt II), *107*
A/OA-37 (Cessna Dragonfly), *80*
AB.204 (Agusta [Bell]), *36*
AB.212 (Agusta [Bell]), *38*
Aeritalia F-104 Starfighter, *148*
   G91R, *10*
   G91T, *10*
   G91Y, *12*
Aeritalia/Aermacchi/EMBRAER AMX, *36*
Aermacchi M.B.326, *16*
   M.B.339 Veltro, *18*
Aero L-39 Albatros, *32*
Aérospatiale AS 332 Super Puma, *26*
   CM.170 Magister, *20*
   CM.170 Super Magister, *20*
   CM.175 Zéphyr, *20*
   SA 316/318/319 Alouette, *22*
   SA 321 Super Frelon, *24*
   SA 330 Puma, *26*
   SA 341/342 Gazelle, *28*
   SA 361 Dauphin, *30*
   SA 365 Dauphin 2, *30*
   SA 365 Panther, *30*
   SA 366 Dolphin, *30*
AEW Defender (Britten-Norman), *76*
Agusta A 129 Mangusta, *34*
Agusta (Bell) AB.204, *36*
   AB212, *38*
Agusta (Sikorsky) ASH-3 Sea King, *40*
AH-1 (Bell HueyCobra), *44*
AH-1 (Bell SeaCobra/Improved SeaCobra/SuperCobra), *46*
AH-64 (Hughes [McDonnell Douglas Helicopters] Apache), *130*
Airfox (IAR-317), *22*
Airguard (Xian F-7), *294*
AJ 37 (Saab Viggen), *235*
Ajeet (HAL), *128*

Albatros (Aero L-39), *32*
Alizé (Dassault-Breguet), *82*
Alouette (Aérospatiale), *22*
Alpha XH-1 (Atlas), *22*
Alpha Jet (Dassault-Breguet/Dornier), *104*
AMX (Aeritalia/Aermacchi/EMBRAER), *14*
Apache (Hughes [McDonnell Douglas Helicopters] AH-64), *130*
AS 332 (Aérospatiale Super Puma), *26*
ASH-3 (Agusta [Sikorsky] Sea King), *40*
ASW/ASV Defender (Britten-Norman), *76*
Atlantic 1 (Dassault-Breguet), *84*
Atlantique 2 (Dassault-Breguet), *84*
Atlas Alpha XH-1, *22*
   Impala, *16*
Aurora (Lockheed CP-140), *150*
AV-8 (British Aerospace Harrier), *60*
AV-8 (McDonnell Douglas/British Aerospace Harrier II), *170*
Aviojet (CASA C-101), *77*

B-1 (Rockwell), *226*
B-52 (Boeing Stratofortress), *48*
'Backfire' (Tupolev Tu-26), *274*
'Badger' (Tupolev Tu-16), *270*
'Beagle' (Ilyushin Il-28), *138*
'Bear' (Tupolev Tu-95/142), *278*
Beech T-34 Mentor, *42*
   T-34C Turbine Mentor, *42*
Bell AH-1 HueyCobra, *44*
   AH-1 SeaCobra/Improved SeaCobra/SuperCobra, *46*
Black Hawk (Sikorsky EH/UH-60), *248*
'Blackjack' (Tupolev Tu-?), *280*
'Blinder' (Tupolev Tu-22), *272*
BO 105 (Messerschmitt-Bölkow-Blohm), *195*
Boeing B-52 Stratofortress, *48*
'Brewer' (Yakovlev Yak-28), *296*

British Aerospace AV-8 Harrier/Matador, *58*
   Buccaneer, *54*
   Canberra, *56*
   Harrier, *58*
   Hawk, *61*
   Hunter, *64*
   Lightning. *66*
   Nimrod, *68*
   Sea Harrier, *70*
   Strikemaster, *72*
   T-45 Goshawk, *62*
Britten-Norman AEW Defender, *76*
   ASW/ASV Defender, *74*
   CASTOR Islander, *74*
   Defender, *74*
   Maritime Defender, *74*
   Trislander, *74*
   Turbine Defender, *74*
Bronco (Rockwell OV-10), *228*
Buccaneer (British Aerospace), *54*

Canberra (British Aerospace), *56*
C-101 (CASA Aviojet), *77*
CASA C-101 Aviojet, *77*
CASTOR Islander (Britten-Norman), *74*
Cayuse (Hughes [Mcdonnell Douglas Helicopters] OH-6), *134*
Cessna A/OA-37 Dragonfly, *80*
   T-37, *80*
CM.170 (Aérospatiale Magister), *20*
CM.175 (Aérospatiale Zéphyr), *20*
CNIAR IAR-93, *254*
Commando (Westland), *292*
Corsair II (Vought A-7), *272*
CP-140 (Lockheed Aurora), *150*
Crusader (Vought F-8), *286*

Dagger (IAI), *143*
Dassault-Breguet Alizé, *82*
   Atlantic 1, *84*
   Atlantique 2, *84*
   Lancier, *106*
   Mirage III, *86*
   Mirage IV, *90*
   Mirage 5/50, *92*
   Mirage 2000, *94*

301

Mirage F1, *97*
Super Etendard, *102*
Dassault-Breguet/Dornier Alpha Jet, *104*
Dauphin (Aérospatiale SA 361), *30*
Dauphin 2 (Aérospatiale SA 365), *30*
Defender (Britten-Norman, *74*
Defender (Hughes [McDonnell Douglas Helicopters] Model 500), *134*
Dolphin (Aérospatiale SA 366), *30*
Dragonfly (Cessna A/OA-37), *80*
Draken (Saab 35), *232*

EA-6 (Grumman Prowler), *122*
Eagle (McDonnell Douglas F-15), *161*
EH-60 (Sikorsky Black Hawk), *248*
EMB-326 Xavante (EMBRAER), *16*
EMBRAER EMB-326 Xavante, *16*

F-1 (Mitsubishi), *210*
F/RF-4 (McDonnell Douglas Phantom II), *157*
F-5 (Northrop Freedom Fighter/Tiger II), *214*
F/FT-5 (Shenyang), *180*
F-6 (Shenyang), *182*
F-7 (Xian Airguard), *294*
F-8 (Vought Crusader), *286*
F-14 (Grumman Tomcat), *125*
F-15 (McDonnell Douglas Eagle), *161*
F-16 (General Dynamics F-16), *112*
F-21 (IAI), *143*
F-104 (Lockheed/Aeritalia Starfighter), *146*
F/A-18 (McDonnell Douglas Hornet), *165*
F/FB-111 (General Dynamics), *118*
Fairchild Republic A-10 Thunderbolt II, *107*
'Fagot' (Mikoyan-Gurevich MiG-15), *178*
'Fantan' (Nanchang A/Q-5), *212*
'Farmer' (Mikoyan-Gurevich MiG-19), *182*
'Fencer' (Sukhoi Su-24), *264*
'Fiddler' (Tupolev Tu-28), *276*
Fighting Falcon (General Dynamics F-16), *12*
'Firebar' (Yakovlev Yak-28), *296*

'Fishbed' (Mikoyan-Gurevich MiG-21), *185*
'Fitter' (Sukhoi Su-7/17/20/22), *256*
'Flagon' (Sukhoi Su-15/21), *262*
'Flanker' (Sukhoi Su-27), *268*
'Flogger' (Mikoyan-Gurevich MiG-23), *189*
'Flogger' (Mikoyan-Gurevich MiG-27), *195*
'Forger' (Yakovlev Yak-38), *298*
'Foxbat' (Mikoyan-Gurevich MiG-25), *192*
'Foxhound' (Mikoyan-Gurevich MiG-31), *200*
'Fresco' (Mikoyan-Gurevich MiG-17), *180*
'Frogfoot' (Sukhoi Su-25), *266*
'Fulcrum' (Mikoyan-Gurevich MiG-29), *198*
FMA IA-58/66 Pucara, *110*
Freedom Fighter (Northrop F-5), *214*

G-2 (Soko Galeb), *250*
G-4 (Soko Super Galeb), *252*
G91R (Aeritalia), *10*
G91T (Aeritalia), *10*
G91Y (Aeritalia), *12*
Galeb (Soko G-2), *250*
Gazelle (Aérospatiale SA 341/342), *28*
General Dynamics F-16 Fighting Falcon, *112*
F/FB-111, *118*
Grumman A-6 Intruder, *122*
EA-6 Prowler, *122*
F-14 Tomcat, *125*
Goshawk (British Aerospace T-45), *62*

H-6 (Xian), *271*
HAL Ajeet, *128*
Harbin Z-8, *24*
Z-9, *30*
Harrier (British Aerospace), *58*
Harrier II (McDonnell Douglas/British Aerospace AV-8), *170*
Hawk (British Aerospace), *61*
HH-3 (Sikorsky Jolly Green Giant), *291*
HH-60 (Sikorsky Night Hawk), *248*
Hornet (McDonnell Douglas F/A-18), *165*
HSS-2 (Mitsubishi), *291*
HueyCobra (Bell AH-1), *44*
Hughes (McDonnell Douglas

Helicopters) AH-64 Apache, *130*
Model 500 Defender, *134*
OH-6 Cayuse, *134*
Hunter (British Aerospace), *64*

IA-58/66 (FMA Pucara), *10*
IAI Dagger, *143*
F-21, *143*
Improved Fouga, *20*
Kfir, *140*
Phantom 2000, *144*
Nesher, *143*
IAR-93 (CNIAR), *254*
IAR-317 Airfox, *22*
Il-28 (Ilyushin 'Beagle'), *138*
Ilyushin Il-28 'Beagle'), *138*
Impala (Atlas), *16*
Improved Fouga (IAI), *20*
Improved SeaCobra (Bell AH-1), *46*
Iskra (PZL Mielec TS-11), *224*

J-1 (Soko Jastreb), *250*
J/JJ-5 (Shenyang), *180*
J/JJ/JZ-6 (Shenyang), *182*
J-7 (Xian), *294*
J 35 (Saab Draken), *232*
JA 37 (Saab Viggen), *235*
Jaguar (SEPECAT), *239*
Jastreb (Soko J-1), *250*
Jolly Green Giant (Sikorsky HH-3), *291*

Kfir (IAI), *140*

L-39 (Aero Albatros), *32*
Lancier (Dassault-Breguet), *106*
Lightning (British Aerospace), *66*
Lockheed CP-140 Aurora, *150*
F-104 Starfighter, *146*
P-3 Orion, *149*
S-3 Viking, *152*
Lynx (Westland), *288*

Matador (British Aerospace AV-8), *60*
M.B.326 (Aermacchi), *16*
M.B.339 (Aermacchi), *18*
Magister (Aérospatiale CM.170), *20*
Mangusta (Agusta A 129), *34*
Maritime Defender (Britten-Norman), *74*
McDonnell Douglas A/OA-4 Skyhawk II, *154*
F/RF-4 Phantom II, *157*
F-15 Eagle, *161*
F/A-18 Hornet, *165*
McDonnell Douglas/British Aerospace AV-8 Harrier II, *170*

McDonnell Douglas Helicopters
AH-64 Apache, *130*
Model 500 Defender, *134*
OH-Cayuse, *134*
Mentor (Beech T-34), *42*
Messerschmitt-Bölkow-Blohm
BO 105, *175*
PAH-1, *175*
VBH, *175*
Mikoyan-Gurevich MiG-15
'Fagot/Midget' *178*
MiG-17 'Fresco', *180*
MiG-19 'Farmer', *182*
MiG-21 'Fishbed/Mongol',
182
MiG-23 'Flogger', *189*
MiG-25 'Foxbat', *192*
MiG-27 'Flogger', *195*
MiG-29 'Fulcrum', *198*
MiG-31 'Foxhound', *200*
Mil Mi-8 'Hip', *202*
Mi-14 'Haze', *204*
Mi-17 'Hip', *204*
Mi-24 'Hind', *205*
Mi-25 'Hind', *206*
Mi-28 'Havoc', *208*
Mitsubishi F-1, *210*
HSS-2, *291*
T-2, *210*
Mirage III (Dassault-Breguet),
86
Mirage IV (Dassault-Breguet),
90
Mirage 5/50 (Dassault-Breguet),
92
Mirage 2000 (Dassault-
Breguet), *94*
Mirage F1 (Dassault-Breguet),
97
Model 500 (Hughes
[McDonnell Douglas
Helicopters] Defender), *134*
Modernized HueyCobra (Bell
AH-1), *44*

Nanchang A-5 'Fantan', *212*
Q-5 'Fantan', *212*
Nesher (IAI), *143*
Night Hawk (Sikorsky HH-60),
248
Nimrod (British Aerospace), *68*
Northrop F/RF-5 Freedom
Fighter, *214*
F-5 Tiger II, *214*
RF-5 Tigereye, *214*
T-38 Talon, *216*

OH-6 (Hughes [McDonnell
Douglas Helicopters]
Cayuse), *134*
Orao (Soko), *254*
Orion (Lockheed P-3), *149*

OV-10 (Rockwell Bronco), *228*

P-3 (Lockheed Orion), *149*
PAH-1 (Messerschmitt-Bölkow-
Blohm), *195*
Panavia Tornado, *217*
Panther (Aérospatiale SA 365),
30
Phantom II (McDonnell
Douglas F/RF-4), *157*
Phantom 2000 (IAI), *144*
PS-1 (Shin Meiwa), *242*
Pucara (FMA IA-58/66), *110*
Puma (Aérospatiale SA 330),
26
PZL Mielec TS-11 Iskra, *224*

Q-5 (Nanchang 'Fantan'), *212*

Rockwell B-1, *226*
OV-10 Bronco, *228*

S-3 (Lockhed Viking), *152*
S.211 (SIAI-Marchetti), *244*
SA 316/318/319 (Aérospatiale
Alouette), *22*
SA 321 (Aérospatiale Super
Frelon), *24*
SA 330 (Aérospatiale SA 330),
26
SA 341/342 (Aérospatiale
Gazelle), *28*
SA 361 (Aérospatiale Dauphin),
30
SA 365 (Aérospatiale Dauphin
2), *30*
SA 365 (Aérospatiale Panther),
30
SA 366 (Aérospatiale Dolphin),
30
Saab 35 Draken, *234*
37 Viggen, *235*
105/Sk 60, *230*
AJ/JA/SF/SH/Sk 37 Viggen,
235
J/Sk 35 Draken, *232*
SeaCobra (Bell AH-1), *46*
Sea Harrier (British
Aerospace), *70*
Seahawk (Sikorsky SH-60),
248
Sea King (Agusta [Sikorsky]
ASH-3), *40*
Sea King (Sikorsky), *291*
Sea King (Westland), *291*
SEPECAT Jaguar, *239*
SF 37 (Saab Viggen), *235*
SF.260 (SIAI-Marchetti
Warrior), *246*
SH 37 (Saab Viggen), *235*
SH-60 (Sikorsky Seahawk), *248*

Shenyang J/JJ-5, *180*
J/JJ/JZ-6, *182*
Shin Meiwa PS/US-1, *242*
SIAI-Marchetti S.211, *244*
SF.260 Warrior, *246*
Sikorsky EH/UH-60 Black
Hawk, *248*
HH-3 Jolly Green Giant, *291*
HH-60 Night Hawk, *248*
SH-3 Sea King, *291*
SH-60 Seahawk, *248*
Sk 35 (Saab Draken), *232*
Sk 37 (Saab Viggen), *235*
Sk 60 (Saab), *230*
Skyhawk II (McDonnell
Douglas O/OA-4), *154*
Soko G-2 Galeb, *250*
G-4 Super Galeb, *252*
J-1 Jastreb, *250*
Orao, *254*
Starfighter (Lockheed/Aeritalia
F-104), *146*
Stratofortress (Boeing B-52), *48*
Strikemaster (British
Aerospace), *72*
Sukhoi Su-7 'Fitter/Moujik',
256
Su-15 'Flagon', *262*
Su-17 'Fitter', *259*
Su-20 'Fitter', *259*
Su-21 'Flagon', *262*
Su-22 'Fitter', *259*
Su-24 'Fencer', *264*
Su-25 'Frogfoot', *266*
Su-27 'Flanker', *268*
SuperCobra (Bell AH-1), *46*
Super Etendard (Dassault-
Breguet), *102*
Super Frelon (Aérospatiale SA
321), *24*
Super Galeb (Soko G-4), *252*
Super Magister (Aérospatiale
CM.170), *20*
Super Puma (Aérospatiale AS
332), *26*

T-2 (Mitsubishi), *210*
T-34 (Beech Mentor), *42*
T-34C (Beech Turbine Mentor),
42
T-37 (Cessna), *80*
T-38 (Northrop Talon), *216*
T-45 (British Aerospace
Goshawk), *62*
Talon (Northrop T-38), *216*
Thunderbolt II (Fairchild
Republic A-10), *107*
Tiger II (Northrop F-5), *214*
Tigereye (Northrop RF-5), *214*
Tomcat (Grumman F-14), *125*
Tornado (Panavia), *217*
Trislander (Britten-Norman), *74*

TS-11 (PZL Mielec Iskra), *224*
Tu-16 (Tupolev 'Badger'), *270*
Tu-22 (Tupolev 'Blinder'), *272*
Tu-26 (Tupolev 'Backfire'), *274*
Tu-28 (Tupolev 'Fiddler'), *276*
Tu-95/142 (Tupolev 'Bear'), *278*
Tu-? (Tupolev 'Blackjack'), *280*
Tupolev Tu-16 'Badger', *270*
  Tu-22 'Blinder', *272*
  Tu-26 'Backfire', *274*
  Tu-28 'Fiddler', *276*
  Tu-95/142 'Bear', *278*
  Tu-? 'Blackjack', *280*
Turbine Defender (Britten-Norman), *74*
Turbine Mentor (Beech T-34C), *42*

UH-60 (Sikorsky Black Hawk), *248*
US-1 (Shin Meiwa), *242*

VBH (Messerchmitt-Bölkow-Blohm), *175*
Veltro (Aermacchi M.B.339), *18*
Viggen (Saab 37), *235*
Viking (Lockheed S-3), *152*
Vought A-7 Corsair II, *282*
  F-8 Crusader, *286*

Warrior (SIAI-Marchetti SF.260), *246*
Westland Commando, *292*
  Lynx, *288*
  Sea King, *291*

Xavante (EMBRAER EMB-326), *16*
Xian F-7 Airguard, *294*
H-6, *271*
J-7, *294*

Yak-28 (Yakovlev 'Brewer/Firebar/Maestro'), *296*
Yak-38 (Yakovlev 'Forger'), *298*
Yakovlev Yak-28 'Brewer/Firebar/Maestro'), *296*
  Yak-38 'Forger', *298*

Zephyr (Aérospatiale CM.175), *20*
Z-8 (Harbin), *24*
Z-9 (Harbin), *30*

Jaguar GR.Mk 1s show off a diversity of external stores.